INTRODUCTION

Alors que plusieurs centrales nucléaires implantées dans les pays Membres de l'OCDE approchent de la fin de leur durée de vie prévue, les exploitants commencent à se pencher sérieusement sur la question de la prolongation de l'exploitation de ces centrales. Un groupe d'experts de l'AEN a récemment publié un rapport intitulé - Prévision de coûts de l'électricité produite par des centrales nucléaires ou au charbon mises en service en 1995 - dans lequel on a admis une durée de vie économique des centrales de 25 ans. Cette valeur reflète le fait que la plupart des pays Membres escomptent que leurs centrales resteront en service au moins pendant cette période.

Il apparaît toutefois que la durée de vie de certaines centrales existantes pourrait être prolongée si l'on remettait en état certains de leurs composants essentiels, pour qu'ils demeurent conformes aux normes de sûreté et de fiabilité. Prolonger la vie utile d'une centrale est avant tout une solution qui permet d'éviter un déclassement relativement rapide. La décision de mettre une centrale hors service est en général arrêtée à la suite d'une analyse économique dans laquelle on compare le coût de la rénovation de la centrale avec celui de son remplacement par une installation comparable. Il semble le plus souvent qu'il serait économiquement justifié de poursuivre l'exploitation des centrales nucléaires au-delà de leur durée de vie initialement prévue. L'objectif final est d'abaisser autant que possible le coût de la production d'électricité tout en maintenant des marges de sûreté suffisante.

L'Agence pour l'Energie Nucléaire de l'OCDE a décidé d'aborder l'analyse de cette question en organisant, en coopération avec l'Agence Internationale de l'Energie Atomique, un symposium international qui s'est tenu du 24 au 27 février 1987 à Paris, auquel ont participé les représentants de 14 pays Membres de l'OCDE et de l'AIEA et de 4 organisations internationales. Les principaux objectifs de ce Symposium étaient les suivants :

- Passer en revue les pratiques de conception et de maintenance se rapportant à la prolongation de la durée de vie des centrales existantes et futures et déterminer les facteurs susceptibles de la limiter ;

- Etudier les possibilités de réalisation et la viabilité économique de gros travaux de rénovation dans des centrales par rapport à leur déclassement ou à la construction de nouvelles centrales ;

- Indiquer la tendance dans l'évolution des travaux dans le domaine de la prolongation de la durée de vie des centrales.

Certes, les critères applicables à la sûreté et à la réglementation jouent un rôle déterminant dans la prolongation de la vie utile des centrales, mais ce Symposium n'avait pas pour objet de procéder à un examen technique détaillé de ces problèmes. Il s'agissait plutôt de recenser les limites connues à la prolongation de la durée de vie des centrales actuellement en exploitation, d'examiner si ces limites pouvaient être et seraient surmontées grâce à des perfectionnements techniques apportés aux centrales existantes ou nouvelles et de déterminer si les travaux de R-D requis étaient en cours ou étaient prévus.

INTRODUCTION

As several nuclear plants in OECD countries approach the end of their planned lifetime, plant owners are and will be looking closely at the question of extending the operation of these plants. An NEA Expert Group recently published a report - Projected Costs of Generating Electricity from Nuclear and Coal-Fired Power Stations for Commissioning in 1995 - in which the economic lifetime of a plant was taken to be 25 years. This figure reflected the fact that most Member countries expected their plants to remain in service for at least this period.

It is apparent, however, that for some existing plants a longer lifetime could be attained with some refurbishment of critical components to maintain safety and reliability standards. Essentially, life extension is an alternative to early decommissioning. The decision to retire a plant from service is usually based on an economic comparison of the refurbishment costs with those of a comparable replacement. It appears that in many cases it would be economically justifiable to continue operation of nuclear power plants beyond their originally expected lifetimes. The ultimate goal is to make the electricity generating cost as low as practicably achievable while maintaining appropriate safety margins.

A review of this topic was initiated by the NEA at an international symposium organised in co-operation with the International Atomic Energy Agency on 24th-27th February 1987, in Paris, which was attended by representatives from 14 OECD and IAEA Member countries and 4 international organisations. The main objectives of this Symposium were:

- To review experience in design and maintenance practices relevant to life prolongation and to identify lifetime limiting factors in existing and future plants;

- To study the practicability and economic viability of major refurbishment of a power plant as an alternative to decommissioning the plant and building a replacement;

- To indicate the future direction of work in the area of plant life extension.

Although safety and regulatory criteria are key factors in extending plant lifetimes, this Symposium was not intended to review these issues at a detailed technical level. The purpose was rather to identify known limits of the extension of the lifetime of currently operating plants, to discuss whether such limits could and would be overcome by future developments applicable to existing or new plants, and the extent to which the required R&D was underway or planned.

The information derived from the Symposium as presented in these proceedings should be of particular benefit to those responsible for planning major refurbishment work and/or construction of replacement power plants, for long-range planning of decommissioning activities and for analyses of nuclear economics. This information is made public on the responsibility of the Secretary General of the OECD.

PROCEEDINGS OF A SYMPOSIUM ON

NUCLEAR POWER PLANT LIFE EXTENSION

Paris, 24th-27th February 1987

COMPTE RENDU D'UN SYMPOSIUM SUR

L'EXTENSION DE LA DURÉE DE VIE DES CENTRALES NUCLÉAIRES

Paris, 24-27 février 1987

D
621.481
Sym

organised by the
OECD NUCLEAR ENERGY AGENCY
in co-operation with the
INTERNATIONAL ATOMIC ENERGY AGENCY

organisé par
L'AGENCE DE L'OCDE POUR L'ÉNERGIE NUCLÉAIRE
en coopération avec
L'AGENCE INTERNATIONALE DE L'ÉNERGIE ATOMIQUE

ORGANISATION FOR ECONOMIC CO-OPERATION AND DEVELOPMENT
ORGANISATION DE COOPÉRATION ET DE DÉVELOPPEMENT ÉCONOMIQUES

Pursuant to article 1 of the Convention signed in Paris on 14th December, 1960, and which came into force on 30th September, 1961, the Organisation for Economic Co-operation and Development (OECD) shall promote policies designed:

- to achieve the highest sustainable economic growth and employment and a rising standard of living in Member countries, while maintaining financial stability, and thus to contribute to the development of the world economy;
- to contribute to sound economic expansion in Member as well as non-member countries in the process of economic development; and
- to contribute to the expansion of world trade on a multilateral, non-discriminatory basis in accordance with international obligations.

The original Member countries of the OECD are Austria, Belgium, Canada, Denmark, France, the Federal Republic of Germany, Greece, Iceland, Ireland, Italy, Luxembourg, the Netherlands, Norway, Portugal, Spain, Sweden, Switzerland, Turkey, the United Kingdom and the United States. The following countries became Members subsequently through accession at the dates indicated hereafter: Japan (28th April, 1964), Finland (28th January, 1969), Australia (7th June, 1971) and New Zealand (29th May, 1973).

The Socialist Federal Republic of Yugoslavia takes part in some of the work of the OECD (agreement of 28th October, 1961).

The OECD Nuclear Energy Agency (NEA) was established on 20th April, 1972, replacing OECD's European Nuclear Energy Agency (ENEA) on the adhesion of Japan as a full Member.

NEA now groups all the European Member countries of OECD and Australia, Canada, Japan, and the United States. The Commission of the European Communities takes part in the work of the Agency.

The primary objective of NEA is to promote co-operation between the governments of its participating countries in furthering the development of nuclear power as a safe, environmentally acceptable and economic energy source.

This is achieved by:

- *encouraging harmonisation of national, regulatory policies and practices, with particular reference to the safety of nuclear installations, protection of man against ionising radiation and preservation of the environment, radioactive waste management, and nuclear third party liability and insurance;*
- *assessing the contribution of nuclear power to the overall energy supply by keeping under review the technical and economic aspects of nuclear power growth and forecasting demand and supply for the different phases of the nuclear fuel cycle;*
- *developing exchanges of scientific and technical information particularly through participation in common services;*
- *setting up international research and development programmes and joint undertakings.*

In these and related tasks, NEA works in close collaboration with the International Atomic Energy Agency in Vienna, with which it has concluded a Co-operation Agreement, as well as with other international organisations in the nuclear field.

Les enseignements tirés du Symposium, tels qu'ils sont présentés dans le compte rendu, devraient être particulièrement utiles aux responsables de la planification des travaux majeurs de remise en état et/ou de la construction de centrales nucléaires de remplacement, et à ceux chargés de planifier les activités de déclassement à long terme et d'analyser les aspects économiques de l'énergie nucléaire. Ce compte rendu est publié sous la responsabilité du Secrétaire général de l'OCDE.

TABLE OF CONTENTS

TABLE DES MATIERES

Session I - Séance I

IMPLICATIONS OF PLANT LIFE EXTENSION

CONSEQUENCES DE LA PROLONGATION DE LA VIE DES CENTRALES

Chairman - Président : M. R. VIDAL (France)

Session II - Séance II

PLANT AND COMPONENT LIFETIMES

DUREE DE VIE DES COMPOSANTS ET DES CENTRALES

Chairman - Président : Mr. V.J. STREICHER (F.R. of Germany)

Session III – Séance III

PROJECTS OF PLANT LIFE EXTENSION

PROJETS DE PROLONGATION DE LA DUREE DE VIE DES CENTRALES

Chairman – Président : Mr. D.R. HOSTETLER (United States)

Session IV – Séance IV

REFURBISHMENT EXPERIENCE AND MONITORING

EXPERIENCE ET CONTROLE DES TRAVAUX DE RENOVATION

Chairman – Président : Dr. G. SCHÜCKTANZ (F.R. of Germany)

Session V – Séance V

ECONOMIC ANALYSES ON PLANT LIFE EXTENSION

ANALYSE ECONOMIQUE DE LA PROLONGATION DE LA DUREE DE VIE
DES CENTRALES

Chairman – Président : Mr. T.T. FLETCHER (United States)

Session VI - Séance VI

CLOSING SESSION

SEANCE DE CLOTURE

Chairman - Président : Mr. P.R. PARKMAN (United Kingdom)

SUMMARY OF SESSIONS - RESUME DES SEANCES

OPENING ADDRESS

H.K. Shapar
Director General of the OECD Nuclear Energy Agency

Ladies and Gentlemen

1.   I am happy to welcome you to this Symposium and to the OECD. I believe that for some of you this is the first time that you are attending a meeting sponsored by the OECD Nuclear Energy Agency.

2.   As you know, we are an inter-governmental agency, and as such the greater part of our dealings is with government representatives. However, we fully recognize the benefits to be obtained from close co-operation with the nuclear industry of our Member countries and I am grateful for the presence of the industry representatives here as well as, of course, of the government representatives.

3.   You may be interested to know the present range of our activities, and these can be found in two small booklets entitled "NEA Activities" and "NEA Newsletter", copies of which are available in this room. Here at the Agency we cover many aspects of nuclear power development and you will undoubtedly be familiar with many of them.

4.   We have all heard that, in the end, the success or failure of nuclear as a source of energy will depend, among other things, on economics. As some of you may be aware, the Agency recently published a comparative report on the costs of generating electricity from nuclear and coal-fired power stations. The report concluded that in most OECD countries, nuclear power had a very clear economic advantage over coal for base-load electricity generation. In fact, it is often said that the three main advantages of nuclear are economic, environmental and its contribution to energy security.

5.   However, as everyone knows, oil prices have fallen to a level where the nuclear advantage would be reduced if kept at this level. Additional efforts are needed to make the cost of nuclear electricity generation as low as practicably achievable, whilst maintaining appropriate safety margins.

6.   In our generating cost report, the lifetime of the plant was taken to be 25 years. This reflected the fact that most Member countries expected their plants to remain in service for at least that period. If we were to apply that assumption to every plant in the world, it would appear that 37 plants would reach the end of their lifetime in 1990 and as many as 160 plants in 2000. If my memory serves me well, I recall that the maximum term of a nuclear power plant license in the United States is 40 years (subject to renewal), but you start counting at the date of issuance of the construction permit rather than the operating license.

7.   When nuclear power plants were being started up in significant numbers in the 1970s there was no experience base for projecting physical lifetime, although designers did consider lifetime factors in specifying materials and component designs. It seems to be still too early to specify with confidence what physical lifetime should be expected on average. However, there is more knowledge now on behaviour of critical components which could determine or influence lifetimes.

8.   Thus, although we cannot expect to be able to define lifetime expectations very precisely, it does not seem to be too early to start discussing the question of nuclear plant life extension. That is why we organised this Symposium. It appears to us that in many existing plants a longer lifetime could be attained with some refurbishment and monitoring. If significant plant life extension really can be realised, we can expect to see some reductions in nuclear electricity generating costs.

9.   One of the objectives of this Symposium is to indicate future directions of the factors influencing plant life extension. You are the ones who can tell us, and I hope that your discussions will be of particular benefit to planners and analyists in our Member countries. We expect that the results of this Symposium will also be reflected in our future studies. I would therefore like to wish you a most successful meeting and I very much look forward to hearing the results of this Symposium.

10.   I would like to express our thanks to the IAEA, which co-operated with us in the organisation of this Symposium, and also to Electricité de France for arranging the field trip to Chinon, as well as all those who have made written contributions.

11.   I hope to see you all again at our reception this evening, which will take place in Salle A in the Château at 6 pm.

12.   Finally, I would like to introduce Mr. P.R. Parkman of the United Kingdom Central Electricity Generating Board, who will be the Chairman of the Symposium. Mr. Parkman is now Head of the Board's Nuclear Safety Operations Branch, has a wide range of experience in plant operation and is familiar with both the technical and economic aspects of plant life extention. ...

OPENING ADDRESS

P.R. Parkman
Central Electricity Generating Board
London, United Kingdom

Mr. Shapar, on behalf of the delegates here from no less than 13 of the OECD Member countries and also the delegate from India, I would like to thank you for that warm welcome, and your staff for making the arrangements for us to gather here at what I understand may be the first international Symposium on nuclear plant life extension. The increasing interest in this subject is clearly reflected in the substantial number of delegates attending.

When nuclear power plant was being constructed and commissioned in the 1960's and early 70's, they were built to the best engineering standards of the day. At that time, however, life limiting features were not predictable with any certainty. Hence, as a prudent measure, comparatively short amortization periods were ascribed to these large capital investments. As operating experience has been gained, it has been confirmed in a large number of plants that extension of operating lifetimes is an option, maintaining safety and reliability standards by selective refurbishment. The report by an NEA Expert Group, to which you refered, assumed the economic lifetime of nuclear plant to be 25 years, reflecting Member countries' expectation that their present plant will remain in service for at least that period. As a substantial proportion of plant approaches its "nominal" retirement age, system economics and capacity planning make it increasingly urgent to search a conclusion on nuclear plant lifetimes and their extendability because of comparatively long construction lead-times.

The papers to this Symposium address the engineering and economic considerations of life extension feasability, with speakers largely representing the viewpoint of utilities and manufacturers, rather than Governments as is the usual OECD practice, but with additional input from IAEA and NEA, who have collaborated in preparing this Symposium, as well as from the IEA. Although a most important factor, detailed safety considerations have been quite deliberately omitted from the Programme, since this is well covered in various expert discussions. However, in Session II we will have a report from the Workshop of the Pressure Circuit Integrity Expert Group that met here last week, and also one from the IAEA, putting the principle safety aspects into the broader perspective to be considered by the delates to this meeting.

We are fortunate to have session chairmen who are eminent in their particular fields. Mr. Vidal, Manager at CEA for Research and Development on Light Water Reactors, chairs the first session later this morning, reviewing the implications of nuclear plant life extension in broad terms. This afternoon, Mr. Streicher, responsible for the Kraftwerk Union Monitoring Division's Laboratories, will chair the session devoted to assessment of the impact of component lives on nuclear power plant lifetime. On Wednesday morning, Mr. Hostetler chairs the session on Plant Life Extension Projects. He is Project Manager for Surry Unit 1 Life Extension Pilot Project, and Vice-Chairman of the NUPLEX Steering Committee. That session is followed in the afternoon by one on refurbishment Experience and Monitoring, to be chaired by Dr. Schücktanz who is the General Manager in Kraftwerk Union's Reactor Technology Division in charge of primary system component design for nuclear power plant. The session on Economic Analysis of Plant Life Extension on Thursday morning, chaired by Mr. Fletcher, Senior Managing Economist and Director of Product Consulting at Data Resources Inc., completes the presentation of formal papers.

Apart from a short time for immediate queries after each paper, a period has been reserved at the end of each session for delegates to question speakers and to put their own viewpoint. In addition, in the closing session chaired by me, a substantial period has been allocated for discussion after summaries of each session by the Session Chairmen. I look forward with interest to that debate when I hope that as many delegates as possible will participate. Although we can hardly expect to reach firm conclusions on nuclear plant life extension, I hope at least that we will have clarified the key issues to be addressed when choosing between decommissioning and life extension.

The week will end with a visit to Chinon as guests of EDF, by all those who registered for this fieldtrip, to see the reactor internal repair techniques on A3 using advanced robots, and the A1 reactor which has been turned into a museum.

However, before we launch into this intensely interesting and vitally important subject, may I introduce Mr. Horiuchi, Deputy Director for Science & Development at NEA and Martin Crijns, acting head of NEA's Nuclear Development Division and our organising secretary, Soichi Mori who have been responsible for arranging this Symposium.

SESSION I

IMPLICATIONS OF PLANT LIFE EXTENSION

SEANCE I

CONSEQUENCES DE LA PROLONGATION DE LA VIE DES CENTRALES

Chairman – Président

R. VIDAL

(France)

PROLONGATION DE LA DUREE DE VIE DES TRANCHES NUCLEAIRES : ASPECTS TECHNICO-ECONOMIQUES

L. Bertron
Electricité de France
Paris (France)

RESUME

L'importance qu'ont prise les centrales nucléaires REP dans l'ensemble des moyens de production d'électricité justifie qu'un effort particulier soit consacré à l'appréciation de leur durée de vie et ceci d'autant plus qu'elles ne risquent pas d'être touchées à moyen terme par une obsolescence économique due à l'apparition sur le marché de moyens de production plus performants.

La prolongation de la durée de vie des équipements nucléaires ne doit en aucun cas se faire au détriment de la sûreté d'exploitation. Il est donc nécessaire de s'assurer et d'apporter la preuve que les différents équipements sont toujours à même d'assumer leur fonction sur le plan de la sûreté. Ceci suppose un suivi en exploitation du vieillissement des composants et l'adoption d'indicateurs de vieillissement à partir desquels les décisions de remise en état ou de remplacement devront être prises sous peine de devoir arrêter l'installation.

Le choix entre la réparation ou l'arrêt pourra se poser dès lors qu'il concerne un équipement lourd pouvant nécessiter des interventions de longue durée et des travaux complexes en milieux actifs.

Une étude technico-économique, prenant en particulier en compte le gain de prolongation de durée de vie espéré par le remplacement, doit permettre de prendre la décision la plus opportune.

NUCLEAR UNIT LIFE EXTENSION :
TECHNICO-ECONOMIC CONSIDERATIONS

ABSTRACT

The outstanding place of PWR power plants among the overall power generating facilities indicates the need for particular attention to be paid to
assessing their expected useful life. The more so as they are not, in the
medium term, exposed to the risk of becoming financially absolute which might
result from more efficient generating tools entering the market.

Yet, in no case should plant life extension affect safety in operation.
This makes it necessary to ascertain and produce evidence that the various
items of equipment remain equal to their function in terms of safety. Components ageing problems should be steadily monitored and ageing indicators
adopted, allowing decisions of refurbishing or replacement to be made to avert
plant shutdown.

The alternative between repair works or shutdown will possibly arise in
the case of heavy equipment likely to require protracted repairs and intricate
works in radioactive environment.

A technico-economic study, making allowance for anticipated savings in
life extension through replacement operations, should help make the most
appropriate decision.

Au cours de la dernière décennie, les centrales thermiques à flamme ont vu, dans certains pays, leur participation à la production d'électricité se réduire de façon importante pour des raisons économiques compte tenu de l'augmentation du coût des combustibles fossiles, au profit de la production d'électricité d'origine nucléaire.

Déjà, en France, et ce sera encore plus vrai dans les prochaines années, la production d'électricité est assurée pour l'essentiel par l'hydraulique et le nucléaire, le thermique à flamme n'étant plus appelé que pour fournir au réseau de la puissance en réserve ou en pointe. La réalisation du programme nucléaire s'est accompagnée d'un vaste programme de déclassement de tranches classiques, en particulier des tranches à fioul victimes d'une obsolescence économique précoce alors que leur état technique autorisait encore un fonctionnement prolongé.

Le remplacement d'équipements d'un certain âge par des matériels plus économiques n'est pas une nouveauté. Les différents paliers techniques du termique classique 125 MW, 250 MW, 600 MW et 700 MW trouvaient tous une justification économique soit par un effet de taille, soit par un gain de rendement ou de productivité.

L'avenir des tranches REP, toutes jeunes encore puisque leur moyenne d'âge ne dépasse guère 5 ans, sera-t-il soumis à la même évolution ? Notre esprit, façonné par 2 siècles d'accélération continue de progrès, a du mal à imaginer qu'il pourrait en être autrement. Pourtant, les centrales REP présentent, par rapport à leurs aînées, des caractéristiques particulières qui permettent d'envisager pour elles une plus grande résistance aux phénomènes d'obsolescence économique et technique.

D'abord, la structure des coûts donne aux équipements REP existants une forte valeur d'usage car ils permettent d'importantes économies de combustible en se substituant à des centrales de coût proportionnel élevé et on ne voit pas de raison pour que cette situation change d'ici de nombreuses années. En effet, le coût du combustible REP est beaucoup moins sensible que le coût des combustibles fossiles aux phénomènes politico-économiques qui perturbent le coût d'approvisionnenent, le coût d'approvisionnement de l'uranium naturel n'intervenant que pour 20 % dans le coût du combustible REP. On peut assister à une dérive des prix, on ne devrait jamais connaître de bouleversement comparable aux chocs pétroliers.

Les investissements nécessaires à la réalisation des centrales nucléaires sont et resteront des investissements lourds. Un fonctionnement prolongé des centrales REP retarde les investissements en moyen de remplacement. Des réparations importantes, des refontes de longues durées dont les coûts représenteraient une fraction significative de l'investissement initial peuvent ainsi se trouver justifiées.

Par ailleurs, il ne semble pas que le potentiel d'évolution des REP laisse entrevoir dans un avenir prévisible une réduction radicale des coûts comme ce fut le cas dans le thermique à flamme entre 1950 et 1970, ni une amélioration considérable de la qualité technique, en particulier dans le domaine de la sûreté.

Enfin, aucune autre filière n'apparaît aujourd'hui pouvoir détrôner sur le plan économique la filière eau légère. Les réacteurs rapides, prometteurs par leur cycle de combustible dans la mesure où les coûts de retraitements sont correctement maîtrisés, pourront difficilement, dans les prochaines décennies, si les conditions actuelles du marché du combustible demeurent, rivaliser avec les réacteurs thermiques.

Sur le plan technique, les conditions de fonctionnement d'une chaudière REP sont infiniment moins sévères que celles que connaissent les centrales thermiques à flamme dont on a aujourd'hui une idée assez précise sur leur capacité à supporter de façon satisfaisante le vieillissement. Le circuit primaire d'une chaudière REP fonctionne en monophasique, à basse température (330°C), avec un cycle pratiquement isotherme et des vitesses de circulations constantes. Les sollicitations en exploitation susceptibles d'accélérer le vieillissement sont de ce fait très atténuées. Par ailleurs, sa conception a fait l'objet d'études infiniment plus approfondies que les chaudières classiques. S'agissant de nucléaire, ceci est bien entendu parfaitement justifié. Mais il ne faudrait pas croire, parce qu'on fait des études de rupture de ceci ou de rupture de cela, que les installations nucléaires sont plus fragiles que les centrales thermiques pour lesquelles on ne se livre pas à ce genre d'analyse et où l'expérience montre d'ailleurs que les incidents de ruptures sont très peu fréquents et jamais aussi graves que le laissent supposer les hypothèses prises en compte dans les schémas de ruptures du nucléaire.

Il est donc raisonnable de penser que dans les 3 ou 4 décennies à venir le REP se succèdera à lui-même, avec des progrès possibles portant en particulier sur une meilleure utilisation du combustible mais sans bouleversement technologique pouvant justifier une obsolescence économique pour le parc existant.

Les exploitants de centrales nucléaires auront donc tout intérêt à prolonger aussi longtemps que possible l'exploitation de leurs centrales dans la mesure, bien entendu, où la sûreté de ces installations reste toujours garantie. C'est la raison pour laquelle EDF s'est engagé résolument dans un vaste programme permettant d'aborder tous les aspects liés au vieillissement des installations. Nos collègues américains nous ont devancés dans ces réflexions : l'EPRI et le DOE ont ainsi mis en oeuvre un important programme d'études centré, pour les tranches PWR, sur la Centrale de SURRY 1. Le projet de SURRY 1 est piloté par la Compagnie VIRGINIA POWER et a pour principaux supports techniques WESTINGHOUSE, STONE and WEBSTER et GROVE ENGINEERING. EDF participe financièrement à ce projet ce qui permet des échanges très fructueux.

o

o   o

Les évaluations de durée de vie des tranches REP françaises ont été jusqu'ici encadrées un peu arbitrairement par deux valeurs d'origine différente :

- une durée d'amortissement de 25 ans minimum escompté et pratiquement garanti, qui résulte d'une extrapolation des données d'expérience du thermique,

- une durée de vie de conception de 40 ans qui a été appliquée aux analyses mécaniques des composants principaux des chaudières nucléaires.

Entre ces deux valeurs, nous devons nous attacher à cerner l'optimum de longévité (nous nous apercevrons peut-être que l'optimum se situe au-delà de 40 ans). Les objectifs que nous avons assignés à notre programme de travail sont les suivants :

1 - Etablir la liste des matériels dont l'état de vieillissement ne peut être connu à partir des techniques habituelles de maintenance. Sont en principe exclus de cette liste les matériels mécaniques qui font l'objet d'entretien programmé et les matériels d'importance économique secondaire dont la remise en état ne pose pas de difficultés techniques et dont la défaillance ne compromet ni la sûreté, ni gravement la disponibilité.

2 - Parmi ces matériels, établir la liste des matériels sensibles, c'est-à-dire ceux dont la défaillance pourrait à elle seule mettre en cause la poursuite de l'exploitation parce que leur réparation ou leur remplacement est a priori difficile et coûteux. Ces matériels doivent de ce fait faire l'objet en exploitation d'un programme de surveillance approprié.

3 - Pour cette dernière catégorie de matériel, établir un inventaire détaillé des éléments dont on dispose pour évaluer les durées pendant lesquelles ils devraient pouvoir être exploités de façon sûre et fiable, les moyens que nous avons pour en suivre le vieillissement, les possibilités de réparation ou de changement, les durées et les coûts des travaux correspondants.

4 - A partir de cet inventaire, définir les actions d'étude, de Recherche et Développement, de retour d'expérience qu'il est nécessaire d'engager pour améliorer les connaissances là où elles apparaissent insuffisantes.

5 - Déterminer les conditions d'exploitation susceptibles d'atténuer l'effet du vieillissement sur certaines structures, par exemple en réduisant le nombre ou l'intensité des chocs thermiques, en réduisant la fluence des neutrons sur l'acier de la cuve par un arrangement plus favorable des assemblages combustibles, etc...

6 - Proposer des indicateurs technico-économiques à partir desquels une décision de réparation, de remplacement ou d'arrêt de l'installation pourrait être prise.

Il ne faut pas sous-estimer les difficultés de ce programme, car tous les matériels ou composants n'ont pas été traités de la même façon lors de leur conception. L'état de l'art en matière de conception des matériels mécaniques est différent de celui en vigueur pour les matériels électriques ou les structures en béton armé, ceci pour des raisons aussi diverses et variées que l'histoire des techniques, la sensibilité vis-à-vis de la sécurité des populations, la diversité des dommages susceptibles de les affecter, etc...

C'est ainsi, et j'ai déjà eu l'occasion de le souligner, que parmi les matériels couverts par cette réflexion, les composants du circuit primaire principal de la chaudière nucléaire, tel que le définit l'arrêté du 26 février 1974, bénéficient à leur conception de dispositions particulières qui confèrent à leur durée de vie de conception (40 ans) une signification plus précise que pour les autres matériels.

En effet, les règles applicables à l'étude du circuit primaire principal prévoient que soit effectuée, pour chacun de ses composants, une analyse de comportement lors de laquelle sera examinée la résistance de la structure à tous les dommages mécaniques auxquels elle peut être soumise en exploitation et dont il faut prévenir les effets. Cette analyse implique la définition, dès le début des études, de la liste complète des situations de chargement, notamment transitoire, dans lesquelles pourra se trouver le matériel en exploitation. L'étude vise à garantir, par le respect de critères définis par le code (RCCM), que le matériel sera à l'abri des dommages dûs à l'évolution des chargements (déformation ou fissuration progressive, rupture brutale) définis par la liste des situations.

Il suffit que l'exploitant s'assure de la validité des situations prises en compte lors de la conception et comptabilise tout au long de la vie de la tranche les situations réellement vécues. Il dispose ainsi d'un indicateur de vieillissement extrêmement précieux et d'un outil d'aide à la décision très efficace. Lorsque, pour une structure déterminée, le nombre de situations vécues en exploitation atteint la valeur prise en compte lors de la conception, il aura le choix entre les décisions suivantes :

- affiner l'évaluation des dommages en prenant en compte les situations telles qu'elles ont été effectivement vécues en exploitation (les situations prises en compte dans la conception sont toujours des situations enveloppe) et en faisant appel aux moyens d'études les plus performants ;

- en fonction du résultat de cette étude :

  - poursuivre l'exploitation si les marges de sécurité restent suffisantes ou, dans le cas contraire

  - remplacer la structure ou,

  - arrêter l'installation.

Dans le cas particulier de la chaudière nucléaire, on dispose ainsi d'un outil très performant permettant de suivre le vieillissement de la chaudière nucléaire et de prendre les décisions les plus opportunes.

Mais, c'est bien le seul composant mécanique (c'est aussi le plus important à divers titres) qui bénéficie de cet avantage . Le programme que nous avons lancé devra s'efforcer d'élaborer de tels outils pour l'ensemble des composants qui doivent être suivis, en prenant largement en compte de retour d'expérience.

Les composants électriques et électroniques constituent une catégorie à part de matériels dont il est nécessaire de suivre le vieillissement en exploitation.

Pour ces matériels, le retour d'expérience peut s'avérer d'un faible intérêt.

Prenons l'exemple des câbles électriques : aucune comparaison possible avec les câbles qu'on installait il y a 30 ou 40 ans. Nous avons depuis fait beaucoup de progrès : ils sont moins combustibles, ils sont capables de tenir à des irradiations considérables. Mais comment vieilliront-ils ? On peut en avoir une petite idée par des essais en laboratoire, mais il est indispensable de mettre au point des méthodes permettant, en exploitation, de suivre l'évolution de leurs caractéristiques afin d'anticiper sur le moment à partir duquel elles deviendraient insuffisantes.

Les composants électroniques -tous très nouveaux- posent eux aussi le problème de leur suivi en exploitation. A partir de quels critères considérerons-nous qu'un système électronique assurant la conduite et la sécurité d'une fonction d'exploitation atteint un taux de vétusté inacceptable ?

o

o   o

Je pense que des études de fiabilité peuvent répondre à ce genre de question. De telles études ont été engagées pour surveiller la fiabilité du refroidissement des réacteurs gaz graphite de St-LAURENT-DES-EAUX. Ces techniques, mises au point par la Direction des Etudes et Recherches à EDF, seront sans doute appelées à se développer pour les réacteurs à eau sous pression.

La durée de vie de la plupart des équipements industriels n'a guère de limite physique pourvu qu'on leur assure un entretien et une surveillance en exploitation convenables et qu'on procède aux remises en état des différents matériels ou à leur remplacement.

Dans une centrale REP tout, hormis les structures principales de génie civil qui devraient déjouer les siècles, peut être changé y compris la cuve du réacteur. Il suffit d'y mettre le prix.

Le problème de la prolongation de la durée de vie au-delà d'un minimum escompté et pratiquement garanti ne se pose donc qu'en terme économique.

Le plus important est de savoir apprécier très précisément le moment à partir duquel il devient nécessaire, soit pour des considérations économiques, soit pour des considérations techniques, de procéder à une réparation importante ou à un remplacement. Mais la décision relèvera toujours d'une approche économique.

L'établissement de critères de vieillissement basés sur les études de conceptions et les sollicitations véritablement vécues en exploitation, et un programme de surveillance optimisé constituent sans doute la meilleure façon de maîtriser le vieillissement.

Le vieillissement n'est pas une question qui se pose après 25 ans ou après 40 ans. Dès que le bébé est né, il vieillit. Il en est de même pour nos centrales : leur vieillissement doit être suivi dès la mise en exploitation pour ne s'achever qu'au moment de leur arrêt définitif.

U.S. NATIONAL AND REGIONAL IMPACTS
NUCLEAR PLANT LIFE EXTENSION

L. MaKovick and T. Fletcher
Data Resources, Inc.
Washington, D.C., USA

D. L. Harrison
U.S. Department of Energy
Washington, D.C., USA

ABSTRACT

This paper presents the results of a study performed by Data Resources for the U.S. Department of Energy. The purpose of this study was to evaluate the economic impacts of nuclear plant life extension on a national and regional level.

Nuclear plant life extension allows nuclear electric generating units to continue to operate beyond their original 40 year license period. Nuclear generating capacity is expected to reach 104 gigawatts (119 units) in the 1994-1995 period. Nuclear units of the 1970 to 1980 vintage are expected to account for 96% of nuclear capacity.

As operating licenses expire, a precipitous decline in nuclear capacity results, with an average of 5 gigawatts of capacity lost each year from 2010 to 2030. Without life extension, 95% of all nuclear capacity is retired between the years 2010 and 2030. Even with historically slow growth in electric demand and extensive fossil plant life extension, the need for new generating capacity in the 2010-2030 time period is eight times greater than installed nuclear capacity.

Nuclear plant life extension costs and benefits were quantified under numerous scenarios using the DRI Electricity Market Model. Under a wide range of economic assumptions and investment requirements, nuclear plant life extension resulted in a net benefit to electricity consumers. The major source of net benefits from nuclear plant life extension results from the displacement of fossil-fired generating sources. In the most likely case, nuclear plant life extension provides a $200 billion net savings through the year 2030. Regions with a large nuclear capacity share, newer nuclear units and relatively higher costs of alternative fuels benefit the most from life extension. The South Atlantic region accounts for a full third of the national benefits. The Middle Atlantic, California, and New England regions also show above average gains. This paper also discusses the importance of regulatory policies on nuclear plant life extension.

INCIDENCES NATIONALES ET REGIONALES DE LA PROLONGATION DE LA DUREE DE VIE DES CENTRALES NUCLEAIRES AUX ETATS-UNIS D'AMERIQUE

RESUME

Cette communication présente les résultats d'une étude effectuée par Data Resources pour le compte du ministère de l'énergie des Etats-Unis. L'étude visait à évaluer l'incidence économique de la prolongation de la durée de vie des centrales nucléaires sur le plan national et régional.

La prolongation de la durée de vie des centrales nucléaires permet d'exploiter les tranches nucléaires au-delà de la période de 40 ans autorisée initialement. La puissance nucléaire installée devrait atteindre 104 gigawatts (119 tranches) vers 1994-1995. Les tranches nucléaires construites dans les années 70 devraient alors représenter 96 pour cent de cette puissance.

Lorsque les autorisations d'exploitation arriveront à expiration, on enregistrera une chute brusque de la puissance nucléaire installée de l'ordre de 5 gigawatts par an entre 2010 et 2030. Si l'on ne prolonge pas la durée de vie des centrales nucléaires, les déclassements se traduiront donc par une perte de puissance installée de 95 pour cent pendant cette période. Même en tenant compte de la faible croissance actuelle de la demande d'énergie et d'une forte prolongation de la durée de vie des centrales thermiques classiques, il faudra installer, entre 2010 et 2030, une puissance huit fois supérieure à la puissance nucléaire déjà installée.

Les coûts et les avantages de la prolongation de la durée de vie des centrales nucléaires ont été évalués pour un grand nombre de scénarios à l'aide d'un modèle de marché de l'électricité mis au point par la société Data Resources. En tenant compte d'une large fourchette d'hypothèses économiques et de besoins d'investissement, il est apparu que la prolongation de la durée de vie des centrales nucléaires se traduisait par un bénéfice net pour les consommateurs. Les bénéfices nets procurés par la prolongation de la durée de vie des centrales nucléaires résultant principalement du remplacement des unités consommant des combustibles fossiles. L'hypothèse la plus probable montre que la prolongation de la durée de vie des centrales nucléaires entraînera des économies nettes de 200 milliards de dollars en 2030. Ce sont les régions dans lesquelles la part du nucléaire est importante, les tranches nucléaires sont les plus récentes et les coûts des combustibles de substitution sont relativement plus élevés qu'ailleurs qui bénéficieront le plus de la prolongation de la durée de vie des centrales nucléaires. La région atlantique méridionale profitera à elle seule d'un bon tiers de ces avantages. La région atlantique moyenne, la Californie et la Nouvelle Angleterre tireront également des avantages supérieurs à la moyenne. Cette communication traite également de l'importance de la politique réglementaire sur la prolongation de la durée de vie des centrales nucléaires.

ANALYTICAL APPROACH USES DRI ELECTRICITY SECTOR MODEL

National and regional economic analysis of nuclear Plant Life Extension (PLEX) was conducted using the DRI Electricity Sector Model. This model is a formal long run frame work consisting of mathematical equations based upon relationships derived from economic theory, political theory, technological structures, and statistical correlations. The McGraw-Hill/DRI Energy Group maintains this model and databases in order to provide quarterly, long-run forecasts published in the Data Resources Energy Review. The DRI Electricity Sector Model is comprised of the following six submodels: electricity demand, capacity, generation, fuel demand, cost of service, and pricing.

The first submodel is electricity demand. Macroeconomic activity is the most important factor in determining energy consumption. Macroeconomic forecast parameters establish levels of housing stock, commercial square footage and industrial output. These concepts establish a level of total energy consumption consistent with energy end use efficiencies. Evaluation by customer class of the relative economics of electric end uses and alternatively fueled end uses allows estimation of the electric share of total energy requirements. The electricity demand submodel adjusts these electric energy demands which arise from the structural analysis for behavioral responses due to real electricity prices and other economic parameters. Finally, electric energy forecasts are integrated with regional load factor assumptions to construct forecasts of regional electric load duration curves. Load duration curves are ordered electric load levels over a given period of time. The area under the load duration curve is the generation requirement.

Once regional profiles of electric load levels over time are constructed, the capacity submodel calculates additional generating capacity to be added over the forecast interval. Current capacity plans of electric utilities are used in the near term. Assumptions regarding capacity retirements and refurbishment are combined with the new and existing capacity to determine generating capability mixes in the long run.

After installed capacity is estimated, the generation submodel determines capacity utilization by fuel type and interregional power flows. The load duration curve configuration is utilized in a derating dispatch algorithm. Non-dispatched energy, principally Canadian imports, are incorporated in the dispatch analysis.

Generation by fuel type is passed to the fuel demand submodel. Heat rates, based upon historical regional analysis, are used to estimate the Btus of fuels consumed by electric utilities. Fuel demands are a function of consumption and inventory adjustments.

The cost of service submodel reflects the institutional and legal framework of electric utility regulation. Fixed costs of electric production are a function of ratebase, the cost of capital and depreciation rates. Ratebase measures the net investment devoted to electricity production. Variable costs are calculated based upon the cost of fuels consumed and operating and maintenance costs. Net interchange costs reflect the net revenue from interregional sales. These three cost components are combined with miscellaneous expenses to determine the level of revenue electric utilities are required to recover from customers.

Recovery of the cost of service revenue requirements are determined in the pricing submodel. Prices to individual customer classes are calculated based upon cost responsibility. Initial values for fixed cost allocation by customer class are estimated using historical data. Average regional prices are simply the ratio of revenue requirements to energy sales.

In summary, demands are predicted based upon a price and economic scenario. Capacity needs are defined by demands. The resulting capacity mix and demands determine generation fuel shares. Generation by fuel determines variable costs and capacity determines fixed costs. Once costs are allocated, electricity prices are determined and compared to the price scenario used in the demand forecast. Perturbing the analysis in any submodel creates impacts throughout the other submodels. Such integration allows the myriad effects of the nuclear PLEX issue to be quantified on a regional and national level.

ALMOST ALL NUCLEAR OPERATING LICENSES WILL EXPIRE BETWEEN 1997-2030

Currently, 100 nuclear units are on-line in the United States and only 8 of these units are greater than 16 years old. Between the years 1970 and 1986, 78,512 megawatts (MW) of nuclear electric generating capacity entered service in the United States. Over these past 16 years, 95% of current installed nuclear capacity has been completed. Twenty nuclear units are still under construction and nuclear capacity is expected to peak in the 1994-1995 period at 103,579 MW of installed nameplate capacity representing 119 units. When all current construction of nuclear units are finished, 96% of all nuclear capacity is expected to be 1970 to 1990 vintage.

Nuclear electric generating units are licensed by the Nuclear Regulatory Commission (NRC) for 40 years. As a result, the rapid growth of nuclear capacity will be followed by a precipitous decline in nuclear capacity as operating licenses expire. Figure 1 displays the historic and expected path of U.S. nuclear capacity if units are kept in-service until operating licenses expire. In the long run, nuclear capacity peaks at 14% of installed capacity in the United States, as 119 units are fully operational. In 1995, nuclear generating units are expected to account for more than 18% of domestic generation, a greater percentage than installed capacity due to nuclear's role as a base load source of supply. Operating license expirations halve the nuclear share by the year 2015, and the nuclear percentage drops to 2% by the year 2025.

EXPIRING NUCLEAR CAPACITY WILL NEED TO BE PROLONGED OR REPLACED

In order to understand the impact of a rapid loss of nuclear generating capacity in the 2010-2030 period (a loss of about 5,000 megawatts per year or an 18% annual rate of decline), an understanding of future electric generating capacity needs is essential. Capacity needs arise from the supply requirements of electric load growth and the adequacy of current supply resources.

Residential electric energy demand growth is expected to slow in the long run. Residential electric energy sales are expected to increase on average at a 2.7% annual rate between 1985 and 1995. Thereafter, growth slows to 1.6% in the 1995 to 2005 decade and at half this annual rate to 2030.

Non-residential electric energy demands are derived from the demands for commercial services and industrial production. Electricity serves as a factor of production used to provide the level of output produced by the commercial and industrial sectors of the economy. Real output for the economy as a whole (GNP) is expected to increase on average 2-3% per year in the long run. Non-residential electric energy demands are expected to grow slightly more slowly than real GNP over the long run. When the customer class forecasts are aggregated, the long run expected growth in electric energy demand is 1% to 2% per year.

As total electric energy needs increase, so too do the levels of instantaneous maximum demands faced by electric utilities. These peak demands are key variables for electric generation capacity planning. Figure 2 shows the trend in peak demand plus a 20% reserve margin. A 20% reserve margin is generally considered necessary to maintain system reliability. Peak demands are expected to grow in each region of the country at slightly slower rates than

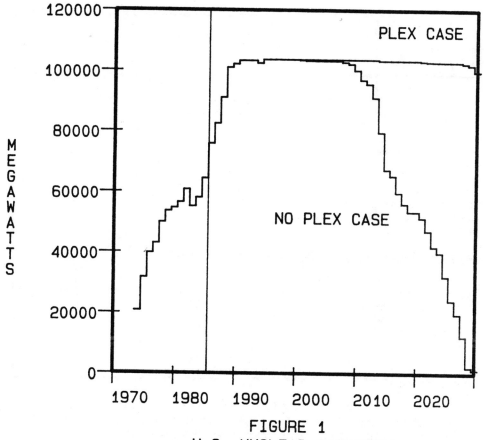

FIGURE 1
U.S. NUCLEAR CAPACITY
(ASSUMES ALL CURRENT PLANTS OBTAINED
CP TO OL CORRECTION)

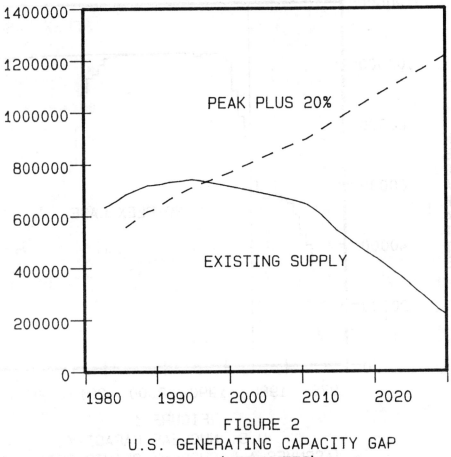

FIGURE 2
U.S. GENERATING CAPACITY GAP
(MEGAWATTS)

energy demands. Load management strategies are expected to be part of the response to load growth over the next several decades, enabling electric utilities to improve load factors.

Figure 2 also shows the expected share of peak demand that can be provided by current generating capacity, both installed and planned. Much of the current capacity in the United States is old. Over 18% of the coal-fired plants in the United States are older than 30 years. For oil and gas units, 22% and 18% respectively are more than 30 years old. Even assuming over three quarters of existing fossil capacity will be extended for 20 years of additional operation, a significant retrogression of generating capacity is expected in the post-2010 period. This data is based on the capacity plans published in the North American Electric Reliability Council reports. Planned coal and nuclear projects completion dates and other data are monitored continuously by DRI. Retirements of existing generating units to the year 1994 are based upon North American Electric Reliability Council reports. Beyond the year 1994, a total of 56 gigawatts of coal-fired capacity is assumed retired without extended service lives. This represents only 23% of coal capacity that is considered obsolete (over 20 years old and smaller than 300 MW). The remaining coal-fired capacity is assumed to be refurbished and to remain in service an additional 20 years. Similarly, the majority of oil and gas fired capacity is assumed to be refurbished for service life extension. The gap that emerges between capacity needs and existing supply planning is displayed in Figure 2.

The interplay of forecast demand growth and capacity expansion plans leads to the conclusion that approximately 810 gigawatts will need to be built over the 2010 to 2030 time period. New capacity to replace expired nuclear operating license units accounts for 12% of this new capacity need. Current installed capacity is 696 gigawatts. By the year 2030, installed capacity needs are 80% greater than current levels. Combining the needs of load growth with capacity replacement due to retirements, construction requirements by the year 2030 are 1.5 times the current level of U.S. installed generating capacity. Thus, even at half the projected load growth, all of the expired nuclear license units would still have to be replaced by new generating capacity. If nuclear PLEX investments are competitive with new generating unit costs, then the benefits of a nuclear PLEX program seems relatively insensitive to the uncertainties of electric load growth. Thus, the need for power is clearly present, and nuclear PLEX provides one means of meeting the future need.

NUCLEAR PLEX PROVIDES A NET BENEFIT UNDER MOST PLAUSIBLE SCENARIOS

Nuclear PLEX is an energy option which provides an opportunity for a benefit to society. Figure 1 displays the path of installed nameplate nuclear capacity assuming 20 years of PLEX. Given the uncertainty surrounding capital cost estimates for nuclear PLEX, a range of estimates were considered. Figure 3 shows the three levels of nuclear PLEX capital cost escalation and the assumed path of new coal-fired unit capital costs. In the middle-case, a nuclear PLEX costs roughly 1.2 times the cost of a new coal-fired unit. Given the past cost estimation record in the nuclear industry, a realistic albeit conservative assumption was chosen for the mid-case.

The middle-case nuclear PLEX capital cost forecast suggests that a net $200 billion savings is possible through the year 2030. Nuclear PLEX capital costs, higher than new coal units, are more than offset by fuel savings provided by continued nuclear operation. Table I is the projection of average national electric energy prices in the no nuclear PLEX case. Table II shows the change in electric energy prices in the middle-case nuclear PLEX scenario from the no PLEX case. Note, the large impact on the fuel cost line item. During the nuclear PLEX investment period, fuel costs are slightly higher due to nuclear downtime and replacement power from a capacity mix absent new and more efficient replacement units. Also evident is the expected positive impact on the fixed cost components; pre-tax return on equity, debt service, and depreciation. This price effect is small on a percentage basis but translates into $200

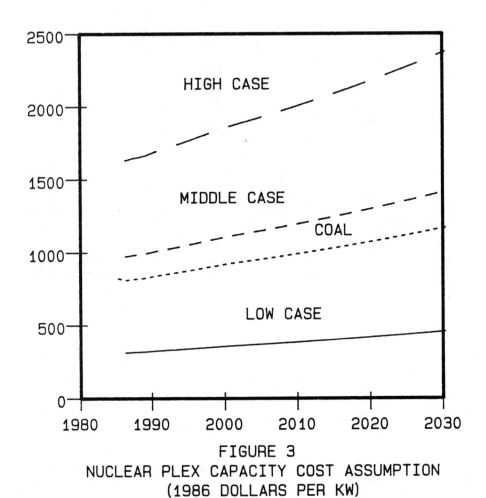

FIGURE 3
NUCLEAR PLEX CAPACITY COST ASSUMPTION
(1986 DOLLARS PER KW)

Table I
Average Electricity Price
NO PLEX Case
(Cents Per KWH)

	YEARS					
	1985	1995	2000	2010	2020	2030
New England	8.52	9.52	12.71	23.94	43.78	82.28
Middle Atlantic	8.02	9.24	12.23	21.91	39.49	74.01
South Atlantic	6.11	8.15	11.15	21.47	41.06	77.28
East North Central	6.40	7.73	10.04	19.22	37.13	71.10
West North Central	5.94	7.32	9.50	19.06	38.60	73.83
East South Central	5.18	7.50	10.16	19.95	38.96	75.87
West South Central	6.14	8.01	11.01	21.37	38.14	72.28
Mountain 1	5.53	6.66	8.03	12.89	28.40	64.04
Mountain 2	7.50	7.56	9.46	16.39	34.62	75.27
Pacific 1	3.91	4.91	6.36	12.43	28.03	59.88
Pacific 2	7.75	9.95	14.29	28.17	46.91	81.28
United States	6.40	8.04	10.79	20.56	38.68	73.80

Table II
Components of Average Electricity Price
UNITED STATES
(Cents Per KWH)

	YEARS					
	1985	1995	2000	2010	2020	2030

PLEX CASE Minus NO PLEX Case

	1985	1995	2000	2010	2020	2030
Return on Equity	0.00	0.00	0.00	-0.02	0.08	0.22
Debt Service	0.00	0.00	0.00	-0.02	0.07	0.21
Depreciation	0.00	0.00	0.00	0.00	0.02	0.02
O & M	0.00	0.00	0.00	0.00	0.02	0.06
Fuel Cost	0.00	0.00	0.00	0.06	-0.27	-0.96
Cancelled Nuclear Cost	0.00	0.00	0.00	0.00	0.00	0.00
Net Interchange	0.00	0.00	0.00	0.00	-0.01	0.00
Other	0.00	0.00	0.00	0.00	-0.01	-0.06
Average Price	0.00	0.00	0.00	0.02	-0.09	-0.52

Low Cost Case Minus NO PLEX Case

	1985	1995	2000	2010	2020	2030
Return on Equity	0.00	0.00	0.00	-0.02	-0.14	-0.30
Debt Service	0.00	0.00	0.00	-0.02	-0.13	-0.29
Depreciation	0.00	0.00	0.00	0.00	-0.06	-0.16
O & M	0.00	0.00	0.00	0.00	0.02	0.06
Fuel Cost	0.00	0.00	0.00	0.01	-0.30	-0.96
Cancelled Nuclear Cost	0.00	0.00	0.00	0.00	0.00	0.00
Net Interchange	0.00	0.00	0.00	0.00	-0.01	-0.01
Other	0.00	0.00	0.00	0.00	-0.01	-0.06
Average Price	0.00	0.00	0.00	-0.03	-0.62	-1.72

Higher Availability Case Minus NO PLEX Case

	1985	1995	2000	2010	2020	2030
Return on Equity	0.00	0.00	0.00	-0.02	0.08	0.22
Debt Service	0.00	0.00	0.00	0.02	0.07	0.21
Depreciation	0.00	0.00	0.00	0.00	0.02	0.02
O & M	0.00	0.00	0.00	0.00	0.03	0.07
Fuel Cost	0.00	0.00	-0.02	-0.06	-0.52	-1.40
Cancelled Nuclear Cost	0.00	0.00	0.00	0.00	0.00	0.00
Net Interchange	0.00	0.00	0.00	0.00	-0.01	-0.01
Other	0.00	0.00	0.00	0.00	-0.01	-0.07
Average Price	0.00	0.00	-0.02	-0.09	-0.34	-0.96

billion through the year 2030. The net benefit in the middle cost case arises even though significant capital expenditures are required to continue plant operation. Further, a 1.5 year net downtime was assumed. As a result, the PLEX case results show lower nuclear plant utilization levels during the PLEX investment period. Obviously, if capital costs and downtime are not required for nuclear PLEX but rather life extension is limited solely to recovery of the lag between license dates and operating dates then few additional costs are involved and significant displaced fuel cost savings are available.

Results of the nuclear PLEX high capital cost case suggest that the breakeven capital costs of the nuclear PLEX option are in the upper range of the capital cost estimates. On the other hand, the results of the low capital cost case suggest a cumulative net benefit in excess of $800 billion through the year 2030. Table II shows the change in national electricity prices in the low capital cost nuclear PLEX case.

The displacement of more expensive fossil fuels is a key parameter in the nuclear PLEX cost benefit calculation. One aspect of the nuclear PLEX policy may be to improve the availability and resulting plant factor of nuclear units. Increasing average nuclear utilization from 62% to 72% by 2030 doubled the mid-capital cost case benefits. Table II shows the change in national electricity prices in the higher nuclear availability scenario. Likewise, stronger coal price paths also increase the benefits of nuclear PLEX.

REGIONAL EFFECTS OF NUCLEAR PLEX

At the regional level, the impacts of nuclear PLEX are varied. The relative levels of benefit from the nuclear PLEX scenario follow the nuclear shares of the regions. A full third of the benefit falls in the South Atlantic region. The South Atlantic region has one quarter of total installed nuclear capacity in 1986. In that region, nominal electric energy prices average two percentage points lower due to nuclear PLEX. Other regions which show greater than average benefits include Middle Atlantic, California, and New England. These four regions together account for half of all nuclear capacity installed in 1995. Table III shows the distribution of nuclear resources at a regional level. Regions with large nuclear share and relatively higher costs of alternative fuels are the regions which benefit the most from nuclear PLEX. Although the mountain regions do not have a great dependence on nuclear capacity, nuclear PLEX impacts are felt due to power wheeling. Due to problems associated with siting new fossil units in California, the replacement capacity for California (PAC2 region) nuclear capacity falls into the mountain regions. Power wheeling is assumed to increase in the Western region of the United States in the long run due to load growth in areas where powerplants can not be locally sited. In the East, the New England and Middle Atlantic regions rely heavily on nuclear capacity in the generation mix. In these two regions displaced fossil fuels are expensive, being comprised of oil and natural gas. Nuclear PLEX competes with one additional source of power in the long run - Canadian imports. In all cases, Canadian imports were assumed to increase significantly in the short run and begin to decline by the turn of the century. This reflects the assumption that Canada and the United States will not agree to build new capacity in Canada that is dedicated to the U.S. market.

Regional electricity prices do not change dramatically in the forecasts. However, price impacts due to nuclear PLEX are expected to be significant at the utility level. National and regional price measures dilute the price impact of nuclear PLEX by spreading the savings across all sales in the country or region.

NUCLEAR PLEX REGULATORY ISSUES

The central task of utility regulation has traditionally been seen as protecting the consumer from the high prices and reduced output expected from "natural monopolies" providing electric

Table III
Regional Nuclear Outlook

| | 1986 | | 1995 | |
| | Number of Units | | Percent | |
	Online	Under Construction	Capacity	Generation
New England	8	1	30	33
Middle Atlantic	15	4	20	25
South Atlantic	24	3	17	20
East North Central	20	5	17	21
West North Central	8	3	10	14
East South Central	8	0	19	22
West South Central	4	3	6	9
Mountain 1	1	0	1	1
Mountain 2	2	1	17	22
Pacific 1	3	0	6	4
Pacific 2	6	0	12	16
United States	99	20	14	17

Sources: DRI @ENG/NUCPLANTS Database
Nucleonics Week, Oct. 30, 1986

service.   Alfred Kahn writes, "The essence of regulation is the explicit replacement of competition with governmental orders as the principal institutional device for assuring good performance."(1)   From this "public interest" perspective, regulators are assumed to make decisions designed to achieve economic efficiency. On the other hand, many social scientists have long recognized the role of electric utility regulation as a mechanism to resolve political conflicts between consumers, environmentalists and utility firms.(2) This "special interest" theory is used to predict and explain regulation as a political equilibrium rather than as a means to achieve a competitive market equilibrium. Several regulatory issues arise as a result of the nuclear PLEX policy, from both the public interest and the special interest perspective.

From the public interest perspective of regulation, nuclear PLEX gives rise to several issues. First, since the cost and benefit analysis shows an expected net benefit from nuclear PLEX, regulators need to encourage these policies to achieve the welfare gain to society. However, regulators do not make the decisions to invest in nuclear PLEX, rather electric utilities make these decisions. Regulators need to insure that the costs and benefits which confront utility managements reflect the real costs and benefits to society.   For example, an acid rain policy which subsidizes the construction costs of a new coal plant's pollution control technology may result in a distorted relative cost comparison to the nuclear PLEX option.   In this case, society still pays for the true cost of the coal plant through taxes to provide the subsidy, but the utility is biased toward the coal plant when compared to alternative technologies.   Further, the cost and benefit analysis of nuclear PLEX involves certain externalities.   Regulators need access to additional research which quantifies the implicit cost or benefits of unaccounted for aspects of nuclear PLEX. For example, nuclear waste disposal costs may greatly exceed the level of funds being set aside through the Nuclear Waste Disposal Act.   This problem may be large enough to significantly impact the cost and benefit results.   Alternatively, greater fuel mix diversity as a result of nuclear PLEX benefits utilities when dealing with the uncertainty of the future. This benefit has not been quantified. Obviously, a higher nuclear share of the generation mix mitigates the impacts of coal strikes or oil embargoes.   As a result, regulators face a two-part issue. First, the nuclear PLEX cost and benefit analysis must be sufficiently complete and include all real costs and benefits to society. Second, all real costs and benefits need to confront the decision makers in the nuclear PLEX area.

Regulatory policies to implement nuclear PLEX vary in complexity. Perhaps the simplest policy to pursue is to allow operating license extension to recapture the construction permit to operating license period. Prior to 1982, the 40 year license period for nuclear units was begun at the issue date of the construction permit. After 1982, the license period began when the operating license was issued.   Since the useful life of a nuclear plant is much more a function of operating life than elapsed time, recovery of the construction period as continued license operating period provides a policy with relatively low costs and substantial benefits. Furthermore, when operating licenses expire, the actual generation from the unit may fall short of the expected generation for which the plant has been designed. The most likely cause would be extended outage periods unanticipated during the design phase. Regulatory policy designed to extend the operating license period may be appropriate to recover the outage time.   Unless outages have affected the safety of the nuclear systems operation, such extensions also provide significant benefits with few costs.

The public interest may also be served by regulatory policies encouraging restructuring in conjunction with nuclear PLEX.   Nuclear plants which undergo life extension could be reorganized as separate generating subsidiaries of utilities. Efficiency gains may arise for two reasons. First, separate generation facilities would not be subject to state level retail rate regulation.   Regulatory responsibilities would be transferred to the Federal Energy Regulatory Commission (FERC). The FERC could provide centralized, standardized, and specialized regulation when compared to the regulatory environment of numerous state agencies. Second, separate generation entities would allow new financing arrangements such as sale and leaseback contracts. These innovative financing techniques can lower the cost of service.

Whether nuclear unit ownership is restructured or not, regulatory policy needs to address the decommissioning funds issue. If extended life and existing decommissioning charges are expected to accumulate revenues in excess of expected decommissioning charges, then existing decommissioning funds may be tapped to provide a source of funds to nuclear PLEX. However, these funds represent an overcollection from customers and if used for nuclear PLEX represent a subsidized loan to the nuclear PLEX alternative. On the other hand, expected decommissioning costs may be in excess of collections and current charges, in which case current decommissioning rates would have to be increased over the extended plant life. Further research on the nature and costs of decommissioning seems appropriate.

Regulatory action, particularly from the NRC is required in order for nuclear PLEX to proceed. Current efforts underway, including the progress of the Light Water Reactor PLEX Steering Committee, are expected to direct Nuclear PLEX regulatory policy. Relicensing guidelines need to provide a rational path for nuclear PLEX implementation. Well defined procedures, codes, and standards need to be promulgated by the NRC to allow utilities to rationally decide between nuclear PLEX and alternatives. Such a system should insure successful relicensing if a well-defined set of objectives are met. Regulatory objectives should be designed to balance the benefit of increased regulatory review with the cost of increased regulatory review. Such a balance provides cost effective regulation and encourages expediency in nuclear PLEX policy implementation. These objectives should clearly define what types of nuclear plant technologies are considered safe for prolonged operation as well as the number and sequence of life extension certificates required for extended operation. Nuclear PLEX is expected to suffer greatly if the prudence and correctness of PLEX investment is subject to review only after the investment has taken place.

From the special interest perspective of regulation, nuclear PLEX policy may suffer from the current inefficiency of regulatory institutions to resolve political conflict. All too often, legitimate political conflict is waged in inappropriate forums. For example, the Shoreham nuclear powerplant's evacuation planning forum is currently being used to fight the entire nuclear debate. A system which allows investments of $5 billion to be made over a decade and then allows a small number of participants to control the outcome through evacuation planning is a flawed system. The decision to operate the plant ought to have been politically resolved before $5 billion had been spent. Proponents and opponents of nuclear PLEX should be involved in formal debate which can resolve the nuclear issue before investment funds are committed.

CONCLUSIONS

The major conclusion of this analysis is that nuclear PLEX will benefit the electricity consumer under a wide range of plausible assumptions. Future electric load growth would have to be negative before the need for power issues became relevant to the nuclear PLEX issue. Regional impacts are varied. Most of the impacts are expected in the South Atlantic, Middle Atlantic, California, and New England regions. Total regional and national electricity price measures are not as sensitive to nuclear PLEX as utility specific price measures.

REFERENCES

1. Alfred E. Kahn, The Economics of Regulation, Vol. 1 (New York: John Wiley & Sons, 1970), p.20.

2. George J. Stigler, "The Theory of Economic Regulation," Bell Journal of Economics and Management Science (1971).

IMPACT OF PLANT LIFE EXTENSION ON GENERATING COSTS

Y. Inaba
International Energy Agency

ABSTRACT

The paper describes the impact of plant life extension on unit generating cost over the life time of new power plants. Three major energy sources
of electric power are compared : nuclear, coal and oil. It also discusses the
requirement for replacing existing nuclear power plants in OECD countries as a
function of plant useful life.

Although it is difficult to take into account specific conditions for
each OECD country, generally speaking, plant life extension is a very important
factor for the future development of nuclear power. If the plant useful life of
existing nuclear power plants is extended from 30 years to 40 years, the need
of replacing existing nuclear power plants with new ones in the coming 25 years
could be reduced substantially. Extension of plant life with neither incremental capital nor O&M costs will reduce the generating cost of nuclear power
plants by several per cent and could be an important option for future electricity tariff reductions in countries where dependency on nuclear power is
high.

INCIDENCE DE LA PROLONGATION DE LA DUREE DE VIE DES CENTRALES SUR LES COUTS DE PRODUCTION DE L'ELECTRICITE

RESUME

Le rapport décrit l'incidence de la prolongation de la durée de vie des centrales sur le coût unitaire de production de l'électricité pendant la durée de vie des nouvelles centrales. Il compare les trois principales sources d'énergie utilisées pour produire de l'électricité, c'est-à-dire le nucléaire, le charbon et le pétrole. Il examine également les besoins de remplacement de centrales nucléaires actuellement en service dans les pays de l'OCDE en fonction de leur durée de vie utile.

Bien qu'il soit difficile de tenir compte des particularités de chaque pays Membre de l'OCDE, on peut dire d'une façon générale que la prolongation de la durée de vie des centrales jouera un rôle très important dans le développement futur de l'énergie nucléaire. Si l'on porte de 30 à 40 ans la durée de vie utile des centrales nucléaires en service, les besoins de remplacement de ces centrales par de nouvelles unités dans les 25 ans à venir pourraient diminuer considérablement. La prolongation de la durée de vie des centrales nucléaires sans nouveaux investissements et sans augmentation des charges d'exploitation et des dépenses d'entretien entraînera une baisse du coût de la production électronucléaire de plusieurs pourcents, ce qui pourrait constituer un facteur important en vue d'une réduction future des tarifs de l'électricité des pays dont la production électrique repose sur le nucléaire pour une large part.

1. PLANT LIFE AND REPLACEMENT INVESTMENT FOR EXISTING NUCLEAR POWER PLANTS

According to projections by IEA Member governments and IEA Secretariat estimates for France and Finland, nuclear power generation capacity in OECD countries is expected to grow by 172 GW from 206 GW in 1985 to 378 GW in 2000. Since 11 GW of existing nuclear power capacity is currently expected to be phased out by the year 2000 under these projections, additional nuclear capacity of 183GW (172 GW + 11 GW) is expected to be developed in the coming 15 years. In other words, 12.2 GW or more than 12 one GW class nuclear reactors are expected to come on stream every year between 1986 and 2000. These projections were prepared during 1985 prior to the oil price decline and the Chernobyl accident. However, even without the decline in oil prices and the Chernobyl accident, these plans for nuclear power contained various uncertainties including costs of alternative energy sources, future development of electricity demand and impacts of environmental issues.

One of these uncertainties, which has been often overlooked is the requirement for replacing existing nuclear power stations. Since most existing nuclear power plants came on stream after 1970, as shown in Table 1, the

Table 1

AVERAGE AGE OF CAPACITY AND GENERATING UNITS
(Years as of 1st January, 1984)

	Nuclear	Hydroelectric	Solid Fuels	Liquids	Gas
IEA North America					
- Capacity*	9.5	21.0	16.2	19.1	20.9
- Generating Units	10.8	25.8	20.8	22.0	24.6
IEA Pacific					
- Capacity*	8.4	17.7	14.8	13.8	11.9
- Generating Units	9.3	22.3	20.9	15.9	14.6
IEA Europe					
- Capacity*	8.3	22.3	16.0	12.4	15.7
- Generating Units	13.1	25.1	19.1	16.3	22.6
IEA Total					
- Capacity*	9.0	21.0	16.1	15.9	18.1
- Generating Units	11.9	25.0	20.2	19.1	23.0

* Average age per kW. The differences between capacity and generating unit are due to the increasing size of units in recent years.

Source: Secretariat calculations based on data from Power Plant Register (University of Sussex) and other sources (for pre-1955 capacity and units). Excludes units smaller than 30 MW.

average age of existing nuclear power plants is much lower than power plants based on other energy sources. Therefore, the requirement for replacement will take place, at the earliest, in the latter half of the 1990s. This implies that the requirement for replacing existing nuclear power stations should not affect significantly the OECD Member government projections up to 2000. However, this is one of the major factors for nuclear power development beyond 2000 because the size of new nuclear capacity, which should be constructed in the future, could differ substantially depending upon the size of existing nuclear power plants to be phased out. Quite naturally, the amount of replacement investment for existing nuclear power plants is the function of plant life.

Table 2

DEVELOPMENT OF NUCLEAR POWER CAPACITY IN OECD COUNTRIES (GW)

	End of 1964	1969	1974	1979	1985	Phased Out by 1985
Canada	0*	0*	2.7	5.9	11.2	0.5
USA	0.2	3.4	31.7	54.6	81.4	0.1
Japan	–	0.2	3.9	15.1	24.7	–
Belgium	0*	0*	0*	1.7	5.4	–
Finland	–	–	–	1.1	2.3	–
France	–	1.3	2.9	8.0	37.5	0.4
Germany	0*	0.4	3.3	8.8	16.1	0.5
Italy	0.2	0.4	0.6	1.4	1.3	0.2
Netherlands	–	0.1	0.5	0.5	0.5	–
Spain	–	0.2	1.1	1.1	5.8	–
Sweden	–	–	1.1	3.7	9.5	–
Switzerland	–	0.4	1.0	1.9	2.9	–
UK	1.3	4.1	4.3	6.3	7.1	0*
OECD Total	1.7	10.3**	52.9**	110.1	205.6**	1.6**

*   Less than 0.05 GW.
**   Do not add up to total due to rounding.

Source: IEA Electricity Statistics and "Nuclear Power Plants in the World", March 1986.
Japan Atomic Industrial Forum.

Table 3 below shows pure arithmetic calculations of the OECD nuclear capacity to be phased out as a function of plant life based upon the data in Table 2. In reality actual useful life should be different from one reactor to another. Therefore, the figures just show the general trend.

Table 3

NUCLEAR CAPACITY TO BE DECOMMISSIONED IN OECD (GW)

Periods of Phase-out	Plant Life			
	25 years	30 years	35 years	40 years
1986 - 2000	51*	10*	2	0
2000 - 2005	57*	40*	9	1
2005 - 2010	94*	58*	40	9
1986 - 2010	206*	109*	51	10

* Do not add up to total due to roundings.

Source: IEA Electricity Statistics and "Nuclear Power Plants in the World",
March 1986. Japan Atomic Industrial Forum.

As shown in the tables, if the plant life of existing nuclear power plants is less than 25 years, about 51 GW of existing nuclear power capacity in OECD countries would be phased out in the coming 15 years by 2000. Approximately 60 per cent or 32 GW of the 51 GW is located in the U.S. Since no new nuclear capacity is currently planned to come on stream after 1996 in the United States, this suggests a possibility of a decline of the contribution from nuclear power in the United States as early as in the latter half of the 1990s, given the long construction lead time of nuclear power plants in the US, and a plant life of only 25 years. In other OECD countries, the impact of the short plant life (25 years) will be relatively small up to 2000 except for the UK in which approximately 60 per cent of existing nuclear power plants would be phased out if the plant life of nuclear power plants is only 25 years. In the period between 2000 and 2005, nuclear capacity of 57 GW should also be phased out. The capacity to be phased out would increase substantially to 94 GW from 2005 to 2010 reflecting the increase in nuclear capacities commissioned in the first half of the 1980s. As a result, with plant life of 25 years, 206 GW of nuclear capacity would exhaust their useful lives in the coming 25 years by 2010.

However, if the plant life is 30 years long, the requirement for replacement due to phasing out would decline substantially. Nuclear capacity to be phased out from 1985 to 2010 would be halved from 206 GW under the plant life of 25 years to 109 GW. Especially only a little more than 10 GW of nuclear capacity will come to the end of their useful lives by the end of this century, which roughly corresponds with the current phase out schedule of 11 GW by 2000 planned by OECD countries. In fact, most OECD countries assume, on average, plant useful life of around 30 years.

The requirement of decommissioning would decrease further as plant life is extended. Under the 35 year useful life assumption only 51 GW should be phased out in the coming 25 years. If it could be extended to 40 years, the

OECD nuclear capacity, which should cease to operate by 2010, would amount to only 10 GW. In comparison with the 30 year case, which most countries assume, plant-useful life of 40 years would allow 99 GW to operate in the coming 25 years and, thus, will put off the additional problem of replacing existing nuclear capacity of 99 GW or 4 GW per year.

Judging from the projected pace of nuclear capacity development in OECD countries from 1986 to 2000 (12.2 GW per year), the decline in replacement requirements of 4 GW through plant life extension from 30 years to 40 years is by no means negligible. Plant useful life is closely related to the future share of nuclear power in electricity generation especially in countries such as the United States and the United Kingdom, which are the pioneers of peaceful utilization of nuclear power.

2.   IMPACT OF PLANT LIFE EXTENSION ON ELECTRICITY GENERATING COST

Table 4 shows the effect on generating costs of longer plant life extension from 30 years to 40 years assuming no additional capital investment nor operating and maintenance (O&M) costs. In general, as power plants get older,

Table 4

IMPACT OF PLANT LIFE EXTENSION ON GENERATING COSTS*
(1986 U.S. mills/kWh**)

	Plant Life		
	30 years(A)	40 years(B)	(B)/(A)
Nuclear (PWR, 2 x 1100MW)			
(a) 6 year construction lead time	28.7	27.1	0.944
(b) 10 year construction lead time	30.4	28.5	0.938
Coal (2 x 600 MW, with 90% FGD)			
(a) Coal Importing Region ($40/tonne)			
(1) Constant Coal Price	31.3	30.1	0.962
(2) 2% p.a. real increase after 1990	35.3	34.1	0.966
(b) Low Coal Price Region ($30/tonne)			
(1) Constant Coal Price	28.0	26.8	0.957
(2) 2% p.a. real increase after 1990	31.2	30.0	0.962
Oil (2 x 600 MW, with 90% FGD)	55.9	55.0	0.984

*   Details of assumptions, cost components and calculations are presented in Table 5.
**   1000 U.S. mills = $1 U.S.

additional capital investments or O&M costs would be required. However, in the estimates below, future technological progress is assumed to bring about plant life extension from 30 to 40 years without incremental costs.

2.1   Impact on New Power Plants

Indicative generation costs of new oil, nuclear and coal-based power plants commissioned for 1990 are shown in 1986 prices based on a real discount rate of 5 per cent.

The method of calculation is the levelised cost in kWh, which allocates lifetime production cost over lifetime output of electricity. The assumptions used in these calculations are included in Table 5. The heavy fuel oil price of $180/tonne corresponds broadly to crude oil prices in the range of $26-$30 per barrel taking into account future increases in crude oil prices. Separate coal price assumptions are taken for a coal importing region at $40/tonne and an area close to low-cost coal supplies at $30/tonne. Additional results are shown for escalating real coal prices after 1990.

Generating costs of nuclear power plants can be reduced approximately by six per cent if plant useful life is extended from 30 years to 40 years without any additional capital investment. In comparison with generating costs by coal or oil, plant life extension for nuclear-based plants has a higher impact on generating costs reflecting its high capital-intensiveness.

2.2   Impact on Replacement Investment

The estimates above do not take into account the cost reduction which could be brought about by postponing replacement investment for ten years. If a nuclear power plant is expected to exhaust its useful life, for instance, in the year 2000, the owner of the plant should make replacement investment by that time so as to avoid a capacity shortage beyond 2000. However, if plant life could be extended for 10 years, the existing plant would be replaced by 2010 rather than 2000. Capital cost savings, which could be derived from this, could be substantial, although it differs from one case to another depending upon when existing plants are to be replaced. From the viewpoint of electric utilities with existing nuclear power plants, plant life extensions have the same effect as cuts in future capital investments.

Figure 1 illustrates this point based upon the same assumptions as those in Table 5. The horizontal axis shows the year in which an existing nuclear power plant should be replaced under the plant life of 30 years. The vertical axis shows savings in capital investment in 1986 prices which could be realised through the 10-year extension of plant life.

For instance, Point A in the figure indicates that capital investment for an electric utility could be reduced by $846 per kW if it could put off the commissioning of a new plant from 1990 to 2000. In other words, Figure 1 shows break even costs for plant life extension. As long as incremental costs are below the line in Figure 1, utilities would prefer plant life extension to replacement investment if they only consider economics. In reality, the choice of the energy source for replacement is not limited to nuclear power. In addition, Figure 1 does not take into account changes in fuel and O&M costs. Therefore the figure only shows a rough idea on the magnitude of total avoided costs which could be realized through plant life extension.

Table 5
GENERATING COSTS - 5% REAL DISCOUNT RATE (1986 U.S. mills/kWh)
30-Year Plant Life

	Oil with FGD*	Nuclear PWR		Coal with FGD*			
	2 x 600 MW	2 x 1100 MW		2 x 600 MW			
		Lead Time		Coal Importing Region		Low Coal Price Region	
		6 years	10 years	$40/tonne	$40/tonne+2%pa real increase after 1990	$30/tonne constant	$30/tonne+2%pa real increase after 1990
Capital cost	8.5	15.7	17.4	11.5	11.5	11.5	11.5
Operating cost ***	4.2	5.0	5.0	5.0	5.0	5.0	5.0
Fuel cost	43.2	8.0	8.0	14.8	18.8	11.5	14.7
Total cost	55.9	28.7	30.4	31.3	35.3	28.0	31.2
Reference:							
Capacity factor	70%	70%	70%	70%	70%	70%	70%
Construction leadtime	3 years	6 years	10 years	4 years	4 years	4 years	4 years
Capital investment ($/kW)	839	1558	1718	1141	1141	1141	1141
Initial investment ($/kWh)	(777)	(1346)	(1346)	(1035)	(1035)	(1035)	(1035)
(Interest during construction $s/kWh)	(62)	(212)	(372)	(106)	(106)	(106)	(106)
Fuel cost	$180/t			specified above			
Conversion efficiency (net)	36%	34%	34%	36%	36%	34%****	34%****
Heat Rate (kcal/kWh)	2400	2500	2500	2400	2400	2500	2500

* Plant with FGD using high sulphur oil.

** Beside SOx, coal produces various pollutants such as NOx, dust, particules and ashes. The costs of removing these pollutants to meet legal requirements are included in each cost component.

*** Operating cost in this study is directly incurred in a plant. Actual operating cost could be higher with the distributable costs of overhead expenses, which differ by utility.

**** Inland location, lower conversion efficiency.

Quite naturally the higher the vintage of the existing nuclear capacity is, the higher the impact of plant life extension on future cost saving.

Figure 1

SAVING IN CAPITAL INVESTMENT BY 10-YEAR PLANT LIFE EXTENSION –
A MODEL CASE OF A NUCLEAR POWER PLANT (1986 U.S. $ per KW)

Capital Investment
Saving ($/kW)

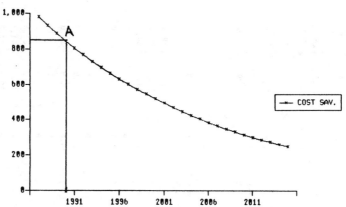

Years for Phase-out under the Plant Life of 30 years.

The figure represents the amount of the gains in opportunity cost realised by putting off the replacement of one nuclear power plant for ten years. For example, A (a case of a nuclear power plant which would be replaced in 1990 under 30-year plant life) indicates savings in capital cost which could be achieved by the plant life extension of 10 years.

Assumptions : Capital Invesment for a new plant 1558 $/kW
              Discount Rate   5%

As shown in Table 6, the share of nuclear power in electricity generation in OECD Member countries differs substantially between countries.

Since the way by which the electricity tariffs are calculated differs substantially between countries, the reduction in generating cost through plant life extension may not directly result in lower electricity tariffs. In addition, since the costs of transmission and distribution are not included in the estimates above, the potential of tariff reduction could be even smaller than those suggested above. However, as shown in Table 6, the share of nuclear power in electricity generation in OECD countries is expected to increase from 17.9 per cent in 1984 to 25.8 per cent in 2000. In particular, more than one third of electricity is projected to come from nuclear by the year 2000 in Belgium, Finland, France, Germany, Japan, Sweden, Switzerland and the United Kingdom. For these countries, plant life extension of nuclear power plants could provide utilities with an indispensable potential for reduction in their electricity tariffs.

Table 6
Fuel Shares of Electricity Generation
Actual 1984 and Projected for 2000
(The data is as a percentage of total fuel)

	Solid Fuel 1984	Solid Fuel 2000	Oil 1984	Oil 2000	Nat. Gas 1984	Nat. Gas 2000	Nuclear 1984	Nuclear 2000	Hydro/Geoth 1984	Hydro/Geoth 2000
North America										
Canada	19.5	12.0	1.6	.7	1.4	1.9	11.9	24.4	65.5	61.0
United States	56.0	59.4	5.0	3.4	12.4	7.3	13.6	17.1	13.0	12.9
Pacific										
Australia	72.5	.8	5.6	6.9	10.0	6.9	.0	.0	12.0	10.6
Japan	14.1	20.1	34.2	13.7	19.0	16.6	20.7	36.1	12.0	13.5
New Zealand	3.7	19.2	.2	1.3	17.2	6.7	.0	.0	78.9	72.7
Europe										
Austria	11.1	13.9	7.2	4.1	12.1	4.7	.0	.0	69.5	77.2
Belgium	33.8	35.2	8.1	5.0	4.9	1.2	50.8	58.0	2.4	.5
Denmark	95.9	87.5	3.7	3.7	.0	.0	.0	.0	.4	8.8
Finland	24.7	27.4	2.5	1.0	1.8	1.0	41.5	48.8	29.5	21.8
France	16.3	5.8	2.6	1.0	1.2	.0	58.9	79.0	21.0	14.3
Germany	61.1	52.3	2.3	2.0	8.5	7.1	23.4	34.5	4.7	4.1
Greece	60.7	73.1	27.7	4.4	.0	2.6	.0	.0	11.5	19.9
Iceland	.0	.0	.1	2.5	.0	.0	.0	.0	99.9	97.5
Ireland	19.6	57.3	19.5	33.8	51.9	2.5	.0	.0	9.0	6.5
Italy	15.5	49.7	40.7	10.4	13.6	5.8	3.8	16.4	26.4	17.7
Luxembourg	44.5	42.9	3.7	2.9	1.6	2.9	.0	.0	50.2	51.4
Netherlands	27.0	33.6	5.4	6.0	61.7	28.8	5.9	31.6	.0	.0
Norway	.0	.0	.3	.2	.0	.0	.0	.0	99.7	99.7
Portugal	2.6	40.5	46.4	3.2	.0	1.8	.0	14.2	51.0	40.3
Spain	41.6	40.5	9.6	2.2	1.7	1.0	19.2	31.3	27.8	25.0
Sweden	1.6	4.0	2.0	.8	.0	.0	41.1	44.3	55.3	51.0
Switzerland	.8	2.1	.6	1.3	.5	1.3	36.5	42.2	61.7	53.1
Turkey	33.1	33.2	23.0	2.1	.0	4.8	.0	8.9	43.9	51.0
United Kingdom	45.3	55.6	32.5	2.9	.9	.0	19.1	38.9	2.1	2.6
Total OECD	40.4	43.1	10.5	4.3	10.3	6.7	17.9	25.8	20.9	20.1

Hydro/Geothermal includes solar and wind in 2000
Source: Country submissions and IEA Secretariat estimates.

3.   CONCLUSION

Although it is difficult to take into account specific conditions for each OECD country, generally speaking, plant life extension is a very important factor for the future development of nuclear power. If the plant useful life of existing nuclear power plants is extended from 30 years to 40 years, the need of replacing existing nuclear power plants with new ones in the coming 25 years could be reduced substantially. Extension of plant life with neither incremental capital nor O&M costs will reduce the generating cost of new nuclear power plants by several per cent and could be an important option for future electricity tariff reductions in countries where dependency on nuclear power is already high.

PRELIMINARY STUDY OF NPP LIFE EXTENSION EFFECTIVENESS IN COUNTRY EXTENDING ELECTRICITY PRODUCTION EXCLUSIVELY ON NUCLEAR POWER PLANT PRODUCTION (CSSR CASE)

S. Novak
IAEA
Vienna, (Austria)

ABSTRACT

The first units with the reactor of WWER-440 type will come to the end of their planned life in CSSR very shortly after the year 2000. Without the life extension of the first generation of NPPs, the construction of new NPPs should be considerably expanded to cover CSSR national economy demands. A few variants of the Nuclear Power Programme development were analysed to assess the economic impact of NPP life extension using economic criteria used in countries with a central planning economy. Methodological approach and results of analyses are discussed for country scheduling to use nuclear energy only for electricity production expansion.

ETUDE PRELIMINAIRE DE L'EFFICACITE DE LA PROLONGATION DE LA DUREE DE VIE DES CENTRALES NUCLEAIRES DANS UN PAYS FAISANT REPOSER LE DEVELOPPEMENT DE SA PRODUCTION D'ELECTRICITE UNIQUEMENT SUR L'ENERGIE NUCLEAIRE
(Cas de la Téchcoslovaquie)

RESUME

En Tchécoslovaquie, les premières tranches équipées d'un réacteur de type VVER-440 arriveront à la fin de leur durée de vie prévue très peu de temps après l'an 2000. Si la durée de vie de cette première génération de centrales nucléaires n'était pas prolongée, il faudrait développer considérablement la construction de nouvelles centrales nucléaires pour couvrir les besoins énergétiques de ce pays. Un petit nombre d'options de développement du programme nucléaire ont été analysées pour évaluer, sur la base des critères de rentabilité retenus dans les pays à économie planifiée, l'impact économique de la prolongation de la durée de vie des centrales nucléaires. L'approche méthodologique et les résultats des analyses sont examinés pour un pays envisageant de n'utiliser que le nucléaire pour développer la production d'électricité.

In 1995, the nuclear fraction of the total installed capacity in Czechoslovakia is expected to be as high as 25%. Twelve units of the VVER-440 and six units of VVER-1000 with the total capacity of 11 280 MWe are planned to be in operation in 2000. The first units with WWER-440 reactors will come to the end of their planned life very shortly after the year 2000. Due to the shortage of fossil fuel the construction of new fossil power plants is not planned. The only alternative to extend electricity production is to build and operate nuclear power plants. If the NPPs were closed down according to their planned life, an increased number of new NPPs would have to be built to cover not only the increasing demand for electricity but also the production of the old, decommissioned nuclear power plants. The capacity development is shown in Fig. 1 and the marked area represents the capacity of NPPs that should be built to exceed the "normal" demands in electrical capacity and to replace the shut down NPP if the 25 years NPPs life is not extended .

It can be supposed that units replacing those decommissioned will have a capacity of approx. 1000MW and further about 1500MW per unit. The group of NPPs coming to the end of their lives and the group of NPPs replacing them by units with higher capacity is shown in Fig. 2 as scenario 1. It must be pointed out that only these particular capacities are shown. The capacities necessary to cover the increasing demands of national economy in electricity are not taken into consideration here as their number is the same, independent of the NPP's life extension policy.

As the second scenario, the life extension of the first generation of NPPs is considered (for WWER-440 and WWER-1000) - Fig. 3. Three years for refurbishment are supposed as the very conservative time schedule. Due to the shutdown for refurbishment, the extra capacity unit must be available to replace the above mentioned shut down units for refurbishment. Only one extra 1000 MW (WWER-1000) unit is required to replace consecutively the capacities of NPPs shut down for refurbishment. Despite the fact that during some periods its capacity is higher than the capacity of units under refurbishment, the differences inside the whole network capacity are relatively small and the electricity output of different considered scenarios is approximately the same.

Another considered scenario (Fig.4) with the 5 years life extension (up to 30 years) without refurbishment followed by 10 or 20 years further life extension after refurbishment can be considered if the technical conditions of NPP components and systems are good and are adequately checked. Other scenarios could be considered but only principally different approaches were analysed.

To assess different scenarios it can be useful to show the flow of expenses and incomes (Fig. 5) in a qualitative form. For the first scenarios it is possible to show expenses of three main types: investment costs, direct operational costs and decommissioning costs. For other scenarios refurbishment expenses should be added and expenses for decommissioning are postponed. An important question that was not studied is the possibility to use money accumulated during the life time for NPP decommissioning, for NPP refurbishment and life extension. The next questions are which part of accumulated money can be used for NPP refurbishment and/or which period of plant operation (normal and/or extended) would be available to collect money for decommissioning after the life extension period.

The integral of discounted income over the NPP planned lifetime should be higher than the integral of discounted expenses to gain a profit. The time of integration is longer if the plant life extension takes place and the time of expenses integration must include the period of decommissioning.

It is supposed that the NPP electricity production is the same in all scenarios. Then the following optimization criterion was used [1]:

$$N_{VTp} = \sum_{T=1}^{T_p} N_{VT} \cdot q^{-T} \stackrel{!}{=} min \; [crowns]$$

The year T=1 is when the first NPP unit comes to the end of its planned lifetime.

N_{VTp} — discounted total operational expenses during period of time T_p

N_{VT} — total operational expenses in the year T (sum of operational expenses of all NPP in operation in year T for particular scenario).

As the basic scenario was taken the alternative shown in Fig.2 and other scenarios were compared with this.

Total operational expenses consist of investment and other loans interests, fuel costs, operational material costs, water supply costs, maintenance and repair costs, personnel wages and salaries, burn-up fuel storage costs, decommissioning costs and others (technical services e.g.).

After detailed consideration of different types of expenses, taking into account technical and economical characteristics of new plants and those to be refurbished, neglecting expenses with very small differences between different scenarios the equation for different scenario expenses is:

$$\Delta N_{VT_p}^i = \sum_{T=T_1}^{T_p} \left[\alpha_{11} J_a^z - \alpha_k J_0^i + 0{,}015 J_a^z \left(1 - a_{main.} \right) + N_{dac_T}^z - N_{dac_T}^i \right] \cdot q^{-T}$$

where

ΔN^{i}_{VTp} difference between discounted operational expenses of basic scenario and scenario i during period of time T_p [crowns]

$$\alpha_n = \frac{\varkappa^n \cdot p}{\varkappa^n - 1}$$

$\varkappa = 1 + p$

p ... discount rate

n ... NPP planned lifetime (years)

$$\alpha_k = \frac{\varkappa^k \cdot p}{\varkappa^k - 1}$$

k ... NPP life extension (year)

For each year T

$$J^z_a = i^z_a \cdot N_z$$

i^z_a ... specific investment costs of new plants - basic variant [crowns/MW]

N_z ... replacing capacity [MW]

$$J^i_i = i^i_o \cdot N_o$$

i^i_o ... specific costs of refurbishment [crowns/MW]

N_o capacity refurbished [MW]

$0,015 \ (1 - a_{maint.})$ ... expressed higher maintenance expenses for refurbished unit (if $a_{maint.} = 1$ then the scenarios are equivalent from the point of maintenance expenses)

N^z_{deeT} ... decommissioning costs in the year T (1st. scenario)

N^i_{decT} ... decommissioning costs in the year T (other scenario)

The results of calculations are in Figure 6. The expense differences between scenario 1 (basic) and scenario 2 (Fig. 3) are shown. Scenario 2 represents old NPPs life extension about 10 or 20 years with 3 years of shutdown for refurbishment. The 20 years NPP life extension is to be efficient up to ratio $i_a^z : i_o^i = 1 : 1,2-1,1$. The shorter life extension period (10 years) is to be efficient up to ratio 1:1,4-1,6. The influence of more expensive maintenance is also shown.

Comparison of basic scenario and scenario 3 (Fig.4) is quantitatively the same as before. The longer the life time extension the more effective it is, if the refurbishment expenses do not increase considerably due to extended operation without refurbishment.

The refurbishment shutdown period influence on ΔN_{VZT} was not analyzed. This was studied in EPRI report [2]. Preliminary results for NPP with WWER-440 reactor taking into account the experience with manufacturing, building, operating and maintenance of these units, real costs of new plants and conservative presumption that a few main components should be replaced has shown [3] that WWER NPP life extension is the way to an effective electricity production that must be seriously considered in long range planning and relevant support to this way should be given in the near future.

REFERENCES:

[1]   Novak, S.:   NPP Life Termination and Problems of Life Extension
                        (in Slovak), Jaderna energie (to be published)

[2]   Extended life operation of light water reactors: Economic and
      Technological Review Vol. 1, Summary, EPRI NP-2418, Volume 1, June
      1982

[3]   Novak, S: NPP Main Components Replacement for Life Extension
                        (in Slovak), Jaderna energie (to be published)

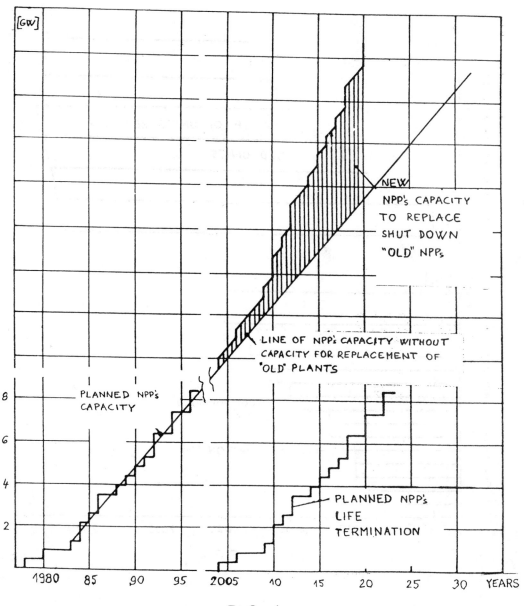

FIG. 1.

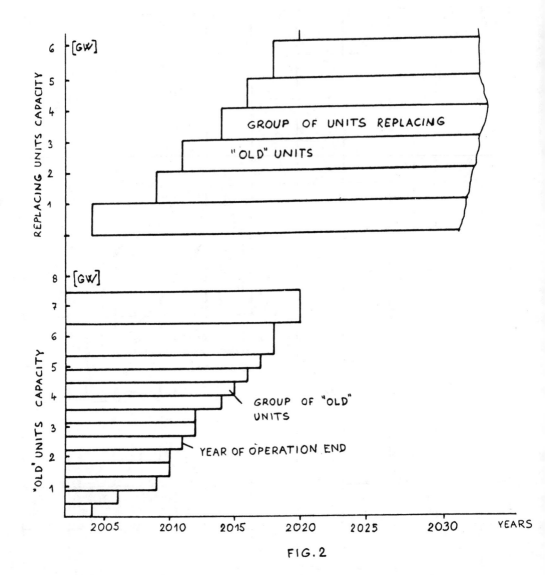

FIG. 2

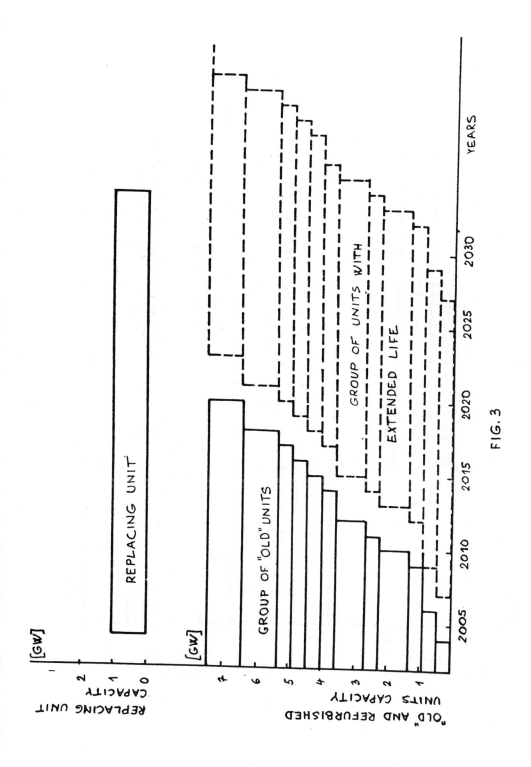

FIG. 3

- 55 -

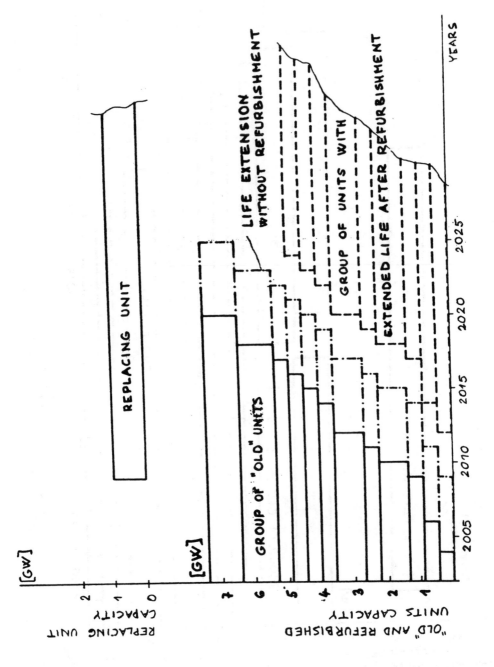

FIG. 4

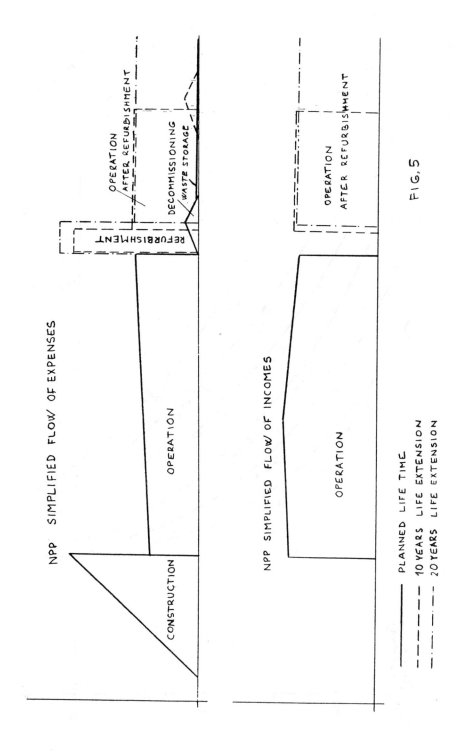

NPP SIMPLIFIED FLOW OF EXPENSES

CONSTRUCTION

OPERATION

REFURBISHMENT

OPERATION AFTER REFURBISHMENT

DECOMMISSIONING

WASTE STORAGE

NPP SIMPLIFIED FLOW OF INCOMES

OPERATION

OPERATION AFTER REFURBISHMENT

——— PLANNED LIFE TIME
----- 10 YEARS LIFE EXTENSION
—·—·— 20 YEARS LIFE EXTENSION

FIG. 5

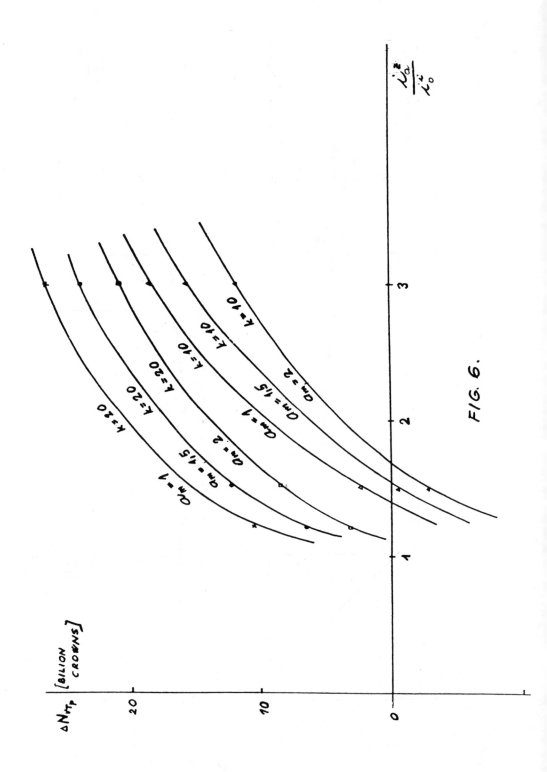

FIG. 6.

DISCUSSION

R. VIDAL, France

Quelle est la réglementation en France concernant les centrales nucléaires ?

L. BERTRON, France

Il n'existe pas à proprement parler de réglementation fixant la durée de vie des centrales nucléaires. L'exploitant doit être en mesure, à tout instant, d'apporter aux organismes de sûreté la preuve que les systèmes participant à la sûreté des installations sont capables d'assumer leur mission et ce indépendamment de leur âge.

R. VIDAL, France

Quel est le temps nécessaire pour les travaux de rénovation des centrales à l'issue d'une période de fonctionnement de 25 ou 30 ans ?

L. REYNES, France

Un arrêt de longue durée de 2 à 3 ans pour remise à niveau d'une centrale nucléaire, a souvent été considéré dans les études économiques concernant l'extension de la durée de vie des centrales nucléaires.

L'analyse que nous faisons à EDF nous conduit à penser que cette hypothèse de travail ne sera pas confirmée par la réalité.

Nous pensons plutôt que la nécessité de réparer ou remplacer certains composants, apparaîtra de façon plus étalée dans le temps. La prolongation de la durée de vie se présentera donc davantage comme une politique d'entretien soutenue avec de grosses réparations ou chargement de composants à l'occasion de visites quinquennales ou décennales que comme une refonte de l'installation au terme de sa durée de vie de conception.

Cet étagement des travaux dans le temps devrait présenter, par ailleurs, un avantage économique sur l'arrêt unique de longue durée.

S. NOVAK, IAEA

Three years was used in the study as the upper limit on time taken for refurbishment. No detailed analyses of refurbishment period were made.

C.J. MARCHESE, United Kingdom

It is not always possible as was suggested by one speaker to use the capacity margin to accommodate outage for refurbishment. For example in the United Kingdom much of the 20 to 25 per cent capacity margin is needed to cover the winter peak. Outages in winter can be economically quite damaging. Therefore we need to ensure the refurbishment outages in the U.K. certainly do not last longer than one year.

L. VIDAL, France

Les centrales refroidies au gaz sont-elles comparées aux centrales à eau ?

C.J. MARCHESE, United Kingdom

Unlike LWRs, there are definite life limiting features for gas-cooled reactors (such as the graphite core) and therefore a more cautious approach is necessary for such plants.

A. MARTEL, France

Les centrales françaises refroidies au gaz carbonique ont un coeur composé de graphite représentant une masse importante. Le vieillissement de ces installations est partout dû à des phénomènes de corrosion à la fois du graphite et des aciers des structures.

Il n'est pas envisageable de remplacer ces composants dans ce type de centrales, ce qui exclut une opération de prolongation de leur durée de vie.

La durée de vie technique qu'il est raisonnable de considérer pour ces centrales est de l'ordre de 25 à 30 ans et il est probable que l'intérêt économique conduira à les exploiter jusqu'à leur fin de vie technique.

R.S. HART, Canada

We believe that in CANDU we can replace various components, as they come to the ends of their differing useful lives, within a 90 day period which can be scheduled in off-peak periods.

J. BOYER, France

L'augmentation des performances des composants est-elle possible et compatible pour leur remplacement dans le cadre de l'extension de durée de vie, ou faut-il que les composants conservent leurs performances initiales, notamment vis-à-vis des critères de sûreté et du fonctionnement général de la centrale ?

A. REMOND, France

Il n'existe pas de réponse unique à la question posée : chaque centrale dispose de marges particulières sur des composants principaux, marges qui sont généralement mises en évidence lors du démarrage et du début d'exploitation. Dans la majeure partie des cas, ce sont les installations les plus anciennes qui disposent du plus de marges, et il est alors possible, lors d'un remplacement de composant principal, d'exploiter la marge générale disponible. Une telle augmentation de performance nécessite de prendre en considération l'ensemble des systèmes et circuits et nécessite un complément de licensing.

A l'opposé, des unités modernes ont mieux cerné les capacités maximales d'usage des matériels et il y a généralement moins de marges disponibles.

La réponse dépend, en conclusion, de chaque modèle de chaudière, des composants tels que réellement installés et du mode d'exploitation ultérieurement souhaité.

L. REYNES, France

Je partage la position exprimée par M. Remond sur les possibilités d'augmentation de puissance des réacteurs au cours de programme d'allongement de la durée de vie. J'ajouterai qu'une telle opération nécessite la vérification du dimensionnement de tous les systèmes, en particulier des systèmes de sûreté. Elle se conçoit bien, au cours d'un arrêt de longue durée de refonte de l'installation. Dans la mesure où les opérations liées à l'allongement de la durée de vie se feraient ponctuellement au cours de visites quinquennales ou décennales, une telle refonte de l'installation étalée dans le temps, ne présenterait guère d'intérêt.

En ce qui concerne EDF, nos réacteurs n'ont pas de marges importantes. Il y a une possibilité d'augmenter la puissance de 5 pour cent sur le 900 MW et pratiquement rien sur les 1300 MW. Cette question est indépendante du projet "durée de vie" dans lequel nous n'envisageons pas d'augmentation significative de la capacité.

Par ailleurs, on peut prendre le terme de performances dans un sens plus général. Je voudrais souligner deux aspects qui sont toujours soigneusement considérés dans les études de remplacement d'appareil.

D'abord, la durée de vie qui doit être meilleure que celle de l'appareil qu'on remplace. Ensuite la disponibilité qu'il faut souvent améliorer. Je peux citer en exemple les nouveaux générateurs de vapeur dont nous avons demandé l'étude à FRAMATOME qui seraient susceptibles de remplacer les premiers appareils des unités de 900 MW pour lesquels nous avons de sérieux doutes sur leur longévité. Ces aspects seront très probablement décrits par M. Remond de FRAMATOME dans la communication qu'il présentera ultérieurement.

D.L. HARRISON, United States

In the US, as long as safety requirements are met, enhancements in performance are allowable. Furthermore, there may be deviations from regulatory technical specifications and on requirements for operation only if the licensee presents acceptable justification to the NRC.

SESSION II

PLANT AND COMPONENT LIFETIMES

SEANCE II

DUREE DE VIE DES COMPOSANTS ET DES CENTRALES

Chairman – Président

V.J. STREICHER

(Federal Republic of Germany)

SAFETY ASPECTS OF NPP AGEING AND OTHER
IAEA ACTIVITIES RELATED TO PLANT LIFE EXTENSION

S.Novak, M.Podest
International Atomic Energy Agency
Vienna (Austria)

ABSTRACT

    As nuclear power plants in IAEA Member States are getting old, the
IAEA, in accordance with requests from Member States, has commenced its
activities with regard to problems of NPP ageing and life extension.
Information on topics that were discussed during Working Group and Technical
Committee Meetings on Safety Aspects of NPP Ageing are presented in this
paper. The content of the state of the art report "On Safety Aspects of
Ageing", which is currently under development, is outlined. Safety aspects
of ageing and life extension have been included in IAEA activity and in
addition, technical aspects of NPP life extension have been discussed at
varying lengths at IAEA meetings in recent years. Future IAEA activity will
be scheduled based on the recommendations made at the IAEA International
Symposium on Safety Aspects of Ageing and Maintenance of NPPs.

QUESTIONS DE SURETE LIEES AU VIEILLISSEMENT DES CENTRALES NUCLEAIRES ET AUTRES ACTIVITES DE L'AIEA RELATIVES A LA PROLONGATION DE LA DUREE DE VIE DES CENTRALES

RESUME

Compte tenu du vieillissement du parc nucléaire dans les pays Membres de l'AIEA, l'Agence Internationale de l'Energie Atomique a entrepris d'étudier, conformément aux demandes de ses pays Membres, les problèmes du vieillissement des centrales nucléaires et de la prolongation de leur durée de vie. Ce rapport présente des informations sur les thèmes abordés dans le cadre des réunions du Groupe de travail et du Comité technique sur les questions de sûreté liées au vieillissement des centrales nucléaires. Le contenu du rapport sur l'état des connaissances intitulé "Questions de sûreté liées au vieillissement", actuellement en cours de préparation, est examiné. L'AIEA ne s'intéresse pas seulement aux questions de sûreté liées au vieillissement et à la prolongation de la durée de vie. Au cours des dernières années, les aspects techniques de la prolongation de la durée de vie des centrales nucléaires ont été également débattus sous différents angles dans le cadre de réunions de l'AIEA. Les activités futures de l'Agence seront programmées en tenant compte des recommandations formulées lors du colloque international de l'AIE sur les questions de sûreté liées au vieillissement et à l'entretien de centrales nucléaires.

INTRODUCTION

For more than 30 years nuclear power plants have been supplying electric energy to national grids and the 382 nuclear power plants (NPP) in 26 countries have produced the equivalent of approx. 560 mill t coal in mid-1986. This figure is comparable to one year's consumption of coal in the USA or the USSR.

Some of these NPPs are, of course, already approaching or are even beyond the end of their planned lifetime, which, for most designs, was estimated at 25-30 years of operation. Whether or not measures should be taken to extend this lifetime by refurbishment of the worn or obsolete components, becomes an important economic question in a number of countries in the "nuclear family". However, long before the end of design lifetime is reached, age-related processes can potentially affect the safety of NPPs in operation, if appropriate measures are not taken.

It is evident from the figure below showing the breakdown of power reactor ages that the age of power reactors in Member State countries is increasing.

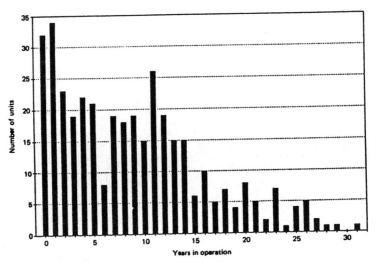

Age distribution of power reactors (completed years) (December 1985). Source: IAEA Power Reactor Information System (PRIS).

The number of NPPs which will reach the age of 25 or 30 years during the period between 1990 and 2000 is shown in Table 1 (taken from the IAEA Power Reactors Information System - PRIS).

TABLE 1:   Number of Nuclear Power Plants reaching 25 or 30 years of operation within the years 1990-2000

Years of operation	Year										
	1990	91	92	93	94	95	96	97	98	99	2000
25	37	41	48	53	63	69	84	99	118	144	160
30	14	15	22	24	29	37	41	48	53	63	69

It can be seen that if in 1990 37 plants are 25 years old and 14 are 30 years old, the relevant figures by the year 2000 will increase to 160 or 69 respectively. The question of the safe operation of rather "old" plants and the question of NPP life extension as an alternative to decommissioning will therefore be of growing importance worldwide.

The IAEA, in accordance with requests from Member States, has commenced its activities with regard to questions of NPP ageing and life extension. These activities are undertaken by two divisions in the Department of Nuclear Energy and Safety, i.e. the Division of Nuclear Power and the Division of Nuclear Safety.

SAFETY ASPECTS OF NPP AGEING

These problems were included in the IAEA Division of Nuclear Safety programme in accordance with recommendations made by the Scientific Advisory Committee in 1984. The first Working Group Meeting was held in 1985 and the following topics were discussed by experts from the USA, FRG, UK and Italy:

- General aspects of ageing during NPP operation:
  - nominal
  - extreme situations

- Mechanisms of deterioration that can be categorized as ageing

- Mechanisms of most concern to NPPs

- Which safety-related components are most susceptible to age-related degradation

- Ageing failures - incipient, degraded, catastrophic

- Detection of age-related degradation

- Methods and sources for ageing data collection

- Methods for mitigation of ageing effects:
  - during design
  - during operational phase

- Methods for ageing study and analyses, modelling possibilities

- Regulations and standards concerning NPP ageing phenomena

- Recommendations for managing these phenomena during:
  - design
  - operation

- Approach to this issue in different countries

- Possibility of international cooperation, role of the IAEA.

It was generally agreed that much more concern should be devoted to this issue by all Member States. As a first step it was decided that available information be collected for preparation of "The State of the Art Report on Safety Aspects of NPP Ageing", the first draft of which was prepared during this meeting.

The document is intended to give basic information on the following to Member States with NPPs in operation and also designing and constructing NPPs:

- time-related deterioration mechanisms related to components, structures and systems used in NPP environment

-   relationship of material degradation to component degradation due to ageing

-   relationship between the ageing of components, systems and structures and NPP safety

-   identification methods of this phenomenon in NPP operation and by means of experiment

-   approaches to mitigate its impact on the safe operation of NPPs

-   the activity in Member States to research this phenomenon.

The table of contents of the first draft is shown in Annex I.

The Technical Committee Meeting on Safety Aspects of NPP ageing took place in September 1986. Twenty experts from 12 countries operating NPPs for more than 5 years took part in discussions which were held in four sessions:
-   the exchange of general information on the approach to safety aspects of NPP ageing in Member States
-   the exchange of experience with different ageing phenomena at NPPs, relationship between NPP ageing and safety, critical components and system determination
-   monitoring of ageing during NPP operation life
-   methods and provisions to handle ageing phenomena in NPPs.

Information on approaches to safety aspects of NPP ageing was presented by participants from France, FRG, Italy, Sweden, UK and USA. However, only the USA (NRC) has a broad programme for Nuclear Power Plant Ageing Research, the results and ongoing scheduled activity of which was also presented.

Participants from all countries presented their experience including methods and regulations applied in handling these phenomena.

There are three general approaches presently in use by Member States to address the capability of "aged" components performing their function during normal and accident conditions. Basically these are as follows:

A   Preconditioning the component by accelerated testing or natural ageing to some advanced life condition followed by experimental test to accident conditions or earthquake environment. This is commonly referred to as the qualified life approach.

B   Annual, biannial or ad hoc review of the plant's operating
     experience to identify components that are deomonstrating
     reduced reliability. Exchange or refurbishment is required
     prior to restart for problem equipment.

C   Use of only "well tried" equipment that has demonstrated high
     reliability under conditions that are comparable to normal and
     accident conditions. Limited use of accelerated ageing methods
     are allowed for "well tried" equipment to address some
     environmental conditions such as normal radiation, that may not
     have been part of the conditions upon which the reliability of
     the equipment was based.

All of the above approaches utilize continuing evaluation through
field experiences, periodic plant testing to assure proper functioning,
surveillance checks and preventive maintenance activities to assess ageing
during normal operation.

The second part of the TC Meeting was devoted to the above mentioned
first draft of the State of the Art Report discussion.

In addition to detailed discussions of the content of different
sections and their amendments based on participants' contributions and
updated information, general proposals will be taken into account during the
final preparation of the document. The document should cover both active
and passive components and systems ageing phenomena and should express the
distinction between them. Many participants expressed the opinion that the
document was dealing with a rather delicate issue in the light of possible
public reaction and that it should show a positive approach giving examples
of how safety-related phenomena can be handled during NPP operation.

Preparation of the next draft is ongoing and the final document will
be prepared after the IAEA International Symposium on Safety Aspects of
Ageing and Maintenance which will be held from 29 June to 3 July 1987 in
Vienna. Future IAEA activity will be scheduled on the basis of the results
and recommendations of the Symposium. The IAEA role in international
cooperation in this field is planned to be a subject of the panel discussion.

TECHNICAL ASPECTS OF LIFE EXTENSION

The activities of the Nuclear Power Division concentrate on the
technological aspects of NPP life extension. The main questions related to
this which are covered by the Division programmes are:

- operation of NPPs with a high availability and with a view to
  their life extension;
- the role of maintenance in the life extension policy;
- experience with critical components, such as pressure vessel
  and pressure boundary, steam generators etc., "remedial
  actions", repair and refurbishment;
- trends in the development of techniques for remote and safe
  repair, replacement and refurbishment of critical components.

Problems related to the availability, the role of maintenance with a
view to life extension, maintenance techniques, replacement of some
important reactor components, e.g. steam generators etc., have already been
discussed to a larger or lesser extent at IAEA meetings in recent years such
as:

- the IAEA International Symposium on Nuclear Power Plant Outage
  Experience, 18-21 June 1984, Karlsruhe, FRG

- the IAEA International Symposium on Nuclear Power Plant
  Availability, Maintenance and Operation, 20-23 May 1985,
  Munich, FRG.

Similarly, the activities of the IAEA Interaction Working Group on
Reliability of Reactor Pressure Components have also been oriented to
questions having a high impact on NPP life extension. This Group's studies
also include questions regarding the selection and testing of materials with
a higher resistance to neutron irradiation embrittlement, their structural
integrity and "repairability". Questions concerning pressure vessel life
extension by means of annealing processes are also encompassed. The
activities of this IWG will be extended to include some important components
of the secondary circuit, such as steam generators and turbo-generators.

Similarly, within the activities of another International Working
Group on Nuclear Power Plant Control and Instrumentation as a part of the
life-time assessment and extension, studies are being undertaken and will
continue to be undertaken concerning instrumentation and control system
obsolescence, refurbishment etc.

In addition to this, other aspects of relevance to NPP life extension
are included within the framework of computerized "Power Reactor Information
Systems" (PRIS), i.e.: plant performance dependence on age. The IAEA plans
to establish a joint international programme on the subject of plant ageing,
life-time assessment and extension in its nuclear plant performance studies.

SAFETY ASPECTS OF AGEING IN NPPs
STATE OF THE ART REPORT - FIRST DRAFT

TABLE OF CONTENTS

TECHNICAL ISSUES LIMITING THE LONG-TERM INTEGRITY
OF WATER REACTOR PRESSURISED COMPONENTS AND THEIR FITTINGS

N.R. McDonald
Nuclear Safety Division
OECD Nuclear Energy Agency

ABSTRACT

The paper reports on a recent workshop conducted by the Principal
Working Group on Primary Circuit Integrity of the OECD-NEA Committee on the
Safety of Nuclear Installations. The workshop sought to identify broad
technical issues that required further study as a contribution to determining,
in a safety context, the long-term integrity and hence service life of water
reactor pressurised components and their important fittings.

The workshop identified no specific technical limitations which would
rule out on structural integrity grounds the extension of service lives for
pressurised components and associated fittings beyond current expectations.
Rather, there are a number of areas in which more understanding and, in
particular, better and more realistic property and performance data will be
required for assessment purposes if the necessary confidence in maintaining
adequate safety margins is to be obtained. The Principal Working Group will
be taking actions on a number of these matters.

PROBLEMES TECHNIQUES LIMITANT L'INTEGRITE A LONG TERME DES COMPOSANTS SOUS PRESSION DES REACTEURS A EAU ET DE LEURS EQUIPEMENTS ANNEXES

RESUME

Le document rend compte d'une réunion de travail organisée récemment par le Groupe principal de travail n° 3 du CSIN (Comité sur la sûreté des installations nucléaires) : Intégrité du circuit primaire. Les participants à la réunion de travail se sont attachés à définir s'il existe des problèmes techniques de portée générale dont il convient d'approfondir l'étude pour contribuer à déterminer, du point de vue de la sûreté, l'intégrité à long terme et donc la vie utile des composants sous pression des réacteurs et de leurs équipements annexes.

S'agissant de l'intégrité des structures, il n'y a, selon les participants à la réunion, aucun obstacle technique particulier à la prolongation au-delà des prévisions actuelles de la vie utile des composants sous pression et de leurs équipements annexes. En revanche, les participants ont observé qu'il faudra approfondir les connaissances dans certains domaines et réunir des données plus précises et plus réalistes sur les propriétés et les performances, pour pouvoir atteindre le degré de confiance requis quant à notre aptitude à maintenir des marges de sûreté appropriées. Le Groupe de travail principal prendra des initiatives à propos d'un certain nombre de ces questions.

The work of the OECD-Nuclear Energy Agency in the area of primary circuit integrity is performed under the direction of the Committee on the Safety of Nuclear Installations (CSNI) by its Principal Working Group No. 3. The Commission of the European Communities shares in the Secretariat of this Group. The main thrust of the work of PWG 3 has been to address selected topics in fracture mechanics and nondestructive examination where the pooling of information and understanding from national programmes will be mutually beneficial. In response to the growing interest in plant life extension the Group has turned its attention to the possible long-term degradation of primary circuit component integrity with age.

This paper reports on some findings of a workshop conducted by the Working Group last week. The workshop sought to identify broad technical issues that required further study as a contribution to determining, in a safety context, the long-term integrity, and hence service life, of water reactor pressurised components and their important fittings. The central objective was to recommend priority subjects on which the Working Group might usefully focus attention during the next few years.

The Working Group has immediately proposed actions on some matters in response to the workshop findings and other possible actions are being further studied. Given the immediacy of these events and the fact that the Working Group itself and the NEA have yet to fully review the outcome of the workshop this paper can be no more than a summary and personal interpretation by the author, for which he accepts sole responsibility. The major contribution of ideas from the 40 workshop and Working Group members and particularly from the discussion leaders and workshop chairman, Dr. R.W. Nichols, are, however, gratefully acknowledged. It is planned that the workshop will be fully reported at a later date.

Some background observations should be made about the workshop's discussions. There was no explicit time frame for defining "long-term integrity" nor for our purposes was any particular "service life" target appropriate to gauge technical limits. This can only be done at the levels of national decision making. Specific decisions on overall plant life extension will be determined by operational, economic and public policy considerations to which "technical limits" of component integrity will be an input but, in most cases, probably not the determining factor. The replacement of a reactor pressure vessel is almost certainly impractical so its degradation to a condition where regulatory requirements for safety could not be satisfied would spell the end of overall plant service life. For most other components, however, repair or replacement seems feasible in principle so that the costs of these activities rather than technical limits of functionability per se would be the key consideration in plant life extension decisions. The timing and frequency of repair or replacement will, of course, also affect the decisions so that the identification of service life limits remains highly important for all components. It is simply that no a-priori limit or target time can be set in an exercise such as the present one.

The workshop included important fittings such as supports, fasteners and reactor internals in its discussion because of their possible role in limiting plant service life and the similarity of degradation phenomena and assessment methods to those for the pressurised components themselves. One important consideration in this respect was that some of these items, for example reactor internals, while replaceable in principle, are not closely monitored so that impending failures are not forecast. Also some phenomena, for example mechanical effects such as wear and fretting, are so design dependent that they must be tackled on a plant specific basis.

The final observation is that the technical limits we are concerned with are not simply the inherent capabilities of the components to continue to function safely and effectively. Of equal importance will be our capability to determine this and to satisfy utility management and regulatory authorities that it is so. Such assessment will, in turn, require the existence of criteria against which judgments and decisions can be made. This range of interacting technical factors is used as a framework in this paper to report the workshop findings, although not all facets were the subject of workshop discussion.

The technical limits to be considered are:

1. Phenomena causing a loss of safety margins or component function.

2. Information on which to base assessments.

3. Ability to assess the loss of function.

4. Criteria for decisions.

1.   PHENOMENA CAUSING A LOSS OF SAFETY MARGINS OR COMPONENT FUNCTION

The phenomena of interest are those which can cause degradation of structural integrity - loss of toughness properties and of load carrying capacity and the development of structural defects.

a)   Loss of toughness properties:

. Neutron irradiation of reactor pressure vessel steel:

   - There is much information and code guidance for up to 40-year service from a number of ongoing national and international programmes;
   - Accurate extrapolation beyond 40-year service requires resolution of many uncertainties (dose rate, spectrum, temperature and composition effects; attenuation through the RPV wall, fracture mechanics and small specimen correlation);
   - Post-annealing behaviour requires detailed study if annealing option is to be implemented (toughness targets, re-embrittlement rate).

. Neutron irradiation of core internal structures and fasteners:

   - More knowledge required as there is likely to be a significant loss of fracture toughness, particularly in welds at very high fluences (10^{21} $n/cm^2 > 1$ Mev);
   - Helium embrittlement requires study;
   - Composition effects require study.

- Thermal ageing:

  - More information is required for coarse grained RPV welds and high impurity steels;
  - Thermal ageing effects need consideration in austenstic core-structure steels.

- Strain ageing:

  - This is not a problem except perhaps in non-PWHT repair welds.

b) <u>Loss of load carrying capacity and development of cracks</u>:

- Creep:

  - This is not a problem in LWR structures.

- Fatigue:

  - Extensive results and understanding achieved by International Committee on Crack Growth Rate point to a need for modification of code guidance (ASME XI);
  - Optimisation of water chemistry requires attention.

- Corrosion/erosion and corrosion:

  - This is generally well understood but optimisation of water chemistry needs better understanding;
  - More work is required on irradiation assisted corrosion of austenstic steel.

- Stress corrosion cracking (SCC) and environment assisted cracking (EAC) of stainless steel:

  - Extensive studies have led to good understanding;
  - Synergistic effects of irradiation on SCC of stainless steel requires much more work;
  - Optimisation of water chemistry requires further study.

- Stress corrosion of RPV steel in high temperature water:

  - There are recent indications that this requires study.

c) <u>Effect of repair and maintenance work</u>:

- Repair and maintenance of some specific components has been extensively studied (e.g. BWR pipe cracking);
- The effects of repair welding of the RPV and piping without PWHT require review;
- Repair of reactor internals needs much more discussion;
- Remedial measures for steam generator tubing are being given on-going attention.

2.   INFORMATION ON WHICH TO BASE ASSESSMENTS

The availability of reliable information relevant to the assessment of specific components and plants is perceived as a more significant technical obstacle than knowledge about the degradation phenomena themselves.

a)   Original design and property information:

- Maintenance of records is important;
- There are questions on the relevance of archive data to specific locations in the real structure (property measurement techniques have also been refined since older reactors were constructed);
- Selection and application of (conservative) generic data requires study.

b)   Changes in properties and development of defects:

- Relevance and use of surveillance data at long times;
- ISI of the RPV is well defined;
- Is acquisition, assessment and archiving of in-service inspection (ISI) data adequate;
- The ISI of cast austenstic steel structures requires more investigation;
- Surveillance, inspection and monitoring of core internals requires particular consideration;
- Philosophy of surveillance and ISI programmes needs careful reconsideration (difficult problems of best allocation of resources);
- Correlation of small specimen and laboratory tests to real materials and structural behaviour needs validation;
- There is a need to obtain data from decommissioned components;
- The availability of data, such as from ISI, on the real condition of containment structures and liners requires attention for long-term integrity assessment purposes.

c)   Operational data:

- Decisions required on what information to record and archive; pressure, temperature, load cycles, local strains; water chemistry, neutron fluence;
- Define technology to do this and where to apply it;
- Are records of maintenace and repair work adequate.

d)   Information on component performances and degradation from Licence Event and Incident reports:

- A rich and growing source of information but careful attention is required to the quality of input and to the extraction and appropriate application of useful findings.

3.   ABILITY TO ASSESS THE DEGRADATION/LOSS OF FUNCTION OF A COMPONENT

The available information must be applied to the assessment of the future ability of the component to perform its function with the maintenance of requisite safety margins.

a)   Input information (as in 2 above):

b)   Models of behaviour require further study and development:

    - Phenomenological behaviour;
    - Predictive models to assess extrapolation of basic behaviour and accelerated test results to long-term behaviour.

c)   Structural Integrity Assessment Methodologies:

    - There is considerable understanding of elastic and elastic/plastic fracture mechanics at theoretical and laboratory level and up to stable crack growth and instability stage;
    - There is a need for validation of fracture assessment methods through bench mark exercises using results of large-scale tests;
    - Margins (degree of conservatism) for different applications of fracture mechanics in safety assessments need further consideration.

d)   Availability of skilled and experienced personnel:

    - Policies which discourage the retention of the necessary skilled people (at both the basic and applied levels) could preempt the ability to perform the necessary assessments with the required level of confidence.

4.   CRITERIA FOR DECISION

        A basic question is how much (if any) degradation of inherent structural integrity can be accepted toward the end of service life of a component. This raises issues which are not new but are given a new focus in the context of projected service life extensions. For example, are the standards and criteria to be applied those for the as-built plant, current ones or is a case-by-case approach adopted to the specific plants for which life extension is proposed. The approach will be specific to each country, dependent on its laws, regulations and procedures. The measure of confidence in integrity assessments that would be required to permit very specific, as opposed to generic and conservative, decisions to be taken will require progress on a number of the technical issues cited above. The workshop did not attempt to address this area but identified the value of a dialogue between fracture mechanics, non-destructive examination and regulatory experts to achieve a better mutual understanding of the technical issues involved and the basis for national approaches.

SOME FOLLOW-UP ACTIVITIES

        The workshop has provided the Principal Working Group on Primary Circuit Integrity with a number of recommendations on subjects already included in its programme or deserving early attention. The response of the Working Group and of the Committee on the Safety of Nuclear Installations to those recommendations will be developed over time, taking account of resources, priorities and other complementary international activities, particularly in the IAEA. Some specific actions have already been set in train or are under investigation.

- A Specialists meeting will be held in October 1987, hosted by Sweden, on the topic of Life Limiting and Regulatory Aspects of Core Internals and Pressure Vessels.

- A workshop on Safety Assessment of Flawed Structures is proposed for 1988 to bring together fracture mechanics and non-destructive examination experts and regulators. This workshop will include consideration of the philosophy of in-service inspection (what are, or should be its objectives and how will these be best achieved, particularly having regard to long-term integrity assessment).

- The Fracture Assessment Group already established within PWG 3 will proceed with a programme to undertake bench mark exercises to validate fracture assessment methodologies, using the results of large-scale test programmes on vessels and pipes underway in a number of countries. This will, inter alia, include the question of the application of laboratory-scale test data to real structures.

- A workshop is proposed on Inspection and Remedial Technique in Steam Generators, hosted by France in spring 1988.

- A number of important non-destructive examination issues are already under investigation in the Programme on Inspection of Steel Components (PISC) under the aegis of the OECD-NEA and the CEC-JRC Ispra. These include round robin inspections of stainless steel and steam generator tubing. A view is being sought from the PISC Managing Board on the question of in-service inspection of concrete containment vessels and their steel liners.

- Other matters already under investigation include:

  - The development by corrosion, water chemistry and fracture experts of further guidance on the effects of chemical environment for integrity assessment purposes;
  - The development of further review and guidance material on continuous monitoring of plant service conditions;
  - The use of the NEA Incident Reporting Systems to contribute information on the leakage and failure of piping systems.

CONCLUSION

The workshop has identified no specific technical limitations which would rule out on structural integrity grounds the extension of service lives for pressurised components and associated fittings beyond current expectations. Rather, there are a number of areas in which more understanding and, in particular, better and more realistic property and performance data will be required for assessment purposes if the necessary confidence in maintaining adequate safety margins is to be obtained. The Principal Working Group on Primary Circuit Integrity of the OECD-NEA Committee on the Safety of Nuclear Installations will be taking actions on a number of these matters.

LIFE PREDICTION STUDY OF REACTOR PRESSURE VESSEL AS ESSENTIAL TECHNICAL FOUNDATION FOR PLANT LIFE EXTENSION

H. Nakajima, N. Nakajima and T. Kondo
Japan Atomic Energy Research Institute
Department of Fuels and Materials Research
Tokai-mura, Ibaraki-ken 319-11, Japan

ABSTRACT

The life of an LWR plant is determined essentially by the limit of reliable performance of the components which are difficult to replace without high economic and/or safety risks. Typical of such a component is the reactor pressure vessel (RPV).

The engineering life of an RPV of a given quality of steel is considered to be a complex function of factors such as the resistance to fracture, which has deteriorated due to neutron irradiation and thermal aging, and generation of surface flaws by environmental effects such as corrosion and their growth under operational load that varies during steady state operation and transients.

In an attempt to evaluate the engineering life of an RPV of an LWR, a preliminary survey was made by applying a set of knowledge accumulated primarily in the field of subcritical crack growth behavior of RPV steels in reactor water environments.

The major conclusions drawn are:

(1)   The life of an RPV is dependent on the quality of steel used, particularly with respect to any minor impurities it contains. The key elements known so far are P and Cu for radiation embrittlement, and S for the growth rate of flaws in aqueous environment under reactor load cycles.

(2)   The issue of plant life extension in RPV aspect is found to be optimistic for cases where the steels used satisfy a reasonable level of quality control.

(3)   The importance of providing sound scientific foundation is stressed for the implementation of a practicable life extension scheme; this can be established through intensified studies of flaw growth and fracture behaviours in well defined testings under reasonably simulated service conditions.

LA PREVISION DE LA DUREE DE VIE DE LA CUVE DES REACTEURS, BASE TECHNIQUE ESSENTIELLE POUR LA PROLONGATION DE LA DUREE DE VIE DES CENTRALES NUCLEAIRES

RESUME

La durée de vie d'une centrale à eau ordinaire dépend essentiellement de la limite de fonctionnement dans des conditions fiables des composants qu'il est difficile de replacer sans s'exposer à des risques importants sur le plan économique ou sur celui de la sûreté. La cuve sous pression du réacteur fait précisément partie de ces composants.

On considère que la vie utile d'une cuve sous pression d'une qualité donnée d'acier est une fonction complexe de facteurs tels que la dégradation de la résistance des matériaux à la rupture en raison du bombardement neutronique et du vieillissement thermique ou la formation de défauts de surface sous l'effet de la corrosion et leur évolution en service à cause des variations de charge qui se produisent pendant l'exploitation du réacteur.

Pour tenter d'évaluer la vie utile de la cuve sous pression des réacteurs à eau ordinaire, les auteurs ont procédé à une étude préliminaire en se fondant sur un ensemble de connaissances acquises principalement dans le domaine de la recherche visant le comportement de l'acier des cuves sous pression du point de vue de la croissance des fissures sous-critiques dans les milieux aqueux des réacteurs.

Les principales conclusions tirées ont été les suivantes :

1) La durée de vie d'une cuve sous pression dépend de la qualité de l'acier utilisé, en particulier de sa teneur en impuretés. Les éléments essentiels connus à ce jour sont P et Cu, qui fragilisent les matériaux exposés à l'irradiation, et S, qui accélère la vitesse de propagation des fissures en milieu aqueux lors des variations de charge.

2) Pour autant qu'il s'agit de la cuve sous pression du réacteur, il y a lieu d'être optimiste quant aux possibilités de prolonger la vie des centrales pourvu que les aciers utilisés répondent à des critères raisonnables de contrôle de qualité.

3) Pour mettre en oeuvre un projet réalisable de prolongation de la vie des centrales, on insiste sur l'établissement d'une base scientifique solide grâce à des études plus approfondies sur la dégradation des matériaux ainsi que sur la croissance des fissures et la tenue des matériaux à la rupture dans le cadre d'essais bien définis exécutés dans des conditions d'exploitation fidèlement simulées.

1. Background

After about 20 years of operating history, more than 40 nuclear power plants are either in operation or under construction in Japan. With one exception of earlier magnox type plant, the type of the reactors are shared almost equally by PWR and BWR, and the present availability of those including the planned inspection outage is high over 75%.(1) While a large number of construction and decomissioning of the nuclear power plants are expected to become realistic issues in the next half century.

Referring to an assessment(2) of the nuclear power generation capacity toward the first quarter of the 21st century in Japan, LWR's are predicted to hold predominant position for at least a half century from now.(Fig. 1)

In regard of the time span for such a life cycle, the average life of the power plants will become not only an economic problem but also a global issue. The nominal license lives of nuclear power plants have been set at 30(PWR) to 40(BWR) years typically in the ASME Code, which might have been created with some empirical basis taking into account the factors such as the experiences of fossil plants and ample safety margin for uncertainty in nuclear applications.(3)

The list of the Japanese plants(4) are summarized in Table I, where the ASME design life time is marked. The histograms of the assumed number of decomissioning of LWR plants in the four countries are shown in Fig. 2, in which plant life was obtained simply by applying tentatively the criterion of the norminal lives of PWR and BWR as 30 and 40 years respectively. In USA, the ASME designated norminal life time of LWR is becoming a present day issue. The similar age in Japan is predicted to come in the year around 2000.

Within last quarter century, the world's nuclear technology has established a level of maturity to attempt the prediction of essential life of the power plants. Substantial advances made in various aspects of nuclear technology are additional factors of improving realistic life estimation and possible extension of the plant life. Under such circumstance, there have been already carried out extensive surveys on the possibility of plant life extension in both the economic as well as the technical aspects in some countries.(3),(5),(6)

The present paper describes a technical aspect of the plant life prediction focusing on the reactor steel vessel which is considered to control directly the engineering life of the total system. Some conclusions are then drawn in what type of research works are to be made in providing scientific and technological bases for the life prediction and thereby extension.

2. Basic consideration for residual life prediction of LWR's(7)

Being composed of variety of components, a nuclear power plant must be kept in healthy condition with well balanced integrity of those parts. With a simple logic, it has been pointed out that the life controlling components are such that the repair or replacement of those is difficult, and even if possible, it is extremely costly and time consuming. Categorization of such an aspect is summarized in Table II. Identification of each specific case for those components, in the event of damage, will become rather important first step in the procedure of plant life prediction. Based on the activities of technical survey made in various parts of the world(3) as well as the technical assessment group in the authors' institute(7), it is now a consensus that the integrity of the reactor pressure vessel is a typical and perhaps the most important component in determining the plant life.

Large amount of knowledge has been accumulated in the field of materials and structural engineering for reactor components in past. While, the studies in such fields have not necessarily been oriented toward the life prediction. In order that the knowledge accumulated and the research potentials cultivated are oriented to such a direction, an intentional reorganization and some appropriate reinforcement of the present activities may be required. Along with such a line, a conceptual scheme of the sequencial procedure for each major component has been composed as illustrated in Fig. 3. Provided that the program in each category of component attains certain level of maturity, the effort should be devoted toward a more coordinative direction, (see top left of the figure noted as the synthetic process) i.e. compromizing all the sets of major components in assessing the life of the total plant system.

3. A scenario for residual life prediction of a reactor pressure vessel and
   its engineering parameters
   3.1 Scenario
       It has been recognized in general that the physical limit in the structural integrity of a reactor pressure vessel is the occurrence of either through well penetration of flaws or fast instable fracture. This concept is the basis of the flaw evaluation procedure of the ASME Code Section XI.(8) Such catastrophic conditions will never occur unless at least the two factors are satisfied, i.e. material degradation by aging and flaw growth to a critical size.
       The time dependent degradation, i.e. aging, of the material is expected to proceed with neutron irradiation, thermal aging and other environmental effects. It reduces the size of allowable flaws in the structure. Then the physical limit of insuring the integrity of the structure is determined by referring it to the predicted flaw(crack) growth trend by the time of the planned next inspection per each specific part of the copmonents, of which interval is, e.g. approximately 10 years.
       Figure 4 illustrates schematically the relationship of those two processes of material degradation and damage, in which the concepts of the engineering life and economic life are indicated. According to the knowledge generated in the field of materials research in last 15 years, the engineering life of the reactor vessel has been found to be controlled more strongly by the quality of the steel used than formerly believed. Namely the steepness of the two trend curves in Fig. 4 are strongly dependent on the impurity contents of the steel.

3.2 Effect of material quality on the performance of reactor vessel structure
    relevant to the residual life
       In past 20 years a revolutional progress has been made in the quality assurance of large scale steel products. The progress has been closely reflected in the heavy section steel technology for ligth water reactor pressure vessel. The followings are typicals of the relationship of the metallurgical factors and the structural performance.

(a) Material degradation aspect
       The well known effects of the irradiation embrittlement of the steels is strongly controlled by the content of impurities in steel, e.g. copper and phosphorus.(9),(10) Copper is also known to be locally increased by welding in some older fabrication procedures. Phosphorus can also cause the temper embrittlement which corresponds to a typical thermally produced aging effect.
       Steels manufactured in modernized steel plants have substantially low impurity levels relative to earlier cases, and the trend of the aging degradation is, thus, much slower and of smaller extent than it used to be.

(b) Flaw(crack) growth aspect

Surface flaws that might be formed on the surface of the structural steel can be grown by repeated mechanical loading. Some incipient flaws that are of the size below the detection limit of in-service inspection(ISI) process are assumed to be potential in growing in their size under operational cyclic loading particularly when they are in direct contact with water. The effect of accelerated crack growth of nuclear pressure vessel steels in simulated LWR water environment was first found by the authors' group in 1969.(11) After various aspects of research efforts devoted by several laboratories particularly later by the ICCGR(12), a voluntary international study group of 50 organizations from 11 countries, it is now almost established that the crack growth acceleration observed in high temperature water is mainly attributed to the existence of small amount of sulfur remained in steel.(13) Figure 5 shows one of the results of the Japanese domestic testing round robin carried out by 10 organizations on the effect of sulfur on the crack growth rate. The upper and lower edges of the test range correspond respectively the materials used in the oldest and latest plants in Japan.(14) Steels containing sulfur over 100 ppm have substantial sensitivity while those less than approximately 40 ppm have been found to be almost immune from the environment assisted crack growth. It should be noted that all the critical elements described above are the residual impurities in steel, and the levels of the content are closely related with the level of advancement in the steel making technology.(Fig. 6)(15)

4. An analysis on the sensitivity of RPV life on the suspected controlling parameters

It is of interest to know how the key engineering parameters described above would affect the life of the RPV of LWRs. An attempt was made to assess the relative difference between the following typical contrast using a computation code developed by the authors.(16),(17)

Case 1
    vessel: made of average quality steel
    flaw growth rate: ASME Section XI reference curve

Case 2
    vessel: made of modern low impurity high quality steel
    flaw growth rate: Japanese domestic testing round robin(Fig. 7)

In the computation, the following factors were taken into account in addition to the basic mechanical parameters;
(1) environment-assisted crack growth rate
(2) fracture toughness value after neutron irradiation
(3) flaw geometry(aspect ratio)

The results were obtained as to see the influence of each of the parameters to the residual life for given equal intial flaws.(Fig. 8) In these results it is clearly resolved that the predicted life of a typical RPV of modern LWR can be several times longer than the values obtained from the conventional set of material and flaw growth trend. In more detailed sensitivity analysis, considerable part of the difference in those two crack growth curves has been found to be attributed to the shape of the reference curve(Fig. 7) and in particular to that of lower ΔK range. In the latter sense, there may be also substantial possibility for older plants to obtain an assessment much more optimistic than that is made at the present because the da/dN data available at the moment for low ΔK range are still scarce and uncertain. The values for low ΔK range used at present are suspected to be overestimated because of the uncertainty.

5. Fundamental research works required
In order that the life prediction be made with adequate accuracy, extended research works in the field of basic engineering may be necessary. Suggested parameters to be dealt in such a research are summarized in Table III. Although the analysis given above is of very preliminary nature, it suggests a high potentiality of the plant life extension and encourages an intensive implementation of the fundamental works for providing the data relevant to life prediction.
A direction for planning such fundamental research programs are illustrated in Table IV.

6. Conclusions
(1) It was pointed out that the essential life of a LWR plant is controlled most strictly by the integrity of reactor pressure vessel, and that forming the scientific and technical basis for predicting the engineering life of the vessel is one of the most important first steps in answering practically the demand for the plant life extension.
(2) The life of a RPV is strongly dependent on the quality of steel used, particularly with respect to its contents of minor impurity elements. The key elements known so far are P and Cu for the radiation embrittlement, and S for the growth rate of flaws in aqueous environment under reactor load cycles. Most of those elements have been reduced along with the progress of steel making technology, thus the higher potentiality for extension being expected in the newer plants.
(3) The issue of plant life extension in RPV aspect is found to be optimistic for the cases where the steels used satisfy a reasonable level of quality control. Although close determination of the critical levels of the steel quality may be the matter of future study, the above will apply in principle to most plants except a limited number of very early ones.
(4) For implementation of a practicable life extension scheme, importance of providing a sound scientific foundation is stressed, which can be established through the intensified studies of the material degradation as well as the flaw growth and fracture behaviors in well defined testings under reasonably simulated service conditions.

Reference
(1) Genshiryoku Hatsudenjyo Unten Kanri Nenpo in Fiscal Year 1985, edited by Agency of Natural Resources and Energy, September 1986.
(2) Vision of Nuclear Power, edited by An Investigation Committee on ALL-round Energy, July 1986.
(3) C. A. Negin et al, EPRI-NP-2418, June 1982.
(4) Nuclear Power Plants in the World As of June 30-1986, edited by Japan Atomic Industrial Forum Incorporated, September 1986.
(5) L. D. Bustard et al, Trans. ANS, vol. 52, p. 461, 1986.
(6) P. P. Stancavage, Nuclear Engineering International, Vol. 31, p. 43, 1986.
(7) Report on Plant Life Prediction of LWR's, edited by Technical Assesment Group at JAERI, to be published in 1987.
(8) ASME Boiler and Pressure Vessel Code, Section XI, ASME, 1980.
(9) L. E. Steele et al, ASTM STP 870, p.863, 1985.

(10) US Nuclear Regulatory Guide 1.99, Revision 1, 1977.
(11) T. Kondo et al, Proc. of 1st Intern. Conf. on Corrosion Fatigue, p.539, 1972.
(12) R. L. Jones, NUREG/CP-0067, vol. 1, p. 93, 1986.
(13) W. H. Bamford, ASMT STP 801, p.405, 1983.
(14) H. Kitagawa et al, NUREG/CP-0067, vol. 1, p. 135, 1986.
(15) T. Iwadate, private communication on steel making technology at JSW.
(16) N. Nakajima et al, JAERI M-report 84-208, 1984.
(17) H. Takahashi et al, NUREG/CP-0067, vol. 2, p.411, 1986.

TABLE I   LIST OF LWR PLANTS IN JAPAN

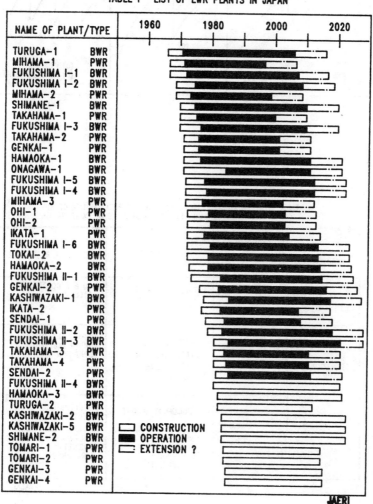

TABLE II CATEGORIZATION OF CONTROL COMPONENTS FOR PLANT LIFE DETERMINATION AND THEIR ADDITIONAL FEATURES

JAERI

	Class. A	Class. B	Class. C
REMARKS	REPLACEMENT : NO REPAIR : POSSIBLE CONTROLS ENGINEERING LIFE	REPLACEMENT : POSSIBLE REPAIR : POSSIBLE CONTROLS ECONOMIC LIFE	REPLACEMENT : PLANNED NO DIRECT RELATION TO LIFE
EXAMPLE	RPV, CONCRETE STRUCTURE, CABLE	HEAT EXCHANGER, STEAM GENERATOR, PIPING etc.	FUEL ASSEMBLY, CONTROL ROD, DETECTOR etc.
DEGRADATION	(a)	(a) or (b)	(b)
	TIME	TIME	TIME

(a) : REPAIR
(b) : REPLACEMENT
------- : LIMITATION

TABLE III SUBSTANTIAL FACTORS RELEVANT TO RESIDUAL LIFE OF RPV OBTAINED THROUGH SENSITIVITY ANALYSIS OF COMPUTATION

RESEARCH ITEMS / VARIABLES		FLAW GROWTH	FRACTURE RESISTANCE
MATERIAL FACTOR		• S CONTENT IN STEEL	• Cu & P CONTENT IN STEEL • Kic
OPERATIONAL FACTOR	LOADING	• STRESS AMPLITUDE DURING STEADY STATE CONDITION • delta Kth LEVEL • FLAW GEOMETRY (ASPECT RATIO)	• IMPACT AMPLITUDE UNDER FAULTED CONDITION
	ENVIRONMENT	• COOLANT FLOW RATE	• TEMPERATURE • NEUTRON DOSE
HUMAN FACTOR		• UNCERTAINTY OF CRACK MONITORING (DEPTH,SHAPE, DISTRIBUTION)	• UNCERTAINTY OF NEUTRON DOSIMETRY (TOUGHNESS)

JAERI

TABLE IV MATERIAL ASPECTS OF THE ISSUES IN PREDICTING THE LWR/RPV RESIDUAL LIFE

	SCIENTIFIC ISSUES	TECHNOLOGICAL ISUUES		EXISTING ACTIVITY
		TESTING	ANALYSIS	
RESISTANCE TO FRACTURE	MECHANISM OF THERMAL AGING DEGRADATION AND IRRADIATION EMBRITTLEMENT	ACCELERATING TEST METHODOLOGY FOR AGING EFFECT	MODIFICATION OF EXISTING CODES AND/OR FORMATION OF NEW GUIDE LINE	IAEA NPAR
	CRITICAL MINOR ELEMENT IN STEEL (Cu & P)	POST–IRRADIATION TESTING ON ELASTO –PLASTO FRACTURE MECHANICS PROPERTIES		
GROWTH RATE OF FLAWS	SYNERGISTIC EFFECTS OF CHEMICAL AND MECHANICAL CONDITION (EAC)	THREE DIMENSIONAL CRACK GROWTH BEHAVIOR		ICCGR JCF(JAPAN) UKEAC(UK)
	CRITICAL MINOR ELEMENT IN STEEL (S)	EFFECT OF MECHANICAL LOADING SPECTRUM		

JAERI

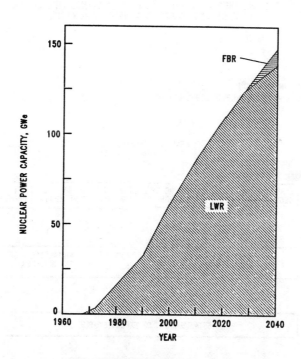

FIG.1   RELATIONSHIP BETWEEN PREDICTED DEMAND OF NUCLEAR POWER CAPACITY AND YEAR IN JAPAN

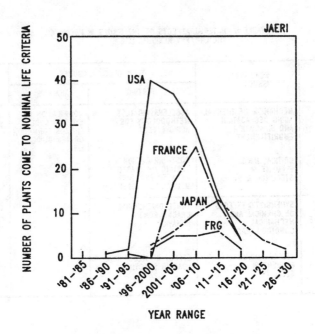

FIG.2 NUMBER OF PLANTS COME TO NOMINAL LIFE CRITERIA
IN EACH FIVE YEARS IN VARIOUS COUNTRIES

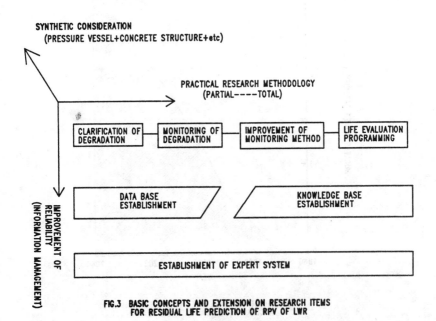

FIG.3 BASIC CONCEPTS AND EXTENSION ON RESEARCH ITEMS
FOR RESIDUAL LIFE PREDICTION OF RPV OF LWR

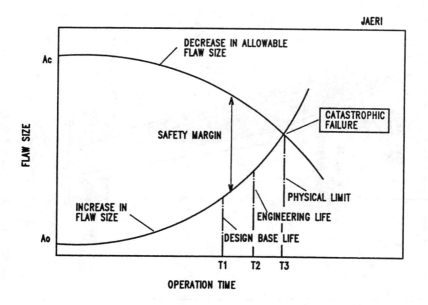

FIG.4 CONCEPT OF LIFE TIME FOR RPV OF LWR

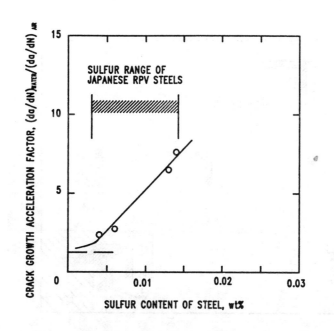

FIG.5 RELATIONSHIP BETWEEN CRACK GROWTH ACCELERATION FACTOR DUE
TO THE WATER ENVIRONMENT AND SULFUR CONTENT OF JAPANESE
RPV STEELS

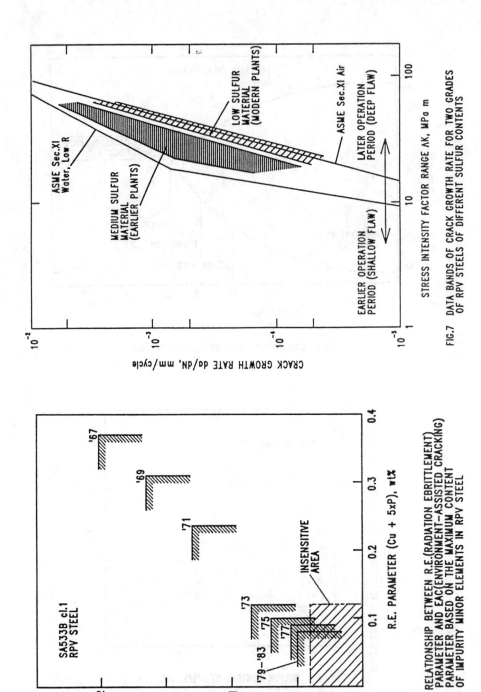

CRACK GROWTH RATE da/dn, mm/cycle

STRESS INTENSITY FACTOR RANGE ΔK, MPa m

ASME Sec.XI Water, Low R

MEDIUM SULFUR MATERIAL (EARLIER PLANTS)

LOW SULFUR MATERIAL (MODERN PLANTS)

ASME Sec.XI Air

EARLIER OPERATION PERIOD (SHALLOW FLAW)

LATER OPERATION PERIOD (DEEP FLAW)

FIG.7 DATA BANDS OF CRACK GROWTH RATE FOR TWO GRADES OF RPV STEELS OF DIFFERENT SULFUR CONTENTS

SA533B cl.1 RPV STEEL

EAC PARAMETER (S), wt%

R.E. PARAMETER (Cu + 5xP), wt%

INSENSITIVE AREA

'67
'69
'71
'73
'75
'77
'79~'83

FIG.6 RELATIONSHIP BETWEEN R.E.(RADIATION EBRITTLEMENT) PARAMETER AND EAC(ENVIRONMENT–ASSISTED CRACKING) PARAMETER BASED ON THE MAXIMUM CONTENT OF IMPURITY MINOR ELEMENTS IN RPV STEEL

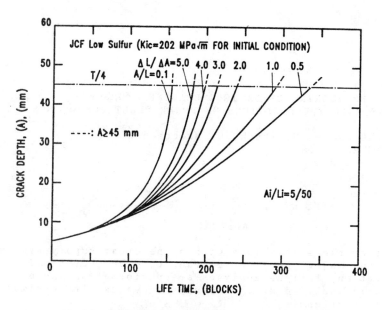

Fig.8(a)   RELATIONSHIP BETWEEN CRACK DEPTH(A) AND LIFE TIME
FOR VARIOUS NEW PARAMETER ΔL/ ΔA

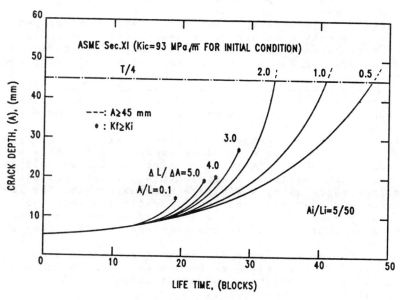

FIG.8(b)   RELATIONSHIP BETWEEN CRACK DEPTH(A) AND LIFE TIME
FOR VARIOUS NEW PARAMETER ΔL/ ΔA

MONITORING OF FATIGUE USAGE FACTORS FOR REPRESENTATIVE LOCATIONS OF POWER PLANT COMPONENTS

G. Schücktanz, M.Miksch, W. Brettschuh
KRAFTWERK UNION AG
Erlangen, FRG

ABSTRACT

Fatigue at critical locations within the steam supply system is one of the major concerns relevant to plant lifetime. Before plant operation, fatigue analyses are performed on the basis of previously analysed design transient events with estimated numbers of occurrences.

During the plant's lifetime it is advantageous to know the actual fatigue as well as the remaining safety margin. The knowledge of the actual usage factors is important for the optimization of load cycles in order to extend the operational lifetime of components.

Furthermore, inservice inspections of sensitive locations can be planned and scheduled accordingly.

The paper presents a new fatigue monitoring system developed by KWU. It allows most accurate and economic online calculation of fatigue usage factors of the installed components by means of microprocessors and takes into account the actual transient history.

For components such as pipes, nozzles, bends etc. whose transients are not completely known a so called Local Monitoring System is applied. Thermocouples are located on such components at the outside wall surface.

The transient non uniform temperature distribution due to regular flow or stratified flow conditions is defined in terms of a heat conduction problem. Temperature distribution as well as stress distribution resulting from elementary transients are calculated in advance using a finite element approach. The resulting response curves for individual locations within the structure can be superimposed using a linear series theory to obtain the temperatures actually measured and thus the thermal stresses.

For components whose transients are known a so called Global Monitoring System is applied based on design transient calculations. An automatic load case indentification system has access to precalculated stress files.

Stress peaks and valleys are arranged chronologically and usage factors are calculated using the Rainflow Algorithm.

CONTROLE DES TAUX D'USURE DE CERTAINS POINTS REPRESENTATIFS
SUR DES COMPOSANTS DE CENTRALES ELECTRIQUES

RESUME

La fatigue en certains points critiques du circuit d'alimentation de vapeur est l'un des principaux éléments intervenant dans la durée de vie des centrales. Avant de mettre l'installation en service, on effectue des analyses de fatigue en prenant en compte des transitoires de référence calculés au préalable sur la base d'estimations de fréquence.

Pendant la durée de vie de la centrale, il est intéressant de connaître le degré réel de fatigue des matériaux ainsi que la marge de sûreté résiduelle. La connaissance des facteurs d'usage effectifs est importante pour optimiser les cycles de charge afin de prolonger la durée de vie utile des composants.

De plus, on peut ainsi prévoir et programmer en conséquence les inspections en service des zones sensibles.

Les auteurs présentent un nouveau système de contrôle de la fatigue mise au point par la société KWU. Ce système autorise, grâce à l'emploi de micro processeurs, un calcul en continu plus précis et plus économique des facteurs d'usage des composants en place et tient compte des transitoires effectivement subis par l'installation.

On emploie une instrumentation spécifique pour les composants tels que les tuyauteries, les tubulures, les coudes, etc. dont on ne connaît pas parfaitement les transitoires. Des thermocouples sont implantés sur la paroi externe de ces composants.

La distribution de la température, qui varie dans le temps, parce que les conditions d'écoulement peuvent être régulières ou stratifiées est définie comme un problème de conduction thermique. On calcule à l'avance au moyen de la méthode des éléments finis la distribution de la température et des contraintes due à des transitoires élémentaires. On peut ensuite superposer les courbes de réponse obtenues aux différents emplacements de la structure en utilisant une théorie fondée sur les séries linéaires pour obtenir les températures réellement mesurées et, par conséquent, les contraintes thermiques.

Pour les composants dont on connaît les transitoires, on emploie un système de contrôle dit global reposant sur le calcul de transitoires de référence. Un système de détermination automatique de la charge a accès à des fichiers de contraintes pré-établis.

Les pics et les creux de contraintes sont classés par ordre chronologique et les facteurs d'usage sont calculés à l'aide de l'algorithme de type "Rainflow".

1. Indroduction

As a rule, the important components of nuclear power plants are designed for a service life of 40 years. In many cases it is desirable from an economic standpoint to extend the service life of components beyond the planned period. This is, however, only possible when the cumulative usage factor and consequently the residual service life of components are known at any given moment in time.
Understanding the mechanisms which influence the service life of components is obviously a preprequisite to determining the residual service life of components.

Life-limiting factors may include:

- Embrittlement of neutron-irradiated material.
- Material degradation due to erosion and corrosion.
- Material fatigue due to cyclic loading.
- Combinations of the above mechanisms, particularly those which include simultaneous material fatigue and corrosion.

Very extensive investigations of the embrittlement of reactor pressure vessel materials have been conducted worldwide. It can be assumed that material property changes induced by neutron irradiation are part of established knowledge. Monitoring programs conducted in individual nuclear power plants ensure that the mechanical properties of the reactor pressure vessel material are known at any given moment in time and that the integrity of the reactor pressure vessel can be established and verified at all times.

Since the operating period of most nuclear power plants to date amounts to a relatively small portion of the total design service life, attention in the past was paid primarily to material embrittlement and less effort has been devoted to the material fatigue of components.
Furthermore, plant operators frequently point out that very extensive in-service inspections are conducted on a regular basis. They contend that these in-service inspections ensure that the probability of defects developing and remaining undetected is extremely low. In the event that a defect should occur and go undetected, it could at worst result in a leak, but not in the failure of the component. Material fatigue problems may thus affect availability, but not plant safety.

This argument is supported by experience which shows that damage due to fatigue is most unlikely to occur. The detection of incipient cracks in feedwater lines in several pressurized water reactors and boiling water reactors, as well as the fracture of several pump shafts, have shown that premature material fatigue, although not necessarily safety related, is definitely a factor to be considered.

2. Fatigue analysis according ot design codes

The verifications required for obtaining a nuclear power plant
operating license include the verification of an adequate margin
of resistance to fatigue for certain components during the
design service life of the power plant. The applicable codes
(e.g. ASME, KTA, etc.) stipulate verification that no impermissible material fatigue shall occur during the service life
of the power plant.
The codes, however, do not require verification of the actual
cumulative usage factor at the end of the service life of the
nuclear power plant. For economic reasons, fatigue analyses
are consequently performed in a very conservative way. It is
only demonstrated that the usage factor is less than 1. A statement on the actual cumulative usage factor at the end of the
planned operating life or at any given moment in time is therefore not possible. For the same reason, comparison of different
components with regard to the degree of fatigue loading is
normally not possible.

Loading specifications, which stipulate pressure and temperature transients for the expected operating and faulted conditions and their frequency for each component, serve as the
basis for the verifications of sufficient safety margin against
crack initiation required by the codes.

Very extensive measurements conducted during commissioning
at various nuclear power plants have shown that there is excellent correlation between the measured temperature and pressure transients and the calculated transients on which the
fatigue analysis is based for a large proportion of the components. On the other hand experience has shown that there are
components the loadings of which cannot completely be specified in advance.

3. Experience gained in nuclear power plants

Temperature measurements were made at the point of connection
of the feedwater lines to the steam generators and reactor
pressure vessels during the course of investigations of the
causes of incipient craking in feedwater lines of pressurized
water reactors and boiling water reactors. Temperature differences of up to 250°C between the upper and lower walls of
pipes were detected during certain operating conditions (hot
stand by and minimum load operation). These temperature differences were caused by stratification of cold feedwater below
hot steam generator water or hot reactor coolant /1/, /2/.
The transition from the cold to the hot layers was relatively
discontinuous. The operating characteristic of the feedwater
valves caused a corresponding cange in the level of the layers.
The result was great cyclic loading and significant fatigue
of the feedwater lines and the downstream feedwater nozzles

which ultimately led to incipient cracking after a relatively short period of operation.

These observations were the impeteus for a decision made during the commissioning of one German 1300 MWe pressurized water reactor in 1982 to provide alle important components with additional instrumentation.

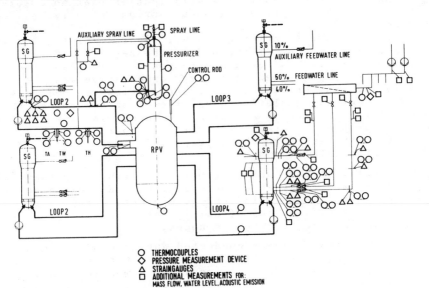

Fig. 1 Instrumentation for Evaluation of Transients in a 1300 MWe PWR-Plant

The aim of this program was to verify the specified load transients and to detect any system malfunctions. A total of 109 strain gauges and 224 thermocouples were installed in addition to the existing process instrumentation. The results of these measurements can be summarized as follows:

- Non-specified thermal loadings are by no means restricted to feedwater lines; a number of other components are subject to thermal loadings which are not apparent from process instrumentation (e.g. temperature stratification in the surge line).
- The mode of plant operation can lead to non-specified additional loadings (e.g. manual actuation of spraying)
- Improper functioning of equipment, particularly of valves, can also cause additional loadings (e. g. leaking valves in auxiliary feedwater lines, Fig. 2).

Load profile measurements have ultimately shown that on-line fatigue monitoring is definitely expedient for the detection of relevant fatigue loading.

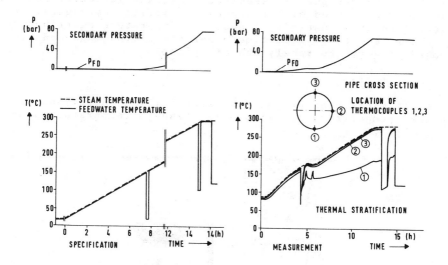

Fig. 2 Comparison of Design Transients and Measured Transients.
SG Auxiliary Feedwater Nozzle

4.   On-line fatigue analysis

The simplest and most widely practised method of "on-line"
fatigue monitoring is counting the load cycles which have actually occured. As long as the specified number of load cycles
is not exceeded, an adequate margin of safety with regard to
impermissible material fatigue should exist.
This method does, however, have a number of weaknesses:

- Direct determination of the actual cumulative usage factor,
  as mentioned above, is not possible.
- If the specified number of cycles for one particular type
  of loading is exceeded, the fatigue analysis must be revised
  to verify sufficient resistance to fatigue.
- As operating experience has shown, non-specified loadings
  can also occur which was not included in the advance prediction
  of fatigue analyses.

A series of on-line fatigue monitoring procedures were developed to avoid these disadvantages. For the most part, they
are based on the detection of actual transient temperature
and pressure loadings using, as a rule, existing process instrumentation, /3/, /4/, /5/, /6/, /7/.
Since process instrumentation is designed to monitor operational processes, it is not necessarily well-suited for measuring relevant thermal loadings on components. This is the
case whenever major temperature differentials occur simultaneously at adjacent regions on the inner surface of a component.
The procedure described below was developed to evaluate the

resistance to fatigue of feedwater lines and feedwater nozzles and can also be used with a number of similar components. In contrast to other methods, transient temperature distributions and their resulting "real-time" operational loadings can be calculated very accurately and efficiently.

4.1 Local monitoring

The local monitoring process is essentially a comparison of measured temperature profiles with standard temperature pro-

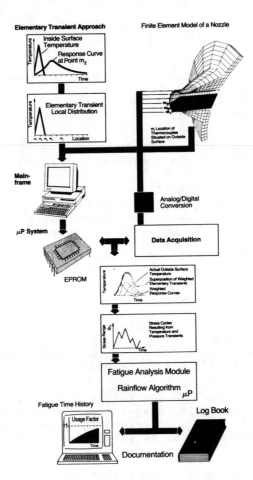

Fig. 3 Local Fatigue Monitoring System

files for which stress fields have been calculated in advance. The component to be monitored, e.g. a feedwater nozzle, is fitted with thermocouples distributed around its circumference (Fig. 3). These thermocouples measure the temperature profiles associated with the prevailing flow conditions in that component.

Standard localized transients calculated in advance for the inner surface of the nozzle serve as a reference in the analysis of these measured temperature profiles. These standard transients result in a clearly defined temperature distribution within the component and thus also in a defined distribution of stresses. The standard transients result also in transient temperature profiles at the location of each thermocouple. Through analysis of actual on-line temperature measurements made at the outer surface of components, loadings can be interpreted as the summation of a very definite number and sequence of standard transients. After this part of the analysis has been completed, the stress fields calculated in advance for standard transients are simply compounded by superposition.
Stresses resulting from internal pressure and from the forces and moments from adjoining pipes are also compounded.
The well-know "rain flow algorithm" can then be used to determine the current cumulative usage factor on-line at any given moment in time.
It goes without saying that the effect of any corrosion occurring can be allowed for by inputting appropriately corrected fatigue curves.

The primary advantages offered by this method are as follows:

- Knowledge of the flow condition at the inner surface of the pipe and of the heat transfer coefficient is no longer of importance, since the stress calculation results from the temperature distribution at the exterior of the component.
- The results are realistic to the largest possible degree, since the stresses are calculated directly from the measured temperature profiles.
- It is a relatively simple matter to continuously monitor the behavior of any defects which may exist in the structure, since the stress distribution is calculated for the entire component anyway.

Local monitoring is suitable for components such as feedwater lines and feedwater nozzles, surge lines, connections of the emergency core cooling system and residual heat removal system to the reactor coolant line, spray lines, etc.

Temperature monitoring without on-line fatigue analysis is sufficient for components which are only subjected to more severe loadings in the event of equipment failures (e.g. valve leakage). It is safe to assume that the equipment in question will be returned to normal operation as soon as possible.

Existing process instrumentation can be employed for detecting loadings on a large number of components and component parts.

4.2 Global monitoring

Measurements made during the commissioning of numerous nuclear power plants have confirmed that for components such as the reactor pressure vessel and the steam generators, operational transients can be predicted in advance with sufficient accuracy. (Fig. 4). If the loading condition sequence is known, the rain flow algorithm can be employed to determine the cumulative usage factor at any given moment in time from the stress values of the advance stress and fatigue analysis.

The loading condition sequence can be documented by the operator personnel manually. It is also possible to call up loading condition sequence information from the plant process computer, since any loading condition can be characterized by certain signal patterns.

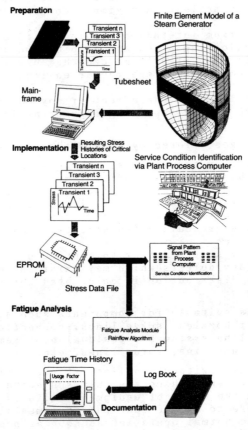

Fig. 4   Globale Fatigue Monitoring System

4.3 Hardware

The fatigue monitoring hardware essentially consists of a system of microprocessors independent of the plant process computer. The system has a modular configuration so that it can
be optimally tailored to the specific needs of the plant in
question and the customer's special wishes (Fig. 5).

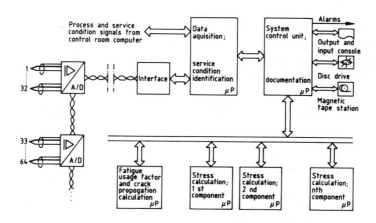

Fig. 5   Hardware of Fatigue Monitoring System

The most important modules are:

- Data acquisition.
  Measurement data are continuously checked for plausibility.
  Measuring errors and implausible values are indicated imme-
  diately.

- Identification of loading conditions

  Each loading condition has a characteristic signal pattern.
  Process signals from process instrumentation forwarded by
  the plant process computer are analysed on the basis of these
  signal patterns. As soon as the loading condition has been
  recognized, the characteristic stresses for that loading
  condition and component are called up from the appropriate
  stress data file, for further processing.

- Stress calculations

  In the case of locally monitored components, the measured
  temperatures are analyzed with the aid of the standard transients which are calculated in advance and available from
  a stored data file. Stresses resulting from internal pressure
  and external forces and moments are then compounded with
  those resulting from temperature transients.

A separate microprocessor is provided for each component monitored.

- Fatigue calculation

This calculation employs the well-known rain flow algorithm to determine the cumulative usage factor based on the current loading condition sequence.

- Calculation of defect propagation.

Growth of any defects which may be present in the component can be calculated at the same time.

- Documentation

The results of the stress and fatigue calculation for each component monitored are displayed individually on a screen. The information not only includes the cumulative usage factor, but rather also the usage accured and stress profile per loading condition or designated period of time. The capability is provided to make the operating personnel more fully aware of the component loading implications of certain modes of operation.
Measured temperatures of locally monitored parts are vividly displayed so that stratification, for example, can be recognized directly and remedial measures such as a less rigorous mode of operation or the repair of leaking valves can be initiated in good time.
Furthermore, the loading condition sequence recognized is fully documented. This ensures that on-line fatigue monitoring can be reviewed as desired at any time.

5. <u>Summary</u>

Through consideration of the actual component loadings, the on-line fatigue monitoring system described here facilitates:

- Selection of the optimum mode of plant operation with regard to minimum component loading and fatigue.
- Improvement of the operators understanding of plant behavior.
- Recognition of malfunctions with plant components.
- Targeted implementation of in-service inspections.
- Timely implementation of countermeasures, e.g. replacement of fatigued piping during scheduled major inspections.
- Ultimately, improvements in plant availability and extensions to plant service life.

6. References

/1/ M. Miksch, G. Schücktanz
"Konstruktive Maßnahmen zur Minimierung von Wärmespan-
nungen in Dampferzeuger-Speisewasserstutzen bei Schicht-
strömung und deren Einfluß auf die Ermüdungssicherheit".
Jahrestagung Kerntechnische Gesellschaft Mannheim,
Mai 1982, Tagungsband.

/2/ R. Braschel, M. Miksch, G. Schücktanz
"Thermal Stratification in Steam Generator Feedwater Lines",
Transaction of the ASME Vol. 106/78-85, Feb.1984.

/3/ "On-line fatigue monitoring with CMS",
Industry review, Nov. 1986, Page 15.

/4/ S. S. Tang. Y.Y. Kuo, P.C. Riccardella
"An On-line Fatigue Monitoring System for Power Plants",
ASME PVP-Conf., Chicago, 1986.

/5/ J. P. Husin, C. Milan
"Transient Monitoring Experience in French PWR Units",
CSNI Specialist Meeting on Continous Monitoring Techni-
ques for Assuring Coolant Circuit Integrity, King' s,
College, London, Aug. 1985.

/6/ R. Pich, K. Erlmann
"Automatische Überwachung der rechnerischen Lebensdauer-
erschöpfung druckführender Bauteile",
VGB-Kraftwerktechnik 63/1983.

/7/ D. Jojewski, L. Speitkamp, T. Kaminski
"Einsatz von Mikroprozessoren bei der Überwachung von
Dampferzeugern"
VDI/VDE - Fachtagung "Automatisierte Meßsysteme, Fellbach,
Nov.1985.

/8/ M. Miksch
"Betriebsbegleitende Ermüdungsüberwachung von Kraftwerks-
komponenten",
Atomkernenergie-Kerntechnik, Vol. 47 (1985) No. 1.

A REVIEW OF THE PERFORMANCE OF THE MAGNOX PLANT OPERATED BY THE CEGB

C.J. Marchese
Nuclear Co-ordination Group
Central Electricity Generating Board
United Kingdom

ABSTRACT

By 1986, the CEGB had 12 Magnox reactors which had operated for more than 20 years since first synchronisation. The capacity involved is 2185 MW(net) and, with 4 other units of a more recent design, has provided the CEGB with a reliable component of base load electrical production.

This paper will review the achievements of these early CEGB Nuclear stations, briefly in terms of their setting to work phase and more fully in their middle years of operation. It will include the current levels of performance and the problems arising from maintenance and plant breakdown.

With this background the factors affecting future operation will be discussed and how they will be incorporated into the CEGB planning process.

BILAN D'EXPLOITATION DES CENTRALES MAGNOX DU CEGB

RESUME

En 1986, l'office central de production d'électricité CEGB exploitait 12 réacteurs Magnox couplés au réseau depuis plus de 20 ans. Ces réacteurs représentent une puissance installée de 2185 MW (net) et fournissent au CEGB, avec quatre autres tranches de conception plus récente, un instrument fiable de production d'électricité en base.

La communication examine le bilan de ces premières centrales nucléaires du CEGB en passant brièvement en revue la phase de mise en service et, de façon plus approfondie, les années d'exploitation qui ont suivi. Elle présente également les résultats actuels et les problèmes découlant de l'entretien et des arrêts.

La communication examine ensuite, sur cette toile de fond, les facteurs influant sur la poursuite de l'exploitation de ces centrales et montre enfin comment ils seront pris en compte dans le processus de planification du CEGB.

INTRODUCTION

The operation of the Magnox power stations operated by the CEGB has been reviewed on several occasions in the past (Broom, Doble, Clarke 1985). The purpose of this review is to bring the symposium up-to-date with the CEGB Magnox scene and prepare the way for a second paper on lifetime extension and economics later in the Symposium. Much of this review concentrates on the six of our plants with operating lives in excess of 20 years but the two younger stations are also included. Operating data is given in Table I. While passing reference is made to other Magnox plants only CEGB data will be given.

BACKGROUND TO THE MAGNOX PROGRAMME

The first British Commercial stations, Bradwell, Berkeley, Hunterston A (operated by the SSEB) and Hinkley Point A were ordered during 1956 to 1957 following a UK Government White Paper in 1955 (Cmnd 9389). They were to follow the successful introduction of Magnox technology at Calder Hall and Chapelcross using natural uranium fuel in a Magnox fuel can, a graphite core and carbon dioxide as a primary coolant. Looking at the CEGB units, the major feature of these first stations were that the two reactor units (all CEGB stations have twin reactor units) were housed in separate buildings. They were a continuation of the earlier steel pressure vessel layout which included separate boilers (steam raising units) which were unshielded. The steel pressure vessel was contained within a concrete shield with penetrations for coolant ducting, and standpipe access at the vessel top for fuelling and control rod access. The design permitted a common steam supply system on all the boilers from both reactors which could then feed the multiple number of turbine generators. The steam supply could also be sectioned into units dedicated to each reactor for start-up and shutdown operations.

The next three stations Trawsfynydd, Dungeness A and Sizewell, ordered between 1959 and 1960, while still having a steel pressure vessel, were designed with further shielding around the boilers. Sizewell marked a departure from previous designs in that it was the first UK station to have a common pilecap services area for the two reactors. This integrated layout with a common services building, irradiated fuel store and decontamination centre, reduced the separation between the reactor centres enabling a reduction in construction costs. The concept of a twin reactor pilecap was accepted for all UK designs thereafter, including Advanced Gas Cooled Reactors, AGRs.

The final two Magnox reactors, Oldbury and Wylfa extended this new design philosophy, and again in common with all subsequent AGRs, a major development, the prestressed concrete pressure vessel was included in the design. This major feature was responsible for the unique increase in thermal capacity of gas cooled units up to the current AGR design of around 1500 MW(th). The increase in unit thermal capacity of the Magnox plants was accomplished by increasing the number of fuel channels from 2564 (Bradwell) to 6150 (Wylfa) in each reactor (Table II).

The graphite structures within the pressure vessel, the fuel elements and the internal arrangements of support, radial core restraint and fuel charge capability above the core, all show a variation between the stations.

The integrity of the pressure circuit was recognised as being of prime importance. The possibility that the reactor pressure vessel might fail was reduced to a negligible level by careful design, construction and pre-service inspection and also by clearly defining operating conditions in advance. In addition, over pressure tests were carried out with margins considerably greater than those required by the normal practice of the day. Although failure of any part of the remainder of the pressure circuit is considered to be unlikely, the consequences of such faults were assessed by studies of hypothetical and severe but credible conditions.

Refuelling of all reactors was designed to be on-load and generally this operation has been maintained throughout the life of each reactor [1]. Therefore the fuel charge standpipes at the top of each reactor and the coolant ducting and other vessel penetrations are important elements of the design and the possibility of their failure had to be addressed in safety cases. This led to defining an operating temperature which, for both depressurisation faults and for other contained faults, ensured that the probability of a fuel channel fire was sufficiently low.

OPERATING EXPERIENCE 1962 TO 1972

In their first ten years, the first 6 CEGB Magnox Stations were constructed and commissioned as scheduled and by inspection of their capacity factors it can be seen that they reached design output with near target availabilities. Although there were difficulties in commissioning the fuelling machines (Broom), the improving resilience of the fuel permitted the design discharge irradiation of 3000 MWd/te (Hardy), as a channel average, to be increased progressively to 4600 MWd/te (Mummery). Refuelling operations and fuel machine problems therefore did not significantly affect electrical production.

However when Bradwell was but 6 years into commercial operation, enhanced corrosion of certain mild steel bolts in the reactor internal restraint structure required a major review of the reactor operating conditions. This event, widely reported (Broom), was found to be due to increased oxidation of mild steel in carbon dioxide at the operating conditions of 400°C at that time. One CEGB station, Berkeley by virture of its lower design operating temperature of 345°C was not affected to such an extent to require alteration of the operating conditions. This event highlighted the extent to which operation can be affected by new materials data not perceived at the time of design of the plant. It also led to a reassignment of the plant ratings, after reducing all gas temperatures to 360°C, downwards from their design value to what is now published by the CEGB as the Declared Net Capability, DNC. The average affect (Table II) of the derating was at the time around 23% but output optimisation since has reduced this to 20%. The effect was larger for the later higher pressure stations and those with steam driven circulators. This review has been shown to be economic and continued operation at the lower ratings is still substantially economic in the CEGB generating system.

A final point to come out of this event was that the structure of Magnox plant maintenance and inspection programmes was also thoroughly reviewed. It led to a requirement to shut down each reactor unit every other year [2] to make an assessment of the rate of oxidation of mild steel components. Based on the pattern of previous operation, the extent of inspection is agreed with the regulatory authority to establish that there is no undue distress apparent in the internal reactor structures.

The main features of the inspection outages after 2 years of operation are as follows:-

(i)   Inspection of the Reactor pressure circuit and boilers (the single largest item excepting the turbine-generators which for some stations, with ranged operation, can also be carried out at other times though with output restrictions).

(ii)   Control Rod actuators and associated electrical equipment on a rotational basis covering about a third of the actuators followed by rod drop testing of all rods. Some other rod maintenance can occur at load.

(iii) Reactor Safety Circuit Checks.

(iv)   Gas Circulator overhaul on a rotational basis to examine electric or steam drives, oil lubrication and gas seal systems.

Given the balance of initial success and some disappointments, overall electrical production from UK Magnox plant was substantial and in 1974 it was possible to say (Broom) that 33% of the worlds' nuclear produced electricity was provided by the United Kingdom.

THE SECOND TEN YEARS 1972-1982

During this period of CEGB Magnox operations, the early stations consolidated their firm foundation as base load generating units at their new operating conditions. The last Magnox units at Wylfa however were having particular difficulties in their commissioning and, due to the timing of the mild steel oxidation derating, were never to reach design output. As mentioned earlier the two last stations, Oldbury and Wylfa, both incorporated the new prestressed concrete pressure vessel design which permitted higher operating pressures. This feature also allowed an increase in size to encompass the boiler (steam raising) units as well, with additional advantages to the development of safety evolution.

The capacity factors over this time for Wylfa show how power raising was affected by problems related to this design change. The new requirement to insulate the pressure vessel liner, in contact with the concrete, was achieved by a matrix of foil fixed by cover plates. These were fabricated on site prior to fitting and had to suffer the buffeting of the high velocity coolant flows. This proved to be a significant challenge to both design and construction but was eventually successfully completed (Barrett). The same problem was to similarly affect the early AGRs and the time taken to install the insulation was not finally dramatically improved until preconstruction manufacture of liner insulation was undertaken at Heysham II. Turning to the major plant items, their operating experience has been as follows:-

(i)   Boilers

The boilers of the last two stations are of the once-through type
to minimise their volume within the vessel. Boiler tube failures had
progressively decreased after a few years of operation, Table III, as
measured by their rate of occurrence, for the earlier steam drum
boiler units. However the Wylfa units appeared to be more markedly
affected [3]. The causes of failure were shown to be both gas flow
vibrational forces and two phase erosion-corrosion in the waterside
of the boiler tubes. The design of the Wylfa boilers were such that
it was possible to plug boiler tubes in which a leak was located, when
the reactor was on-load and the method was successfully developed
(Dean). The technique uses jacks to apply the necessary plugs and has
dramaticaly reduced the losses in production due to tube failure which
previously required off load remedial work.

During this period much was learnt concerning the single phase and
two phase erosion-corrosion, mechanisms causing boiler tube
failure. The two phase mechanism was particularly prevalent in the
Oldbury and Wylfa boilers and considerable success has been achieved
by chemically dosing the boilers and thereby reducing the effects
of two phase erosion-corrosion. In this connection, the CEGB has
obtained much assistance from other Magnox operators notably HIFRENSA
and EdF. Based on an evaluation of the problem using data from
Vandellos (Palomero), the CEGB have used Morpholine and AMP, 2 - amino
- 2 - methyl - propan - 1 - ol, to raise the pH of the feed water at
Oldbury and Wylfa.

(ii)   Gas Circulators

The performance of the main gas circulators showed significant
improvement as the number of both electrical and mechanical faults
decreased over the first nine years of operation of each unit. Since
this time there has been no significant change in the minimal fault
rate [4]. Any one failure of a circulator may not directly lead to
a reactor trip as the design and safety assessment generally permit
operation at a restricted power with a restricted number of
circulators. Energy losses can therefore be minimised.

(iii) Fuel

During this period the Magnox fuel element was improved by increasing
the aluminium content of the uranium bars. A collaborative programme
between the CEGB, SSEB, UKAEA and BNFL led in 1971 to the increase
in aluminium content from a range of 600 to 1300 ppm to 1000 to
1500 ppm. This change decreased the swelling effect produced by
fission products, so that within the uranium bar diameter increase
limit, higher irradiations up to 5500 MWd/te, channel average, could
be achieved. Of the first 2 million fuel elements loaded the failure
rate was of the order of 0.1%. This mark has now been passed and more
than 3 million Magnox fuel elements have been loaded into reactors

still with improving reductions in failure rate currently running near an order of magnitude lower.

(iv) Coolant Ducts and Bellows

By the end of the 1970s all Magnox units were operating successfully with planned outages for inspection and maintenance averaging 10 weeks for each reactor every 2 years. The CEGB introduced ultrasonic inspection of pressure circuit components in 1977 as part of a continuing programme to confirm their high integrity. In 1979 indications from duct bellows unit attachment welds at Dungeness A implied that there could be defects in these welds. Because of these new and unexpected findings, inspections of similar components at Bradwell and Berkeley were brought forward. Improved analysis techniques showed that some features giving adverse indications were due to insignificant point inclusions. In other cases defects were such that metallurgical examination was necessary. Some further units were removed and tested to five times operating pressure and at a range of simulated operating temperatures. By such test cases it has been possible to show that substantial margins exist with the design (Bindon). Further the metallurgical evidence indicates that the welding techniques during construction were the source of some defects and that there has been no in-service growth of such defects.

The units removed for testing have either been replaced or the circuit has been blanked off with a view to future reinstatement. Although time consuming, some additional units have been repaired or replaced and, as a result, no units remain in service which approach the level of defectiveness of any of those pressure tested. Dungeness A and Bradwell were returned to full operation in 1982 following outages lasting two years. Berkeley, which has more bellows units than all the other stations put together and also has the most difficult access problems, will not have all of its 16 circuits available until 1987. Details of the inspection and repair programmes are given elsewhere (Giblin).

These problems produced significant losses in output from these stations over the years 1979 to 1982. Continuing reductions in output have occurred at Berkeley until the present time, as shown by its capacity factors, Table IV. Inspection of Boilers at Sizewell has led to restricted operation and this also shows up in their capacity factors, Table IV.

CURRENT STATUS IN THE 1980's

Following these long outages, the return to higher levels of production has been a credit to the staff involved. The CEGB learnt that a clear plan was necessary before each outage for inspection. There was also a need to agree all criteria for assessment before the inspection and to have specialist staff available for interpretation of the data and to undertake any integrity calculations that were necessary to minimise the downtime of the plant. Finally the teams for any rectification work such as welding or dressing had to be organised. Therefore after much effort, 1984/85 production returned to its normal levels for the plant group as a whole. Given that the plant was nearing the original planned lifetime of 25 years (Wylfa 20 years) assessments took place to evaluate further planned extensions to operating life. This aspect is covered by a companion paper. To finish this review it is relevant to look back over the whole life and indicate those operating features that gave confidence in considering plant life extension as part of the planning process.

SOURCES OF ENERGY UNAVAILABILITY

The CEGB uses a computerised database for recording energy unavailability by plant item using a four digit plant code. This is used to supply many types of performance indicator but for simple analysis, causes of energy unavailability can be divided into the categories [5].

(i)	Total overhaul programme	15.1%
(ii)	Refuelling Losses	0.1%
(iii)	Average Plant Breakdown Loss	3.1%
(iv)	Immediate Breakdown Loss	2.2%
(v)	Other Station Constraints	1.5%
(vi)	Non-Station Constraints	0.1%

Noting that (iv) is part of (iii) the Magnox averages of these quantities since 1981/82 are given along side the source above. While the lifetime capacity factors have been affected for some stations, by the outages mentioned in previous sections, the settled down averages for the 1980s gave us confidence that the plants were still functioning satisfactorily.

As a component of the Immediate Breakdown loss in energy, any trend of an increase in reactor trip rate would have indicated degraded reliability. However to date (1986) the reactor trip rate averaged over life is 0.26 per 1000 hours synchronised to the grid per reactor. Of this value 0.1 is the component due to genuine demands and the remainder is due to spurious action of automatic trip equipment. These values as averages have remained constant throughout the plant lives after the initial commissioning period.

There is therefore no degradation in the reliability of protection systems nor the incidence of faults requiring a reactor trip.

RARE MAJOR FAULTS

A review of unusual faults at CEGB Magnox stations was presented at an IAEA conference in Marseille in 1983 (Cave). This indicated that they were rare, less than 10^{-2} per year, and that none had led to the possibility of a release of the fission product inventory. Since 1983 the CEGB has declared two Site Incidents Alerts which can occur when there is the possibility of an off-site release of radioactivity. The incidents declared were:-

(i) following the lifting of a primary coolant safety relief valve on Trawsfynydd Reactor 1, extremely minor radioactive particles of rust were found beyond the site boundary. (Date 21 February 1986)

(ii)   following the release of carbon dioxide to atmosphere at Sizewell
        when a fuel machine was discharging a consignment of fuel for
        storage. (Date 26 January 1986).

In both these cases, reported to the OECD Incident Reporting System,
the effects for the public were negligible. Therefore in the past 24 years no
serious radiological hazard has arisen from the operation of the CEGB Magnox
reactors.

PLANT IMPROVEMENTS

As with any plant operated over so many years opportunities are taken
to improve the efficiency and output of the plant whenever this proves to be
economically worthwhile. The outlet gas temperatures at several stations have
been reoptimised and increased from 360°C up to a current maximum of 370°C. To
ensure that there is no increase in oxidation rate of mild steel components,
those reactors which have higher moisture content have had additional gas
conditioning equipment installed.

However, as our knowledge of reactor safety has improved by operating
experience and analysis of plant behaviour, modifications have also been
implemented that have been entirely aimed at improvement of the safety status of
the reactors. Examples include:

(i)   Alternative means of reactor shutdown by Boron Ball Shutdown Devices
        (Mitchell)

(ii)   Remote and diverse primary coolant duct valve actuation equipment
        (Green)

(iii)   Remote in-core inspection and repair equipment (Hugh)

(iv)   Improved ultrasonic techniques for standpipe inspection (Morton)

(v)   A Facility for Reactor Engineering Development, FRED, has been
        established at Littlebrook, Kent with facilities for full scale
        manipulator development, testing and training with reactor models

(vi)   Delayed Neutron protection systems to enhance the detection of fast
        fuel element failure events

(vii)   Diverse boiler feed system improvements and loss of boiler feed
        protection systems.

These and many other improvements have been part of a continuing
review process which have placed the Magnox plants in a good position to
continue to operate.

The licensing process in the UK has recently required a Long Term
Safety Review of all Magnox plant. A review of this process to date has been
published (Clarke 1986) and during 1987 final assessments for the two earliest

stations will be made.

CONCLUSIONS

After 24 years of operation of Magnox reactors to generate electricity, the CEGB has supplied 446 TWh from their 16 reactor units of this type. This equates to 337 operating reactor years of experience. Although they have been subject to deratings and several instances of significant engineering problems, they have made a significant contribution to power generation in terms of being both safe and economic. Their cumulative operating experience provides a strong base for assessing continual operation and the possibility of an extension beyond their original planned lifetimes. The economic and technical factors on which a decision could be based are given in a companion paper later in this symposium.

ACKNOWLEDGEMENTS

The work discussed has been carried out on behalf of several Departments within the Central Electricity Generating Board whose permission to publish this paper is gratefully acknowledged.

FOOTNOTES

[1]   Only Berkeley in recent years has been refuelled off-load for significant periods while charge-hall cranes are over-hauled

[2]   Each reactor shall be shutdown after a maximum period of 2 years following consent of the Regulatory Authority to start up that reactor

[3]   A total of 55 boiler tube leaks for 2 reactors from the time of raising power, January 1971, on Reactor 1 until February 1979

[4]   Energy losses from Magnox operation due to gas circulator faults in 1985/6 averaged 0.02% of available energy production

[5] (i) TOTAL OVERHAUL PROGRAMME, includes all planned outages, additions, amendments and over-runs in the year. It includes full outages and restrictions

    (ii) REFUELLING LOSS, includes losses due to off-load and/or reduced load fuelling. It is expressed as a % of energy loss for the year

    (iii) AVERAGE PLANT BREAKDOWN LOSS, is composed of all plant related sources of unavailability excluding those defined by "Other Stations Constraints" and "Non-Station Constraints", the Total Overhaul Programme and Refuelling Loss. It includes Immediate Breakdown Loss, and is expressed as a % of energy loss for the year

(iv)   IMMEDIATE BREAKDOWN LOSS, is a component of average plant breakdown loss and refers to the immediate loss of generation plant which is not planned and is lost to the system under controlled conditions. It is expressed as a % of energy loss for the year.

(v)   NON-STATION CONSTRAINTS, refers to any capability of CEGB plant available at the station side of the Power Station/System boundary which cannot be used to meet demand. It is expressed as a % of energy loss for the year

(vi)   OTHER STATION CONSTRAINTS, refers to a loss of capability at the Power Station boundary not attributable to plant items. It is expressed as a % of energy loss for the year

REFERENCES

Barret, J.D., Nuclear Energy, 1981, 20, No. 2, 189-196.

Broom, T. and Gow, R.S., Phil. Trans. Roy. Soc. Lond. A276, 1974, 571-586.

Bindon, F.J.L., Nuclear Energy, 1983, 22, No. 4, 275-277.

Cave, L. and Clarke, A.W. IAEA Symposium on Operational Safety of Nuclear Power Plants. 1983. IAEA-SM-268/30.

Clarke, A.W. and Marchese, C.J. Nuclear Europe, 1985, No. 1, 13-17.

Clarke, A.W. and Matthews, R.R. Nuclear Europe, 1986, 25, No. 3, 169-175.

Dean, R. Nuclear Energy 1984, 23, No. 2, 97-104.

Doble, B.G., Nuclear Europe, 1982, No. 11, 18-21.

Green, A.A., Cowey, M. and Frankland, E. Nuclear Energy, 1981, 20, No. 2, 201-205.

Hardy, H.K., Bishop, J.F.W., Pickman, D.O. and Eldred, V.W., J. Brit Nuclear Energy Soc, 1963, No. 2, 33.

Hugh, J.R. amd Thompson, V. Nuclear Energy, 1981, 20, No. 2, 153-164.

Mitchell, N. Nuclear Energy, 1981, 20, No. 2, 145-150.

Mummery, G.B. and Hines, G.F. BNES Conference Nuclear Performance, 1973, 1, 1-4.

Morton, J., Ely, R.W.J. and Wooldridge, A.B. Nuclear Europe, 1986, No.6, 20-21.

Palomero, C.F., Pla, E. and Garbett, K. Water Chemistry 3, BNES London (1983) 235-242.

Table I

CEGB MAGNOX STATIONS OPERATING DATA

Station (3)	Construction	(1) Commissioned	Net Rating, MW Design	DNC (2)	Age in 1987 (yrs)
Bradwell	1/57	9/62	300	245	25
Berkeley	1/57	8/62	276	276	25
Dungeness A	7/60	11/65	550	424	22
Hinkley Pt A	11/57	4/65	500	430	22
Oldbury	5/62	4/68	600	434	19
Sizewell	4/61	6/66	580	420	21
Trawsfynydd	7/59	3/65	500	390	22
Wylfa	9/63	12/71	1180	840	16

Note

(1) Mean date for commissioning of all turbine generator sets on site except Wylfa which is the date for the first 3 out of the total of 4 sets.

(2) DNC at Feb 1987.

(3) Each station consists of 2 reactors.

Table II

Station	Channels [1]	T/G [2]	G.C [3]	Derating % [4]	Lifetime CF% [5]
Bradwell	2564	6	6	18	70.7
Berkeley	3265	4	8	0	62.4
Hinkley Point A	4500	6	6	14	74.2
Trawsfynydd	3740	4	6	22	71.8
Dungeness A	3932	4	4	23	69.1
Sizewell	3788	2	4	28	74.8
Oldbury	3308	2	4	28	78.5
Wylfa	6150	4	4	29	68.5

[1]   number of fuel channels in each reactor

[2]   number of main Turbine-generators

[3]   number of gas circulators and boiler units

[4]   % derating from Design Net Rating (DNR) to Declared Net Capability (DNC)

[5]   Lifetime cumulative capacity factor based on DNR until derating and then DNC to end of 1986

Table III

SUMMARY OF BOILER TUBE FAILURES IN CEGB MAGNOX REACTORS
TO 1979

Station	Prior to 1975		Since 1975-79		Change since 1975
	Reactor Years	Total No. of Failures	Reactor Years (1)	Total No. of Failures	
Berkeley	25	10	9	nil	Better
Bradwell	25	107	9	5	Better
Hinkley 'A'	20	1	9	3	Worse [1]
Trawsfynydd	20	39	9	nil	Better
Dungeness 'A'	18	1	9	nil	Better
Sizewell	17	13	9	3	No significant change
Oldbury	14	5	9	1	Better
TOTAL	139	176	63	12	Better

[1] rate then similar to other stations.

Table IV

Capacity Factors over the Past Six Years [1]

	80/1	81/2	82/3	83/4	84/5	85/6
Bradwell	0[2]	3[2]	60	59	79	79
Berkeley [2]	42	0	17	33	32	44
Hinkley Point A	83	81	86	86	93	96
Trawsfynydd	34[4]	88	86	76	86	85
Dungeness A	0[2]	5[2]	86	83	82	84
Sizewell	75	47[2]	59[2]	80	58[3]	65[3]
Oldbury	90	92	91	77	84	88
Wylfa	80	81	84	87	94	90

[1] Capacity factor based on Declared Net Capability for UK financial years (year ending 31 March)

[2] Denotes period of extended reactor outages for inspection of duct work

[3] Denotes period of operation at reduced pressure or reduced numbers of reactor circuits arising from inspection

[4] Denotes year of a large ingress of water following a boiler tube failure and the subsequent outage for remedial work to Reactor 1

A DISCUSSION OF CANDU 300 PLANT LIFE EXTENSION

by R.S. Hart
Atomic Energy of Canada Limited

ABSTRACT

The CANDU nuclear power program recognized from its inception the importance of incorporating maintainability and life extension features into the basic design. This is facilitated by the modular nature of the CANDU design.

The CANDU 300, in providing a station design life of 100 years, significantly advances plant life extension capabilities. All key components are designed for a minimum 40 year life with the provision for easy replacement.

An example of this is the CANDU 300 fuel channel. The fuel channel design has been modified to allow the 208 fuel channels to be replaced within a 90 day outage. Even major equipment can be replaced with a minimum of down time (4 weeks for example for steam generators). This is facilitated by the station layout, which provides 360° access to the five principal buildings, and by spacious and well organized building internal arrangements.

A comprehensive in-service inspection program, in combination with a transient monitoring and recording function within the station control computers is utilized to monitor component status.

The CANDU 300 has been designed utilizing the Atomic Energy of Canada Limited CANDID Engineering system, which incorporates advanced computer aided design and drafting based on 3-dimensional modelling. This has permitted the replacement of all components to be simulated.

EXAMEN DE LA PROLONGATION DE LA VIE UTILE DU REACTEUR CANDU 300

RESUME

Les responsables de la filière CANDU ont pris conscience d'emblée qu'il importait de prendre en compte, dès le stade de la conception, la facilité d'entretien et la possibilité de prolonger la durée de vie de la centrale, tâche facilitée par la conception modulaire du réacteur CANDU.

Le réacteur CANDU 300, théoriquement conçu pour fonctionner pendant 100 ans, représente un progrès considérable quant à la prolongation de la durée de vie des centrales. Tous les composants essentiels sont prévus pour durer au moins 40 ans et sont faciles à remplacer.

Le canal de combustible du réacteur CANDU illustre parfaitement cette conception. Il a été modifié pour permettre le remplacement des 208 canaux de combustible moyennant un temps de disponibilité de 90 jours. On peut même remplacer les gros matériels en réduisant au minimum la durée d'indisponibilité (4 semaines pour les générateurs de vapeur, par exemple). Ces opérations sont facilitées par l'agencement de la centrale qui permet d'accéder par tous les côtés aux cinq bâtiments principaux, ainsi que par des locaux spacieux et une organisation interne rationnelle des bâtiments.

On contrôle l'état des composants grâce à un programme exhaustif d'inspection en service, allant de pair avec une surveillance et un enregistrement des transitoires assurés par les ordinateurs de commande de la centrale.

Le réacteur CANDU 300 repose sur le système CANDID Engineering mis au point par l'Agence de l'énergie atomique du Canada limité et fait appel à des méthodes avancées de conception assistées par ordinateur et d'établissement de projets sur la base d'une modélisation tridimensionnelle. Ces méthodes ont permis de simuler le remplacement de tous les composants.

1.0 INTRODUCTION

The CANDU nuclear power system has evolved over the past 40 years in a carefully planned and systematic manner based on an integrated design, manufacturing and operating approach.

Key features of CANDU include a pressure tube reactor (Figure 1), the use of heavy water moderator and natural uranium fuel, and on-power refuelling.

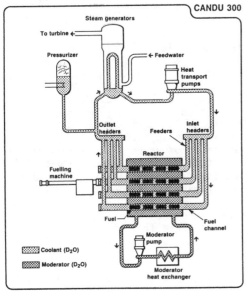

Figure 1   Steam supply system

The CANDU 300, with an electrical output in the range of 400 MW, is the latest in the CANDU family of power stations. Proven technology is used throughout the CANDU 300, updated with innovative features resulting from ongoing Canadian research and development work.

High capacity factors, achieved through the use of proven and tested components, ease of maintenance and ease of component replacement have always been a focus of the CANDU program. This focus is continued in the CANDU 300 which has a plant design life of 100 years and a target lifetime capacity factor of 90%.

Two of the factors that determine the economic design life of a nuclear power plant are the economically achievable design life of each component, and the ease of replacement of each component. Three principal factors determine capacity factor over the life of the station. These are the reliability of station components, the period of continuous full power operation

between scheduled in-service inspection/maintenance outages, and the ease of component maintenance and/or replacement.

The above factors are discussed in the following sections. Although this paper deals primarily with the nuclear steam plant systems, detailed attention has been given to reliability, ease of maintenance and component replacement in all other areas of the CANDU 300 station.

2.0 CANDU 300 OVERVIEW

2.1 General

In order to facilitate an appreciation of the various plant life extension features of the CANDU 300 discussed in subsequent sections, a brief overview of the CANDU 300 is presented below.

2.2 Station and Reactor Building Layout

The CANDU 300 nuclear generating station (Figure 2) consists of five principal buildings and several auxiliary structures. The distribution of equipment and services among the buildings is primarily by function. The principal buildings of the CANDU 300 are, to the maximum extent feasible, self contained "islands" with the minimum number of connections to other buildings. A major advantage of the CANDU 300 station layout is the 360° access to all principal buildings during both construction and operation of the station.

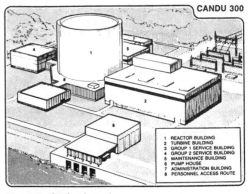

Figure 2   Station Layout

Figure 3 shows the Reactor Building, a conventional post-tensioned concrete structure featuring seven steel bulkheads, optimally positioned around the perimeter wall adjacent to the base slab. All umbilicals from the Reactor Building, ranging from steam and feedwater lines to instrumentation and electrical supplies pass through these bulkheads. There are no other penetrations in the containment structure, except for the airlock and the equipment hatch.

The Reactor Building is encompassed by an annular array of connecting tunnels. This structure (Figure 3),

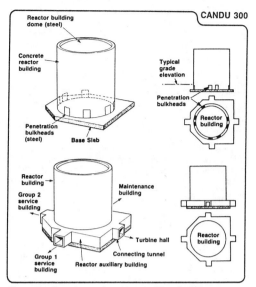

Figure 3   Reactor and reactor auxiliary building arrangement

referred to as the Reactor Auxiliary Building, interfaces with the other principal buildings and accommodates the connecting umbilicals, the Main Control Room, and the Irradiated Fuel Storage Bay.

The Reactor Building arrangement is illustrated in Figure 4, and a plan of the Reactor and Reactor Auxiliary Building is shown in Figure 5. A very large portion of the Reactor Building is accessible during reactor operation, and the arrangement of structures and components facilitates maintenance and component replacement.

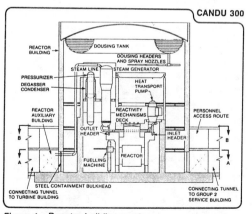

Figure 4   Reactor building section

2.3 Nuclear Steam Plant Systems and Components

Two principal systems in the CANDU nuclear steam plant are the Heat Transport System and the Moderator System. These systems, and the components of these

systems, in conjunction with the reactor assembly are primarily responsible for determining station life. A brief description of these systems and the reactor assembly is therefore provided here.

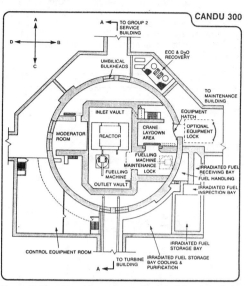

Figure 5 Reactor and reactor auxiliary building base plan

The major components of the CANDU 300 Heat Transport System, shown in Figure 6, are the 208 fuel channels, two steam generators, two electrically driven reactor coolant pumps, reactor inlet and outlet headers and the interconnecting piping.

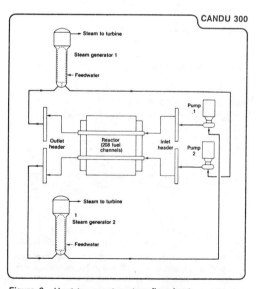

Figure 6   Heat transport system flowsheet

Heavy water coolant is fed to the fuel channels from the inlet headers at one end of the reactor and is returned to the outlet headers at the other end of the reactor. The reactor coolant flow in the CANDU 300 is in the standard CANDU "figure of 8" pattern, with the heat transport pumps in series and the coolant making two core passes per cycle. The equipment arrangement, with the pumps at one end of the reactor, and the steam generators at the other end results in unidirectional core flow.

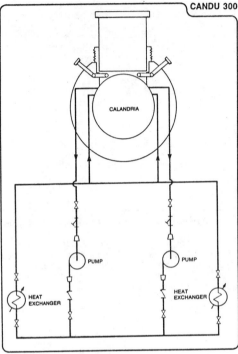

Figure 7 Moderator system

The materials utilized in the CANDU 300 heat transport system are listed in Table 1.

Table 1 Heat Transport System Materials

Steam Generator	• Head	Carbon Steel
	• Tubing	Incoloy 800
	• Tube sheet	Inconel clad carbon steel
Pump	• Casing	Carbon Steel
	• Impeller	Stainless Steel
	• Shaft	Stainless Steel
Piping	• Feeders	Carbon Steel
	• Headers	Carbon Steel
	• Other	Carbon Steel
Fuel Channel	• End Fittings	Stainless Steel
	• Pressure Tube	Zirconium-2 $^{1}/_{2}$% Niobium

The chemistry specifications for the heat transport system coolant are listed in Table 2. No chemicals are added to the heat transport system for reactivity control purposes.

Table 2 Heat Transport System Chemistry Specifications

Parameter	Permissible range
pD at STP*	10.2 — 10.8
Lithium as Li (mg Li/kg D_2O)	0.35 — 1.4
Dissolved Deuterium as mg D_2/kg D_2O	0.5 — 4.0
Dissolved Oxygen as mg O_2/kg D_2O	< 0.01
Chloride (mg Cl/kg D_2O)	< 0.2
Suspended Solids (mg/kg D_2O)	< 1.0
Conductivity (mS/m at 25°C)	0.9 — 3.6

*Standard Temperature and Pressure

Neutrons produced by nuclear fission are moderated by the low temperature heavy water in the calandria. The moderator heavy water is circulated through the moderator system (Figure 7) for cooling and for purification. The materials in contact with the heavy water moderator are summarized in Table 3.

Table 3 Moderator System Materials

Calandria	Stainless Steel
Calandria tubes	Zircaloy 2
Moderator Heat Exchangers	Stainless steel
Moderator Pumps	Stainless steel
Moderator piping and valves	Stainless steel

The chemistry specifications for the moderator system, are listed in Table 4.

Table 4 Moderator Chemistry Specifications

Parameters	Permissible range
pD (at 25°C, as measured on pH meter)	4.5 — 7.0
Chloride (mg Cl/kg D_2O)	< 0.2
Conductivity (mS/m at 25°C)	< 0.5
Boron (mg B/kg D_2O)	< 10
Gadolinium (mg Gd/kg D_2O)	< 1
Dissolved Deuterium/hydrogen (ml D_2/Kg D_2O)	$\overline{< 5}$

The reactor assembly, shown in Figure 8, comprises calandria shell, the end shields, and the sur-

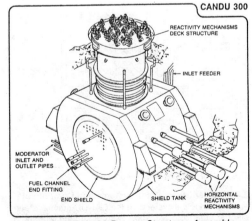

Figure 8 CANDU 300 Reactor Structures Assembly

rounding shield tank. A section through the reactor assembly is shown in Figure 9.

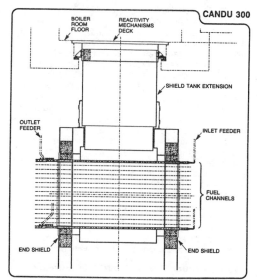

Figure 9   CANDU-300 reactor structures assembly

The calandria shell, with its ends closed by the two end shields, forms a horizontal cylindrical vessel which contains the moderator heavy water at near atmospheric pressure and low temperature (70°C). The end shields comprise an inner and an outer tube sheet joined by the fuel channel lattice tubes, and the outer shell.

The end shields are secured around this periphery to the shield tank end walls. The shield tank encloses the calandria, with the volume between the calandria and the shield tank being filled with light water which is maintained at near atmospheric pressure and low temperature. The space between the inner and outer tube-sheet of each end shield is filled with carbon steel balls and light water. The end shields support the axially-oriented fuel channel assemblies, the calandria supports the vertical and horizontal in-core reactivity control units, and the shield tank extension supports the vertical reactivity control units.

All devices for reactivity control are located between and at 90° to the fuel channels within the low temperature and pressure moderator, and penetrate the reactor from the top or from the side.

Typical of these devices are the mechanical shutoff rods of Shutdown System #1 (Figure 10). These devices feature Zircaloy in-core guide tubes and supports. No devices are inserted into, or chemicals added to the high pressure and temperature Heat Transport System for reactivity control.

3.0 COMPONENT LIFE AND RELIABILITY

Over the past 40 years extensive development effort in Canada has established high component reliability and long component life. Heat transport system coolant pump seals, for example, are an area where

AECL technology is a world leader, with four years of continuous operation established between seal replacements.

Long Component life and high reliability in the CANDU 300 is assured through the utilization of proven components, and the provision of redundancy and on-power maintenance as necessary.

A very high level of standardization, facilitated by the modular notion of the CANDU concept, has always been a feature of CANDU reactors. Standardization, however, has been implemented to an unprecendented degree in the CANDU 300. For example, all key components, including reactor coolant pumps, pressure tubes, steam generators, fuelling machine, and fuel are identical to those now in service in the very successful CANDU 600 stations. In general, however, due to the smaller size of the CANDU 300, only half as many of these components are required. This contributes significantly to overall reliability.

All systems of the CANDU 300 are designed to operate for a minimum of 3 years, with minimum on-power maintenance. The reactor building layout, which provides on-power access to most areas, facilitates maintenance if required. For example, reactivity mechanism drives can be serviced on-power, and a heat transport pump motor can be changed at power (power reduced to 60% as required by reduced coolant flow). Such requirements are rare however (for example, there has never been a need to change a pump motor on a CANDU 600).

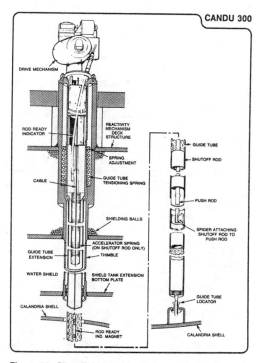

Figure 10   Shutoff and mechanical control absorber unit

4.0 IN SERVICE INSPECTION/MAINTENANCE OUTAGES

In the absence of a requirement for an outage for refuelling, (CANDU reactors are refuelled on-power) CANDU in-service inspection and maintenance outages are determined by other requirements, including maintenance requiring a reactor shutdown, regulatory imposed inservice inspection requirements, or requirements imposed by others (for example, turbine inspections required by insurers).

The CANDU 300 has a target for three years continuous operation between in-service inspections and maintenance outages.

Discussion to date indicates that the inspection requirements imposed by the regulatory bodies and others can be satisfied by the CANDU 300, with three years operation between scheduled outages, except for an inaugural inspection following the first year of operation.

This is accomplished by a comprehensive in-service inspection program, including automated fuel channel inspection by equipment inserted into the fuel channel by the fuelling machine, during scheduled outages, and the provision of on-line monitoring systems, including a turbine generator condition monitoring system.

In-service inspection and maintenance capability is enhanced in CANDU reactors by the relatively low radiation fields associated with the heat transport system. This is attributable to several factors, including material selection (low cobalt content), purification and chemistry control, and the ability to detect, locate and remove failed fuel (utilizing the onpower refuelling system). The latter essentially removes fission products as a source term for major component activation.

5.0 COMPONENT DESIGN LIFE

5.1 General

With the exception of the reactor building structures and the calandria/shield tank assembly, which have design lives in excess of 100 years, all components of the CANDU 300 can be easily replaced (See Section 6). All such components, including steam generators and fuel channels have a design life of 40 years or more. Many major components may therefore be replaced once or twice in the 100 year design life of the station.

The following factors, to a greater or lesser degree, impact on component life and are fully considered in determining the life of CANDU components.
• Creep and growth due to neutron irradiation
• Embrittlement due to irradiation
• Erosion and corrosion
• Fatigue
• Wear
• Thermal creep
• Obsolescence
• Other factors of degradation

Operating experience, experimental data and advanced analytical methods form the basis for determining component life. Life expectancy is verified during plant operation by a comprehensive in-service inspection program which includes the periodic removal of a fuel channel for laboratory inspection, and a transient logging and analysis program that facilitates an ongoing fatigue life evaluation for all key components.

The principal factors affecting the life of some key components of the CANDU 300 are discussed in the following sections.

5.2 Reactor Assembly

All components of the reactor assembly, including the reactivity mechanisms function under low stress, and at low temperatures. These factors together with the moderator chemistry (Table 4) preclude stress-corrosion cracking and all forms of erosion-corrosion.

All CANDU 300 in-core components can be replaced. The reactivity control units can be easily replaced (within 2 or 3 shifts) during routine outages, if necessary. Replacement of the fuel channels is accommodated within a 90 day outage (See Section 6.2). The reactor assembly (See section 3.4) which is not easily replaceable (replacement would require a 24 month outage) is designed to assure a life in excess of 100 years. A paramount consideration in establishing reactor assembly life is the effect of neutron irradiation on reactor materials.

The neutron fluxes and the integrated neutron fluxes for critical CANDU 300 calandria components over the 100 year operation are presented in Table 5. These values are significantly below the threshold fluences for detectable mechanical property degradation.

Table 5 Neutron Fluxes in CANDU-300 Reactor Components

	Max. neutron flux n/cm^2.s >1 MeV	Thermal	Integrated fast neutron flux over 100 years (n/cm^2)
Calandria Mainshell	2.3×10^8	1.3×10^{13}	7.2×10^{17}
Calandria Tubesheet	6.7×10^{11}	1.1×10^{13}	2.1×10^{21}
Calandria Tubesheet/ Lattice Tube Weld	8.3×10^{11}	1.1×10^{12}	2.6×10^{21}

The effect of transmutations on CANDU 300 reactor assembly components has also been considered, and shown to be negligible.

There is a slight change in the absorption cross section of Type 304L stainless subjected to radiation. For example, after 100 years at a thermal flux of 2×10^{13} n/cm^2.s, the absorption cross section changes from 0.23 cm^{-1} to 0.19 cm^{-1}. This does not significantly impact on CANDU 300 core physics.

5.3 Steam Generators

The CANDU 300 utilizes the proven CANDU 600 steam generator design, which consists of an inverted U-tube bundle housed within a light bulb type enclosure, which includes integral steam separating and drying equipment and preheater. Long life for CANDU steam generators is assured by a thorough and conservative approach to design. High recirculation ratios (greater than 5:1) in combination with relatively low heat fluxes are employed. Flow induced vibration is avoided through comprehensive analysis with advanced codes, verified by extensive experimentation. Erosion-corrosion is avoided via an integrated approach to material selection, and both primary side and secondary side chemistry control.

Material selection extends to all secondary side components that contact the feedwater; copper alloys are not permitted in the feed train, stainless steel is used for all low pressure feedwater heater tubes, and titanium tubing is used for condensers on all salt or impure water sites.

Primary side (Heat Transport System coolant) chemistry specifications are presented in Table 2. Steam generator, secondary side chemistry control specifications are given in Table 6, and feedwater chemistry specifications in Table 7.

Table 6 Steam Generator Chemistry Control Specification

Parameter	Permissible operating range
pH at STP	9 to 10
Sodium (ppb)	<70
Chloride (ppb)	<100
Silica (ppm)	<1
Specific Conductivity (mS/m)	0.2 to 2.0
Cation Conductivity (mS/m)	< 0.1
Blowdown (% FPSF)*	
Continuous	0.1%
Intermittent	0.3%

*FPSF = Full Power Steam Flow

Table 7 Feedwater Chemistry Specifications

Parameter	Permissible range
pH at STP	>9.4
Dissolved O_2, (ppb)	<5
Hydrazine, (ppb)	100 — 200
Iron, (ppb)	<10
Copper (ppb)	< 2
Amine	to give required pH
Silica, (ppb)	< 20
Specific conductivity (mS/m)	>0.6
Cation conductivity (mS/m)	< 0.05

CANDU steam generator performance is excellent. In commercial plants over 500 MW(e) only 35 of 540,000 steam generator tubes have been plugged in over 125

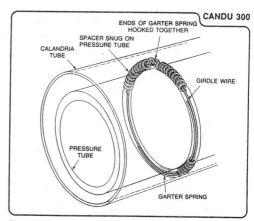

Figure 12   Pressure tube to calandria tube spacer

reactor years of operation, and there is no indication of general steam generator deterioration.

With the design fatigue life and erosion-corrosion allowances, CANDU 300 steam generators will operate satisfactorily for a period in excess of 50 years before replacement is required.

5.4 Fuel Channels

The CANDU 300 fuel channel is shown in Figure 11. There are 208 fuel channels in the CANDU 300, located in a square lattice with a pitch of 286 mm. The pressure tubes, which constitute the heat transport system pressure boundary within the reactor assembly, are concentrically located within the calandria tubes. Four spacers (Figure 12), located along the pressure tube length maintain this concentricity. The annulus between the pressure and calandria tubes is filled with carbon dioxide gas to provide an inert thermal barrier between

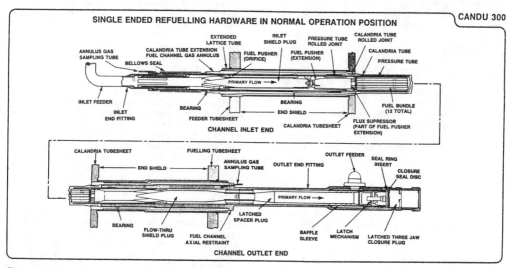

Figure 11   Refuelling hardware in non-refuelling position

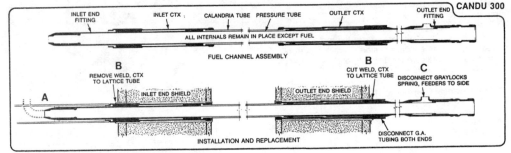

Figure 13 Fuel channel replacement

the hot pressure tube and the cool calandria tube. The pressure tube material for all CANDU reactors subsequent to Pickering Units 1 and 2 is zirconium-2 1/2% niobium.

Pressure tubes are the only component within a CANDU power station that function under a combination of high radiation, high temperature, and high stress.

Two principal factors tend to limit pressure tube life; neutron induced creep and growth and hydriding of the material. The CANDU 300 design accommodates the 300 mm axial creep that will occur over the 40 year design life of the pressure tubes. Hydrogen uptake of the pressure tubes is minimized by material selection and by maintaining favourable temperature distributions over the pressure tube. Pressure tube life, based on hydriding limits exceeds the 40 year design life of the fuel channels.

5.5 Electrical and Instrumentation Cables

Various cables are utilized in the CANDU 300 for electrical power distribution and instrumentation and control, including single conductor, multi-conductor and co-axial cables. All cables used have a projected life of 40 years or more.

Factors contributing to extended life (100 years or longer) for cable systems include:

- Cable materials: various materials are selected for cable insulation, approrpriate to the operating environment (radiation, temperature, etc.), to assure an operating life of 40 years. CANDU cable insulation specifications are continually updated based on Canadian research and world wide operating experience.

- Multiplexing and Data Highways: These substantially reduce the quantities of cable required for instrumentation and control, which facilitates optimum routing and location of cable runs. This, in turn, facilitates cable inspection and eventual replacement.

- Cable Layout: The CANDU 300 features a "radial" cable routing approach within the Reactor Building, in which trunk cabling (power, data highways, etc.), are routed through peripheral accessible areas, and then radially into junction boxes and multiplexer enclosures located on the outside of shielding walls. Individual cables are then routed radially through the shielding walls to the field devices. In this way bulk cabling is always located in low-radiation, accessible areas, with only the final,

individual connections to field devices located in areas of high radiation or temperature. This arrangement assures long cable life and also facilitates easy replacement.

6.0 COMPONENT REPLACEMENT

6.1 General

The CANDU 300 Reactor Building layout and lifting and shielding provisions provide for easy replacement of CANDU 300 components via the airlock or equipment hatch; such replacements are generally accommodated within a routine outage. Exceptions are replacement of the fuel channels (for which special facilities are provided) and the steam generators (which are removed and replaced through the Reactor Building dome).

Fuel channel replacement and steam generator replacement, discussed in the following sections, comply with the general CANDU 300 design requirement that "any major modernization, replacement or repair, must be accommodated within a 90 day outage."

The CANDU 300 was designed utilizing "CANDID Engineering", an acronym for CANDU Integrated Design Engineering. A key element of CANDID Engineering is the full size electronic model of the station created during the design process. This model is utilized to simulate all major maintenance and component replacement activities. The simulation verifies lifting capability, personnel and component access and removal routes, clearances during component movement, radiation fields, and other data pertinent to the maintenance or replacement activity.

6.2 Fuel Channel Replacement

The reactor building layout, the fuel channel design, and replacement tooling designs have been coordinated in the CANDU 300 to facilitate quick and easy fuel channel replacement. Fuel channel replacement proceeds following defuelling of the reactor and decontamination of the heat transport system.

Removal of each channel is accomplished (See Figure 13), by cutting the inlet feeder connection at 'A', cutting the two calandria tube extension to lattice tube welds at 'B' and disconnecting the mechanical outlet feeder connection at 'C'. All cutting is via remote and automatic cutters. The fuel channel is then extracted by a special carrier, which temporarily replaces the fuelling machine in the fuelling machine carriage (Figure 14). The inlet end of the fuel channel is supported as it is withdrawn from the calandria by an extendable mandril as shown in Figure 14.

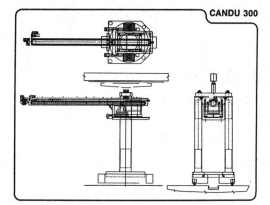

Figure 14   Fuel channel replacement cradle

The fuelling machine carriage, utilizing the normal fuelling machine carriage drive and locating mechanisms, then moves the fuel channel carrier to the Reactor Building perimeter wall and discharges the old fuel channel into a receiving flask as shown in Figure 15. The carrier then receives a new fuel channel assembly, returns to the reactor face. The new channel is installed in a sequence which is the reverse of the removal process. All replacement welds are made by the same remote automatic equipment that was utilized during the original construction installation. The 208 fuel channels can be replaced within a 90 day outage.

6.3 Steam Generator Replacement
The CANDU 300 steam generators can be replaced via an opening in the Reactor Building dome, utilizing a Very Heavy Lift (VHL) crane, in a manner similar to their original installation.

Replacement requires the cutting of an opening in the steel reactor building dome, the cutting of steam and feedwater lines, and the disconnection of instrumentation from the steam generators. The steam generators are then lifted through the dome opening and new steam generators installed utilizing a VHL crane. Various connections to the steam generators are then made. Steam generator replacement requires about 4 weeks.

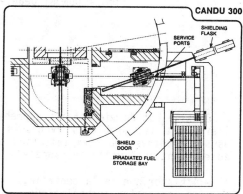

Figure 15   Fuel channel replacement system arrangement

7.0 SUMMARY
High capacity factors and extended station life were principal focuses of the CANDU 300 design effort. Detailed attention has therefore been given to component reliability, ease of maintenance and ease of component replacement.

The resulting CANDU 300 design assures a plant design life of 100 years or more, with a realistic prospect of lifetime capacity factors of 90% or better.

ARRET DEFINITIF DE CHINON A2

DMT - DUMONT Jean - PZC - POUZAC Jean Pierre

RESUME

Dans le but de mieux faire appréhender l'état de la centrale au moment de l'arrêt et les problèmes éventuels que l'exploitant aurait eu à résoudre dans l'hypothèse où l'exploitation de la centrale avait été maintenue, les auteurs ont jugé utile de rappeler :

- l'historique de la centrale,
- sa conception technologique,
- les principaux problèmes rencontrés pendant la vie de la centrale et les moyens mis en oeuvre pour les résoudre.

Dans un premier temps l'exploitant s'est attaché à faire le bilan des problèmes techniques qui auraient pu affecter la sûreté ou pénaliser la disponibilité à court ou moyen terme.

L'analyse effectuée ne laissait pas apparaître de craintes notables dans les cinq années à venir.

L'étude économique périodique d'adaptation du parc de production réalisée par la Direction de la Production et du Transport d'Electricité de France en 1983 montrait que la date optimale de déclassement de l'unité CHINON A2 était juillet 1985. La coïncidence parfaite de cette date avec celle du gréement en personnel des unités voisines B3 - B4 (2 X 900 MWe - REP) a été l'élément complémentaire déterminant la décision d'arrêt en 1985. Cette décision prise suffisamment tôt a permis d'optimiser de façon très sensible l'utilisation du combustible et du personnel de conduite.

La réflexion sur le devenir possible de la tranche est ensuite exposée.

FINAL SHUTDOWN OF CHINON A2

J. Dumont, J.-P. Pouzac
Electricité de France
Chinon (France)

ABSTRACT

In order to gain a better grasp of the condition of the Chinon plant at shutdown and the problems its operator might have had to deal with had the plant been kept in operation, the authors review:

-- The history of the plant;

-- Its technological design;

-- The main problems encountered during its lifetime and how these were solved.

In the first instance, the operator took stock of the technical problems which could have affected the safety of the plant or restricted availability in the short and medium term.

The analysis did not point to any serious problems for the five years ahead.

The periodic economic review of electricity generating capacity carried out in 1983 by the Direction de la Production et du Transport d'Electricité de France showed that the optimal date for decommissioning Chinon A2 was July 1985. The fact that this coincided exactly with the transfer date for personnel in this neighbouring units B3 and B4 (2 x 900 MWe -- PWR) was the additional deciding factor for decommissioning in 1985. Taking the decision early enough enabled the operator to optimise the use both of fuel and of reactor staff.

The authors then discuss the disposal options for the plant.

I - HISTORIQUE

Cette tranche, dénommée au départ E.D.F.2, faisait partie du 1er plan programme "Electro-Nucléaire" décidé par Electricité de France en 1955.

Ce plan comprenait les trois réacteurs de CHINON A :

- EDF 1 -   80 MW électrique
- EDF 2 -   210 MW électrique
- EDF 3 -   400 MW électrique

et le site de CHINON devenait ainsi le premier site Electro-Nucléaire de France.

Ces 3 réacteurs de la filière à Uranium Naturel - Graphite - Gaz (U.N.G.G.) faisaient suite à ceux construits par le CEA sur le site de Marcoule. Ils visaient moins à disposer d'une puissance électrique importante qu'à poursuivre l'expérience du CEA pour :

- acquérir des informations nouvelles,
- développer les capacités des industries intéressées,
- former un personnel qualifié.

Il s'agissait donc d'un programme à caractère expérimental comportant des prototypes de puissance croissante et l'emploi de techniques progressivement améliorées.

Le premier véritable prototype aura été CHINON A1, démarré en 1963, arrêté en 1973, actuellement confiné, aménagé en musée et ouvert au public.

CHINON A2, par sa puissance, sa conception, sa durée de vie et son bon comportement peut être considérée comme véritablement la 1ère centrale électro-nucléaire industrielle d'Electricité de France.

Les premiers travaux de construction de cette centrale ont débuté dans l'été 1959, alors que les premiers travaux d'infrastructure du site et de génie civil d'EDF 1 étaient commencés depuis 1957.

Des dates qui auront marqué la vie de cette installation, on peut retenir :

- 18 Août 1964   1ère divergence du réacteur

- 16 Février 1965   début de montée en puissance

- 24 Avril 1965   puissance maximale possible atteinte

- 14 Juin 1985   arrêt définitif de l'installation.

Au 14 Juin 1985, à l'heure des bilans définitifs, après plus de 20 années de fonctionnement, la tranche totalisait :

- 131.850 heures de marche,
- près de 70 % de disponibilité moyenne dont 86% pour les cinq dernières années,
- 133.374 cartouches d'uranium naturel utilisées,
- 23,6 milliards de kWh de production.

A titre de comparaison on peut dire que pour produire la même quantité d'électricité avec une centrale thermique classique il aurait été nécessaire de consommer un volume de fuel égal à 120 fois le volume de l'Arc de Triomphe alors que le volume d'uranium naturel utilisé par CHINON A2 représente à peu près le volume d'un petit autobus et moins d'une barrique de vin (de Bourgueil ou de Chinon) si l'on ne considère que l'uranium consommé.

II - CONCEPTION TECHNIQUE DE L'INSTALLATION (Voir figure 1)
Le réacteur :

Le coeur du réacteur, d'une puissance thermique de 860 MW est contenu dans un caisson sphérique en acier soudé de 18 mètres de diamètre et de 10 cm d'épaisseur. Il comprend le modérateur et le combustible. L'empilement graphite, servant de modérateur, a la forme générale d'un cylindre à axe vertical de 14,4 m de diamètre et de 8,40 m de hauteur. Il est percé de 2304 canaux verticaux pouvant recevoir chacun 12 éléments combustibles.

Chaque élément combustible est constitué par :

- le combustible, proprement dit, formé par un tube en uranium naturel de diamètre intérieur 23 mm, diamètre extérieur 43 mm, longueur 540 mm. Ce tube contient une âme en graphite,
- la gaine de magnésium - zirconium qui assure l'isolement du combustible en même temps que le transfert de chaleur au fluide réfrigérant,
- une chemise en graphite, dans laquelle est centré, par 4 secteurs, l'élément combustible.

LA GAINE CONSTITUE LA PREMIERE BARRIERE AUX PRODUITS DE FISSION.

Le caloporteur :

Le gaz carbonique (CO_2), sous une pression de 26 bar, est le caloporteur qui transfère les calories du combustible vers les échangeurs de chaleur. Ce gaz, sortant par le haut du réacteur, circule dans des tuyauteries, traverse le côté primaire des échangeurs, est repris par une soufflante et retourne dans le bas du réacteur.

L'ensemble du circuit ci-dessus décrit s'appelle le circuit primaire.

Le circuit primaire :

Il est constitué par :

- le caisson,
- 4 boucles d'échanges comprenant chacune :
  . un circuit chaud, formé de tuyauteries en acier de diamètre 1800 mm,
    reliant le haut du réacteur à l'entrée des échangeurs,
  . les échangeurs constitués de 24 éléments identiques appelés tours,
  . un circuit froid, formé de tuyauteries en acier de diamètre 1400 mm et
    1600 mm et d'une moto soufflante.
  Ce circuit relie la sortie des échangeurs à l'entrée du réacteur.

L'ensemble des circuits chauds et froids comporte des compensateurs de
dilatation permettant la libre dilatation des tuyauteries.

CE CIRCUIT PRIMAIRE CONSTITUE LA DEUXIEME BARRIERE AUX PRODUITS DE FISSION.

Le circuit secondaire :

Chaque tour d'échangeur est constituée d'une bouteille BP, d'une bouteille
HP et d'un surchauffeur.
L'eau du circuit secondaire arrivant aux bouteilles BP et HP est vaporisée,
puis surchauffée et est acheminée vers 2 groupes turbo-alternateurs de
110 MW de puissance unitaire.

Le renouvellement du combustible :

Le renouvellement du combustible en marche (particularité obligatoire sur
les réacteurs UNGG) s'effectue à l'aide de machines de déchargement
combustible que l'on connecte, après équilibre de pression, sur le réacteur.

Pilotage et sécurité du réacteur :

La divergence, la montée en puissance, le contrôle de la puissance, l'apla-
tissement du flux, l'arrêt instantané du réacteur en cas d'anomalie, sont
assurés par 104 barres de contrôle :

- 58 barres de compensation à court terme (barres noires),
- 18 barres de compensation à long terme (barres grises),
- 18 barres de régulation spatiale (barres grises),
- 6 barres de pilotage (barres grises),
- 4 barres de sécurité (barres noires).

III - SURETE DE L'INSTALLATION

Parmi les éléments essentiels participant à la sûreté de l'installation et à
l'absence d'incidents notables pendant toute la vie de la centrale, on peut
noter les suivants :

- sens de circulation du bas vers le haut, du fluide de refroidissement du coeur réduisant considérablement les risques d'obstruction des canaux,
- contrôle permanent de l'intégrité de la première barrière et déchargement immédiat de l'élément combustible en rupture de gaine,
- refroidissement possible, et éprouvé, par thermosiphon du coeur, dès l'arrêt du réacteur, quel que soit le niveau de puissance initial,
- contrôle périodique des composants de la deuxième barrière (hormis le caisson),
- contrôle permanent de l'intégrité des soufflets des compensateurs de dilatation (détection de fuite),
- contrôle permanent de la libre dilatation des tuyauteries.

IV - PRINCIPAUX PROBLEMES TECHNIQUES RENCONTRES PENDANT LA VIE DE LA CENTRALE
   ## - MOYENS MIS EN OEUVRE POUR LES REGLER

De 1965 à 1983 de nombreuses fuites sur les bouteilles BP des échangeurs dûes à des phénomènes de corrosion-érosion, conduisent au traitement de l'eau à la morpholine et au changement de 68/96 bouteilles.

En 1971 des ailettes déflectrices ruptées sont découvertes sur les onglets des coudes du circuit primaire et conduisent à leur arrasage et au remplacement par des grilles flottantes lors des arrêts de tranche de 1972 à 1979. Parallèlement la baisse de la pression CO_2 de fonctionnement de 26 bar à 22 bar est adoptée pour conserver un coefficient de sécurité suffisant.

Des fuites détectées sur 3 soufflets chauds conduisent au remplacement des 12 soufflets chauds simple couche par des soufflets double couche.

De 1976 à 1979 lors des contrôles par ultra-sons (US) des défauts sur 14 caissons de compensateurs de dilatation conduisent au remplacement de ceux-ci.

V - CONTROLES DES BARRIERES PENDANT LA VIE DE LA CENTRALE
Première barrière :

Comme il a été dit précédemment, le contrôle de cette barrière était permanent.
Le système de détection de rupture de gaine (DRG) était toujours opérationnel au moment de l'arrêt du réacteur.

Deuxième barrière :

L'épreuve décennale du circuit primaire étant exclue, les organismes de sûreté ont imposé à l'exploitant des contrôles de substitution.
L'esprit de ces vérifications consistait à examiner, au moins une fois tous les dix ans, toutes les parties sensibles du circuit primaire. Ainsi, toutes les soudures de résistance des composants du circuit primaire ont été contrôlées par gammagraphie ou par US.

Il est à noter que, du fait de la conception même du réacteur, les soudures du caisson ainsi que celles de raccordement des tuyauteries primaires à celui-ci ne pouvaient être contrôlées. Pour ces dernières, l'exploitant s'assurait, à travers le suivi permanent de la verticalité des tuyauteries d'entrée et de sortie du réacteur, que le taux de contrainte au niveau des piètements restait dans des domaines autorisés.

VI - Y AURAIT-IL EU DES PROBLEMES TECHNIQUES QUI SE SERAIENT POSES A COURT OU MOYEN TERME A L'EXPLOITANT SI LA TRANCHE AVAIT CONTINUE A FONCTIONNER ?

- Intégrité de la première barrière :

La maîtrise parfaite de la fabrication du combustible (aucune rupture de gaine depuis 1976) et la bonne disponibilité de la DRG au moment de l'arrêt nous permettent de penser que cet ensemble n'aurait posé aucun problème.

- Intégrité de la deuxième barrière :

Comme nous l'avons vu précédemment, les contrôles étaient limités aux tuyauteries du circuit primaire et aux échangeurs.
L'état représentatif complet de ces éléments ayant été réalisé en 1979, on peut raisonnablement penser qu'aucun nouveau défaut sur cette partie d'installation n'aurait été à l'origine d'un arrêt obligatoire de l'installation. On notera, à ce sujet, que la quasi totalité des défauts découverts sur l'installation étaient d'origine (décollements lamellaires dus aux contraintes de soudage) et seule l'évolution des moyens de contrôle a permis de les découvrir.
Pour ce qui concerne les soudures de raccordement des tuyauteries au caisson et du caisson lui-même, il est certain, dans l'hypothèse d'un prolongement de la vie de la tranche CHINON A2, que l'exploitant aurait eu à prouver, aux organismes de sûreté, la santé de celles-ci.
Compte tenu d'une part, des marges de sécurité prises et du sérieux apporté lors de la fabrication du caisson et, d'autre part, du soin apporté lors de la réalisation des soudures de raccordement des tuyauteries au caisson, la preuve de la bonne santé de ces ensembles aurait pu être apportée.

- Tenue, à la corrosion CO_2, des structures supérieures du réacteur:

L'examen photographique annuel et le suivi de toutes les structures supérieures du réacteur permettaient d'évaluer l'évolution des détériorations provoquées par l'oxydation du CO_2 (tubes DRG et supports). Les derniers examens laissent supposer que ces structures auraient encore pu assurer leurs fonctions quelques années .

<u>- Tenue de l'ensemble des thermocouples</u> :

Le suivi de l'évolution du nombre de ruptures de thermocouples dans le temps et la réserve installée permettent d'assurer que cet ensemble n'était pas une butée pour continuer la vie de la centrale.

<u>- Conclusion</u> :

En regard de tout ce qui vient d'être dit précédemment il est raisonnable de penser, vu du plan technique et de la sûreté, que la tranche CHINON A2 aurait pu continuer de fonctionner, avec une bonne disponibilité, pendant encore au moins 5 ans.

VII - POURQUOI A-T-ON ARRETE CHINON A2 ?
A) <u>Raisons économiques</u> :

Critères de déclassement :

Hormis une éventuelle nécessité technique, le déclassement des matériels de production d'énergie électrique est en général dicté par des considérations économiques, voire des considérations sociales.
Il convient d'arrêter les tranches si les avantages attendus deviennent inférieurs aux dépenses nécessaires à leur exploitation et à leur entretien.
L'étude économique qui s'ensuit consiste à déterminer, pour le maintien en fonctionnement sur une durée de vie restante supposée, d'une part l'apport représenté dans le cadre du système national de production consommation et, d'autre part, les dépenses associées.
La date optimale de déclassement est alors celle pour laquelle la différence entre les avantages et le coût s'annule pour devenir négative.

B) <u>Méthodologie</u>

Pour un matériel considéré et pour chacune des dates possibles de déclassement, on établit le bilan actualisé des avantages que présente le maintien en exploitation jusqu'à cette date et des coûts qu'il implique.
Le montant du bilan actualisé jusqu'à la date retenue représente la "valeur d'usage" vue du jour de l'étude. Cette valeur d'usage peut également être considérée comme la somme que l'on peut investir à un instant donné pour maintenir l'outil de production en état.
L'étude du déclassement est conduite à partir d'un corps d'hypothèses concernant l'évolution au cours des prochaines années des caractéristiques du système production - transport - consommation :

- évolution de la consommation,
- évolution de la structure du parc de production et de sa disponibilité,
- évolution de la structure du réseau.

Les principaux postes du bilan économique comprennent :

a) à l'actif, la valeur attachée à la puissance moyenne disponible du matériel considéré.

Cette valeur comprend elle-même chaque année une "valeur en économie de défaillance", qui exprime la garantie de puissance apportée par le matériel considéré, et une "valeur en économie de combustible" qui dépend de la consommation spécifique de ce matériel, de la nature du combustible utilisé et des prix respectifs des diverses natures de combustibles fossiles et nucléaires.

b) au passif, les dépenses fixes d'exploitation et d'entretien courant, et les dépenses de gros entretien qu'exigerait le maintien en exploitation jusqu'à la date envisagée, ainsi que le coût de la résorption du personnel libéré par le déclassement.

Pour les dépenses fixes d'exploitation et d'entretien courant qui figurent au passif du bilan, les prévisions relatives à des dépenses sont établies à partir des résultats de la comptabilité (moyenne des dépenses en francs constants sur plusieurs années) et dépendent de nombreux facteurs (palier technique, nature du combustible, nombre de tranches sur le site...).

Enfin, il est tenu compte dans le calcul du coût de l'opération de déclassement, notamment de la reconversion du personnel. Ce coût est généralement estimé forfaitairement à deux années pleines des charges relatives au personnel affecté à la tranche à la date du déclassement.

Il n'est pas tenu compte de l'amortissement de l'investissement, considéré comme inéluctable quels que soient les choix retenus.

Des dépenses qui figurent au passif du bilan, on déduit le coût attaché à l'anticipation de renforcements de réseaux qui doit précéder ce déclassement dans certains cas pour éviter de compromettre la sécurité d'alimentation des réseaux régionaux.

C) Application de la méthode à CHINON A2

L'application de la méthode, définie précédemment, à la tranche CHINON A2 est représentée sur la figure 2.

La très nette décroissance du bilan économique annuel de cette tranche à partir de 1984 est due, en grande partie :

- à l'apparition massive des tranches REP,
- aux dépenses fixes d'exploitation et d'entretien propres à la tranche (faible puissance et nombre d'agents relativement élevé).

D) Raisons sociales

La reconversion et le reclassement du personnel d'une tranche arrêtée définitivement est un critère important que les responsables se doivent de prendre en compte suffisamment tôt avant le déclassement des centrales.

A la date de la prise de décision d'arrêt, en plus des considérations économiques exposées ci-dessus, le démarrage, sur le même site de CHINON, des deux tranches B3 et B4 en 1986 et 1987 permettait, si CHINON A2 s'arrêtait suffisamment tôt, un reclassement harmonieux du personnel.

Cette opportunité a été l'élément déterminant dans la décision d'arrêter la centrale CHINON A2.

L'évolution du personnel depuis la notification de l'arrêt de CHINON A2, par la Direction de la Production et du Transport d'Electricité de France, le 12 Juin 1984 pour une date d'effet au 1er Juillet 1985, est représentée sur la figure 3.

VIII - ACTIONS ENGAGEES DES LA NOTIFICATION D'ARRET ET DEVENIR DE LA TRANCHE

Dès la notification d'arrêt, l'exploitant s'est préoccupé :

- de l'optimisation de la dernière charge du combustible,

- des moyens à mettre en oeuvre pour décharger le combustible du réacteur,
- du devenir de la tranche.

Pour l'optimisation de la dernière charge, après accord des organismes de sûreté, une permutation entre les canaux périphériques et les canaux centraux a été entreprise. L'économie réalisée suite à cette opération a été de 80 MF.

Le déchargement final du réacteur s'est effectué du mois d'octobre 1985 au mois de juin 1986 sans problème.

Pour ce qui concerne le devenir de la tranche, un groupe de travail, destiné à inventorier les moyens de démantèlement et de traitement des déchets, a été constitué. Suite à ses travaux une étude technico-économique effectuée par l'exploitant sur les actions qu'il serait raisonnable d'engager a conduit à préconiser à la Direction du Service de la Production Thermique un démontage de toutes les tuyauteries et à leur entreposage, après confinement, dans les locaux échangeurs (voir figure 4).

Cette étude a consisté à trouver le meilleur bilan actualisé entre les dépenses à engager immédiatement et les frais de surveillance à assurer entre le démantèlement partiel et le démantèlement total.

IX - CONCLUSION GENERALE

Plus de deux ans après la décision d'arrêt, compte tenu des difficultés rencontrées pour reclasser les derniers agents libérés, il apparaît confirmé que la date d'arrêt de CHINON A2 devait coïncider avec le gréement du personnel des tranches B3 et B4.

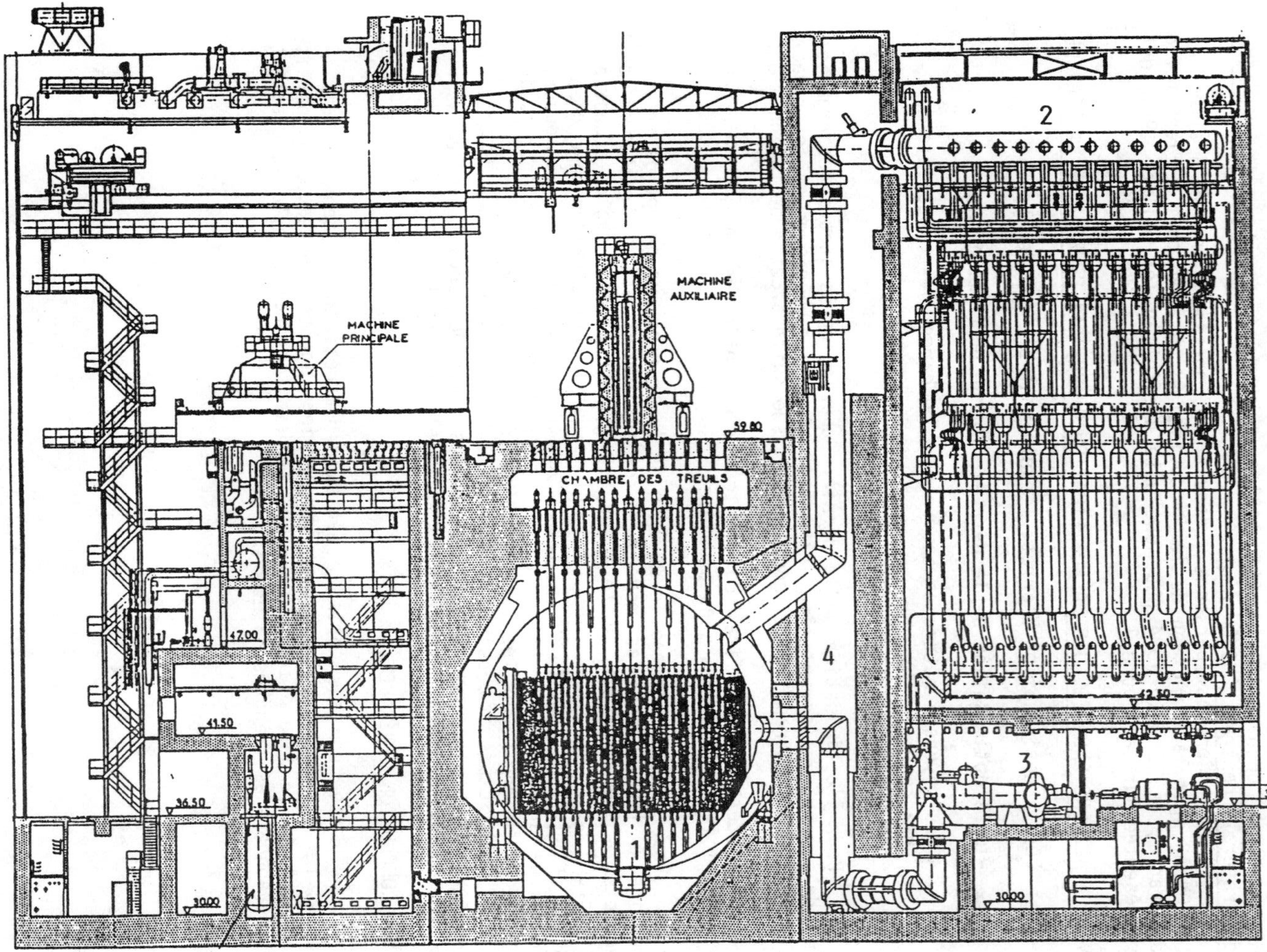

1 Coeur
2 Echangeur
3 Soufflante
4 Circuit primaire

Figure 1 - COUPE TRANSVERSALE - CHINON A2

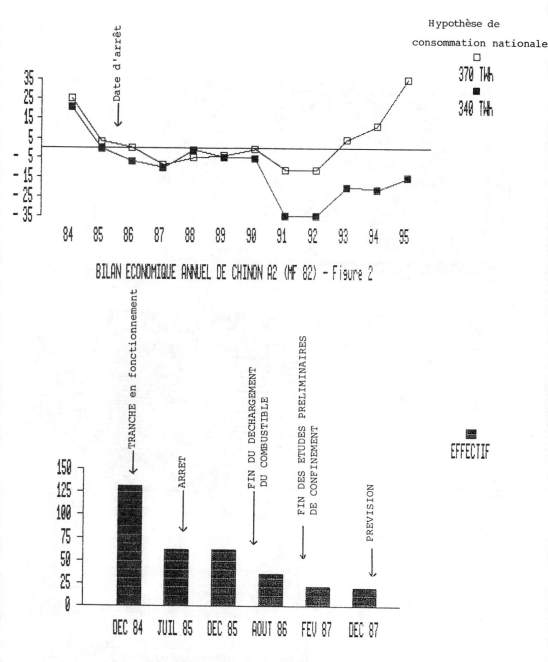

Hypothèse de
consommation nationale

□ 370 TWh

■ 340 TWh

Date d'arrêt

BILAN ECONOMIQUE ANNUEL DE CHINON A2 (MF 82) - Figure 2

TRANCHE en fonctionnement

ARRET

FIN DU DECHARGEMENT DU COMBUSTIBLE

FIN DES ETUDES PRELIMINAIRES DE CONFINEMENT

PREVISION

■ EFFECTIF

EVOLUTION DES EFFECTIFS DE CHINON A2 - Figure 3

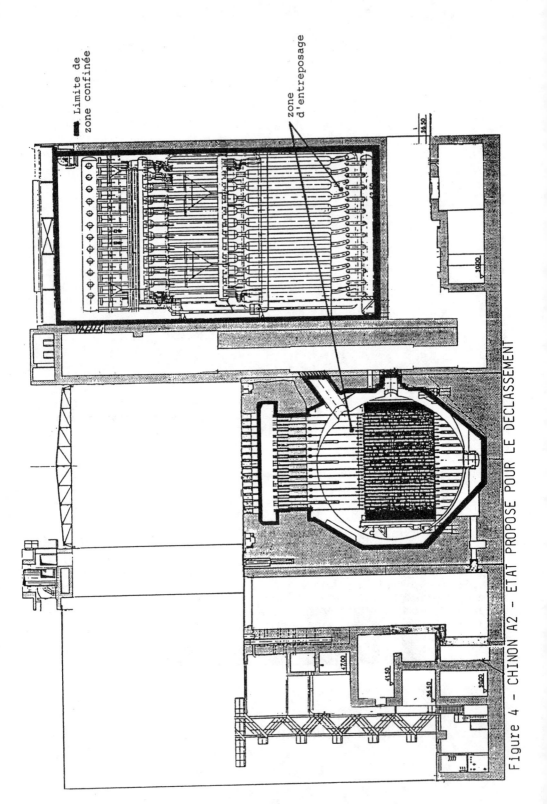

Limite de zone confinée

zone d'entreposage

Figure 4 - CHINON A2 - ETAT PROPOSE POUR LE DECLASSEMENT

- 142 -

SHUTDOWN DECISION FOR THE NUCLEAR POWER PLANT KRB A AT GUNDREMMINGEN

Dipl.-Ing. H.P. Mies, Dipl.-Ing. W. Stang
Kernkraftwerke Gundremmingen Betriebsgesellschaft mbH
Federal Republic of Germany

ABSTRACT

The nuclear power station Gundremmingen unit A (KRB A) was built from 1962 to 1966 as the first of three demonstration nuclear power stations in the Federal Republic of Germany. At the time the twocycle boiling water reactor corresponded to the stage of development of General Electric and had an electrical power output of 250 MW. During its operations from 1966 to 1977, KRB A delivered approx. 15,000 GWh to the public power supply and attained an average capacity factor of approx. 75 %, in several operating years even over 90 %. In January 1977, the facility was placed out of operations due to an accident. The associated repairing and backfitting measures would have led to several years shut-down and considerable costs, without the guarantee of a longterm operating license being granted. For these reasons and also due to progress in the construction of the two 1300 MW units B and C at the same site, it was decided to decommission the facility in early 1980.

DECISION D'ARRET DE LA CENTRALE NUCLEAIRE KRB A DE GUNDREMMINGEN

RESUME

L'unité A de la centrale nucléaire de Gundremmingen a été construite de 1962 à 1966 comme étant la première des trois centrales nucléaires de démonstration en République fédérale d'Allemagne. A cette époque, le réacteur à eau bouillante à deux cycles correspondait à une étape du développement de General Electric et avait une puissance de production électrique de 250 MW. Au cours de son exploitation, de 1966 à 1977, KRB A a fourni environ 15.000 GWh à l'entreprise publique d'électricité et a atteint un facteur de charge moyen d'environ 75 pour cent, dépassant même 90 pour cent pendant plusieurs années d'exploitation. En janvier 1977, l'unité a été mise hors service à la suite d'un accident. L'ensemble des réparations et des mises en conformité auraient dû conduire à la fermeture de l'unité pendant plusieurs années et entraîner des coûts élevés, sans la garantie d'une licence d'exploitation à long terme qui a été accordée. Pour ces raisons, et également à cause de l'avancement des travaux de construction des deux unités B et C de 1 300 MW sur le même site, il a été décidé de démanteler l'unité au début de 1980.

1. Plant Description

KRB A has a dual cycle AEG/GE BWR and is rated at 237 MWe (net). It is located on the Danube River, 80 km northwest of Munich near the Bavarian village of Gundremmingen, Federal Republic of Germany. The 10 acre site is on the plains of the Danube valley and partially covered with forests.

This was the 2nd commercial nuclear power station in the Federal Republic of Germany after the Versuchsatomkraftwerk Kahl. It was the first plant . that had internal steam separators and driers. It was also the first to use in-core startup nuclear instrumentation and an instrument system which provides an improved calibration technique for the fixed in-core power range monitors.

1.1 Nuclear-Steam Supply (NSSS)

The NSSS used the dual cycle principal (Fig. 1). With this principal one portion of the steam was generated in the reactor and passed directly to the turbine, while a 2nd portion of the steam was generated at a lower pressure in an external heat exchanger. This steam was sent to a lower pressure stage of the high pressure turbine.

The reactor vessel is made up of the usual cylinder with hemispherical bottom and top heads (Fig. 2). The top head is flanged and removable. The cylinder is made of seamless forged ring hoops. The hoops had to be annealed several times in order to achieve the required ductility.

Feedwater entered the reactor vessel at the center of the cylindrical portion. Reactor coolant was withdrawn from the bottom of the cylindrical portion and a forced coolant system recirculated it through 3 external loops. Each loop has 1 pump and 1 secondary steam generator. The water then returned to the bottom head of the vessel. The single stage, vertical pumps have mechanical shaft seals.

The shells of the standing U-tube (vertical) steam generators are of
ASTM A302 Grade B (inside plated with stainless steel).

A hydraulic system drove the B_4C control rods. Each of the 89 rods was
provided with an individual drive piston and could be individually inserted
and withdrawn in continuous motion or stepwise by means of a drive switch.
The water was connected to the 89 hydraulic scram accumulators.

Should the pressure in a scram hydraulic accumulator fail when a scram is
triggered off, the control rod could be inserted by applying reactor
pressure via a shuttle valve.

Fig. 3 showes the configuration of the NSSS in the reactor building. The
main characteristics of KRB A are compiled in Fig. 4.

1.2 Safety Systems

A liquid poison system could be manually started to feed a sodium penta-
borate solution into the core. Other safety features were:

- the normal safety valves on the primary steam circuits;
- an emergency condenser system; which served as a heat sink when the primary steam circuit was shut off, in that case the appropriate valves in
  the return pipes to the reactor opened automatically;
- a core spray system; which was triggered by an excessively low level in
  the reactor vessel or a high pressure in the containment;
- flow limiting devices in the steam lines;
- a containment spray system which was triggered the same as the core spray
  system; and
- circuits for containment ventilation and penetration valve closure to
  prevent the escape of radioactivity during an accident.

1.3 Auxiliary Systems

Shutdown cooling was provided by:

- primary steam discharged directly into the main condenser,
- primary water cooled by a closed cycle shutdown cooler, and
- primary water cooled by a clean-up demineralizer cooler.

Reactor coolant purification and makeup was accomplished in a purification system with 2 parallel ion exchangers.

Shield cooling was accomplished via cooling water (35 $^{\circ}$C) tubes in the inner part of the biological shield.

1.4 Reactor Safety System

This system consisted of normally energized relay circuits with parallel normally deenergized lockout delays. The 3-channel system was connected to 2 independent 220-V batteries and evaluated the incoming limit signals of the individual measurements in 2-out-of-3 or, in the case of the neutron flux density, in 3-out-of-6 logics.
The signals were:

- Vessel water level very low
- High containment pressure
- 6 kV auxiliary power failure
- Primary steam line rupture
- Primary steam valve closed
- Primary steam valve "closed signal"
- Neutron flux density high/low
- High reactor pressure
- Low condenser vacuum
- High water level in scram dump tank
- Vessel water level low

1.5 Fuel Handling

Facilities for underwater, off load refueling are provided. The storage pool inside the reactor building has capacity for about 150 % of a core loading. During a typical refueling 25 % of the core had to be replaced every 12 month.

2. History Of Operations

Construction began in 1962 and was completed in 1966.

1966

Initial criticality was achieved in August and zero-power testing finished in September.

The 1st electricity was produced in November and the plant achieved full power in December.

1967

The startup and test programm concluded in February with the completion of the 25 day sustained run.

End of February while shutting down the reactor, a secondary steam relief line failed causing a considerable release of water and steam. We resumed operation after an outage of 1 month for repairs.

The plant was handed over to KRB in April.

We shutdown from July to September to perform modifications to the primary steam line, which included installation of a flow limiter, to ensure steam line isolation in the event of a steam line break. The high pressure feed-water heaters and generator stator winding were also improved during the outage.

1968

A turbine blade failure caused a 1 month outage in January-February.

Turbine blade failures forced another shutdown of 3 weeks in May-June.

Additional turbine blade failures resulted in a 3 weeks outage in August-September.

More turbine blade failures required a 2 month outage beginning in September to effect repairs. The low pressure blading was removed and the plant operated at a reduced power of 155 MWe.

1969

We shutdown for 6 days in January to inspect the low pressure turbine.

A refueling and maintenance outage began in late May. Wet sipping revealed several (67) leaking fuel assemblies. The low pressure turbine was repaired and returned to service. Startup occured in late August.

1970

There was a 6 week refueling and maintenance shutdown from Mai into July. Sipping indicated 33 probable leakers. A turbine inspection was performed.

1971

There was a 5 week outage in June-July for refueling, and turbine and reactor inspections. We identified 38 probable leakers.

1972

A refueling outage occured during May and June. They identified 28 leaking fuel assemblies. The high and low pressure turbines were modified.

1973

A refueling outage was initiated in early May. Sipping revealed 33 leaking fuel assemblies. The main generator was overhauled. Startup began in mid-June.

Copper crud from a feedwater heater was depositing on the fuel assembly inlets causing an increase in core differential pressure which required a shutdown of 5 weeks for cleaning in October-November.

1974

A refueling and maintenance outage commenced in early May. Wet sipping indicated 24 leaking fuel assemblies. Sixteen Pu fuel assemblies were loaded.

1975

We shutdown for refueling and maintenance in May-June. Only 5 leaking fuel assemblies were identified. The reactor vessel and primary system welds underwent ultrasonic testing.

In November during a 41 hr shutdown for repairs in the 220 kV system, repairs were being performed on a primary system cleanup valve (W6) when water in the valve flashed to steam, killing 2 workers.

There was a 79 hr outage in December to test the W6 valve and repair leakage at a steam generator manhole cover.

1976

A refueling and maintenance outage began in May. The outage was extended to allow repairs to feedwater spargers and secondary steam generators. Startup occurred in early October.

A repair of a leak in a primary circulating pump bearing resulted in an 87 hr shutdown in December.

A loss of offsite power caused a reactor trip from 100 % power and resultant high pressure and blowdown to the containment in January.

After this accident the plant never produced nuclear power. During its operations from 1966 to 1977, KRB A delivered approx. 15.000 GWh to the public power supply and attained an average capacity factor of approx. 75 %,
in several years even over 90 %.

3. History and Reasons of Decommissioning

1977 - 1979

The damaged systems have been repaired and improved. Some backfitting
measures e.g. at the fire protection system, in the instrumentation and the
venting system were realized. A step-by-step plan was worked out for further backfitting measures. We checked all primary systems by ultrasonic
testing, acoustic emission and eddy-current testing as far as possible. The
primary recirculation piping had to be partially decontaminated and cut for
inside inspection. Several intergranular stress corrosion cracks have been
found at the safe ends and the welding areas of the primary loop piping.

Our step-by-step plan for backfitting and repair measures ended up with the
following main activities:

- exchange of the complete recirculation loops
- installation of a new
  . high pressure injection system
  . emergency generator
  . primary steam suppression pool
  . emergency control room
- construction of a new building for the above mentioned systems
- construction of a new stuck because of the influence of the new
  units B/C

Because of the overall costs of approx. Mio DM 250 (based on 1980) and no
guarantee for a long time licence (more than 10 years) the shearholders
RWE and BAG decided to decommission the plant. In addition to these reasons, the decision was facilitated by the fact that the new units B and C,
with 1300 MW$_e$ each, have been halffinished at this time and the staff
could be completly transfered to the new company "Kernkraftwerke Gundremmingen Betriebsgesellschaft mbH".

4. Decommissioning Activities

Fig. 5 showes the present status of KRB A.

1980 - 1982

Different decommissioning concepts aiming the stage of "safe enclosure"
have been planned. We decided to start with dismantling activities in the
turbine hall.

1983 - 1987

Because time-saving is not always equal with cost-saving the dismantling
activities in the turbine hall will last until end of 1987.

1988 - 2000

We decided to continue the decommissioning measures in the contaminated
areas of the other buildings and to start the dismantling of the activated
reactor and biological shield in about 5 years from now. If a final storage
facility will be available at that time decommissioning could be finished
at the end of this century.

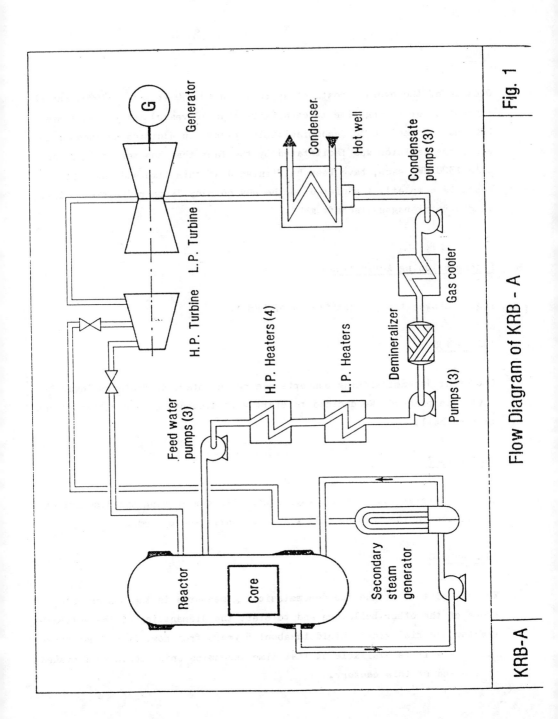

Flow Diagram of KRB - A

Fig. 1

KRB-A

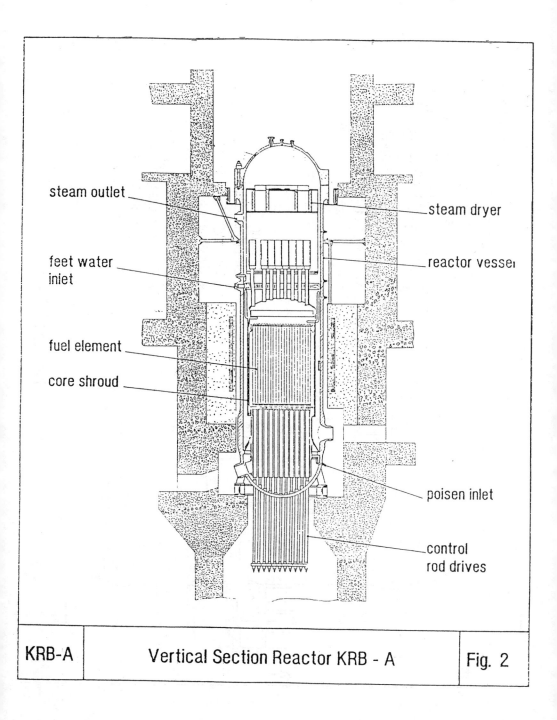

steam outlet

steam dryer

feet water inlet

reactor vessel

fuel element

core shroud

poisen inlet

control rod drives

| KRB-A | Vertical Section Reactor KRB - A | Fig. 2 |

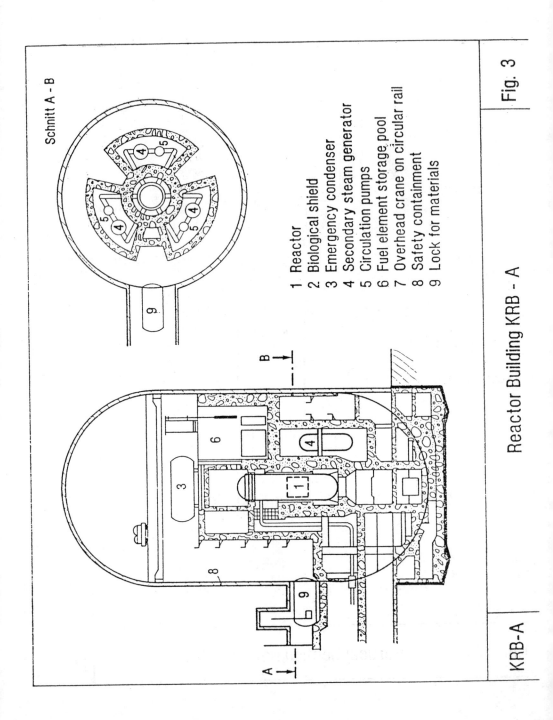

Schnitt A - B

1 Reactor
2 Biological shield
3 Emergency condenser
4 Secondary steam generator
5 Circulation pumps
6 Fuel element storage pool
7 Overhead crane on circular rail
8 Safety containment
9 Lock for materials

Reactor Building KRB - A

Fig. 3

KRB - A

- 154 -

Owner :	Rheinisch-Westfälisches Elektrizitätswerk Essen and Bayernwerk AG, Munich.
Operator :	Kernkraftwerk RWE - Bayernwerk GmbH (KRB).
Address :	D - 8871 Gundremmingen/Donau, Postfach, Federal Republic of Germany
Type :	Dual cycle, boiling light water moderated and cooled.
NSSS Supplier :	GE
Turbine Generator Supplier :	AEG
Arch. Engr. :	AEG / Hochtief
Constructor :	Hochtief AG
Design Output :	801 MW$_t$, 250 MW$_e$ (gross), 237 MW$_e$ (net).
Fuel :	by GE, sintered UO$_2$ pellets, 2.22 % av enrichment, Zirc 2 clad, 6 x 6 array, 36 pins/assembly, 368 fuel assemblies, 2748 mm dia x 3302 m high core, 40. 9 kW/l.
Control :	B$_4$C powder in SS tubes, 60 tubes/assembly, cruciform shape, 89 control assemblies, hydraulic drives; originally had 156 removable boron - SS curtains.
Reactor Vessel :	ASTM - 336, 131 mm thick, 16. 8 m lenght, 3.7 m dia, SS internal clad.
Thermal & Hydraulic :	264 °C coolant in, 286 °C coolant out, 71 atm abs. coolant pressure, 12. 250 t/hr reactor coolant flow, 3 recirc loops each with 1 pump and 1 steam generator, primary steam is at 71 atm abs. and 285 °C.
Containment :	dry, steel, cylinder with hemispherical top and bottom domes, 30 m dia, 60 m height, 26.5 mm cyl wall, 13.5 mm dome wall, 3.55 kg/cm^2 design pressure, 4.75 kg/cm^2 test pressure, 0.5 % vol/day leakage.
Turbine :	by AEG, singleshaft, 2 casings, 1 single flow HP and 1 double flow LP, 1320 mm final stage vane length, 1500 rpm, 0.03 atm abs. condenser vacuum, single condenser.
Generator :	by AEG, 250 MW$_e$, 317 MVA, 1500 rpm, 21 kV, 79 PF, water cooled stator, H$_2$ cooled rotor.
Cost (millions) :	316 DM plus 50 DM for initial fuel.

KRB-A	Main Characteristics of KRB - A	Fig. 4

1 Reactor Pressure Vessel (core unloaded)
2 Fuel Assembly Storage Pool (empty)
3 Turbine / Generator (dismantled)
4 Reactor Building ⎫
5 Turbine House ⎬ Controled Area
6 Smokestack / Purification Building ⎭
7 Workshop ⎫
8 Operations Building ⎬ not Controled Area

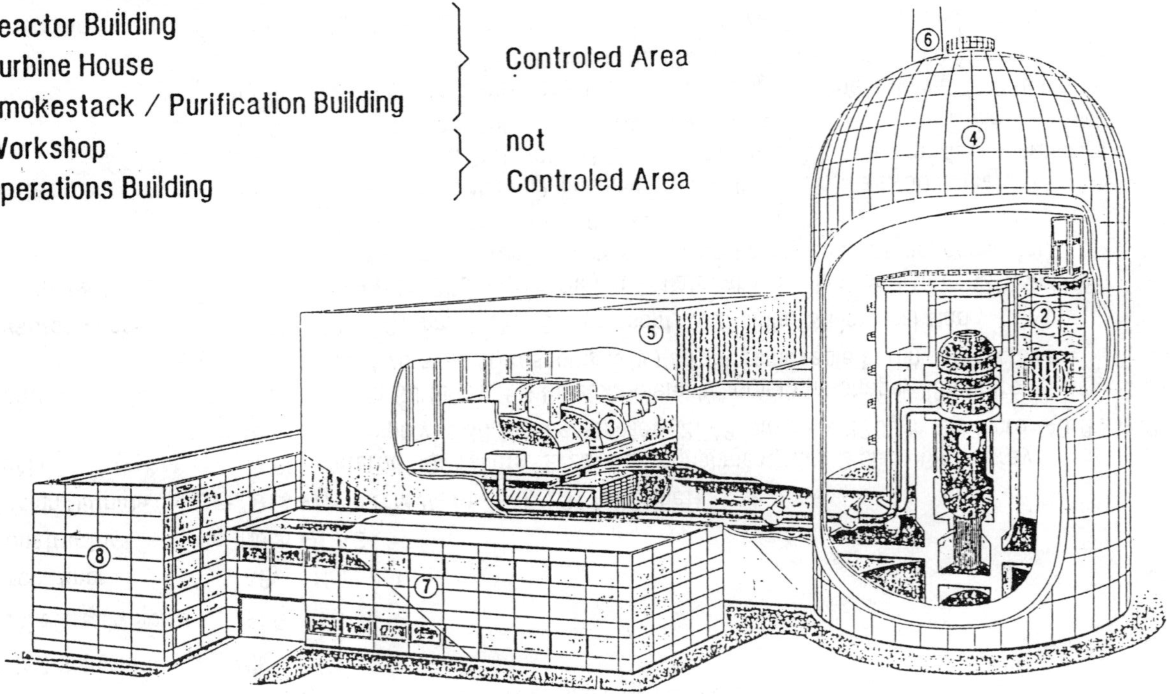

KRA-A

Present Status of KRB - A

Fig. 5

DISCUSSION

V.J. STREICHER, Federal Republic of Germany

Mr. Podest, could you give us information on the Czech efforts on plant life extensions ?

M. PODEST, IAEA

The producer of the pressure vessels of the WWER 440 reactors, i.e. the Skoda-Work, is following irradiation changes in the pressure vessels' steel in a "surveillance programme". Samples are evaluated in facilities of the Nuclear Research Institute, Rez near Prague.

S. NOVAK, IAEA

Operating organisations in CSSR concentrate their efforts for collecting and storing as much operational information as possible for future evaluation. The information system is in operation and international experience is to be used to collect more information, if necessary, for life time extension evaluation.

V.J. STREICHER, Federal Republic of Germany

Can you comment on the cooperation between US NRC and IAEA in the field of plant ageing and decommissioning.

S. NOVAK, IAEA

A USNRC representative took part in the IAEA Technical Committee Meeting on NPP Ageing and in the state-of-the-art Report on Safety aspects of NPP ageing preparation. USNRC officers will present papers during the IAEA Symposium on Safety Aspects of NPP Ageing and Maintenance (29 June-3 July 1987) and the NRC contribution to the state-of-the-art report is extremely valuable.

V.J. STREICHER, Federal Republic of Germany

In the assessment of the phenomena causing a loss of safety, did the NEA Workshop consider abnormal operation conditions (LOCA) ? How are thermal effects (such as pressurized thermal shock) analysed ?

N.R. McDONALD, NEA

Yes. Much of the development and application of fracture mechanics has been concerned with assessing structural behaviour under abnormal loading conditions such as in a LOCA and during pressurised thermal shock. In-service inspection objectives also relate to detecting cracks of critical length for growth under such abnormal loading conditions ; assessments also attempt to take account of the specific localised variations or gradients of stress, temperature and material properties where these are known. The question of continuous monitoring to measure important variations in general and localised parameters is receiving much attention and the Workshop recommended actions to update review and guidance material in these areas.

G. SCHÜCKTANZ, Federal Republic of Germany

Mr. Nakajima mentioned a number of factors affecting the life time of reactor pressure vessels. Has he developed any program to extend the life time of pressure vessels already in operation ?

H. NAKAJIMA, Japan

The first priority in our calculation at the present is to clarify the key engineering parameters relevant to residual life of RPVs. The preliminary results were summarized in the paper. The calculation is still in a preliminary stage; we have not yet developed the program you suggested. However, after some modification based on the fair engineering foundation focused on the actual operational condition, some information will be available.

R. COMINI, Italy

Can Dr. Schücktanz report about the measured "usage factors", obtained from the KWU monitoring system, versus the "expected usage factors" derived from the standard design practice ?

G. SCHÜCKTANZ, Federal Republic of Germany

For components whose loadings can be specified in advance and can be controlled by the plant instrumentation, the actual usage factor is generally much less than the expected one.

For components whose loadings cannot be monitored by the usual plant instrumentation (such as all piping feeding cold water into the primary system) the actual usage factor might be much higher than the predicted one.

N.R. McDONALD, NEA

Are there any fatigue monitoring installations in service or planned for operating power plants ? Can the findings on usage factors in one plant be applied to unmonitored components in similar plant with comparable operating history ?

G. SCHÜCKTANZ, Federal Republic of Germany

The first system to cover the whole primary system of a NPP is just being installed in a 1300 MW unit in the FRG. The unit will go into operation by the end of 87.

The usage factors cannot easily be applied to similar components in other plants as the mode of operation usually varies considerably from unit to unit.

V.J. STREICHER, Federal Republic of Germany

In case of back fitting the fatigue monitoring system in an operating plant, how is the actual usage factor calculated or estimated ?

G. SCHÜCKTANZ, Federal Republic of Germany

The actual usage monitored over a certain period of time can be extrapolated to the past.

M.J. CRIJNS, NEA

I realise that the UK paper referred only to CEGB plants, but would you have information on Calder Hall and Chapel Cross and their life expectancy ?

R. DODDS, United Kingdom

The first reactor at Calder Hall was commissioned in 1956 and thus has been operating for over 30 years. Current plans are that the Calder and Chapel Cross reactors should operate through the 1990s subject to satisfactory economics. The economics depend on the ability of BNFL to sell electricity to the CEGB/SSEB at competitive prices, and the continuation of the CEGB/SSEB to operate their Magnox stations as planned and share the fixed costs of fuel cycle service plants. The Calder and Chapel Cross reactors operate at the lower end of the pressure/temperature range discussed by Dr. Marchese and no life limiting features have been identified that would require these reactors to be decommissioned any earlier than corresponding reactors of the CEGB and SSEB.

V.J. STREICHER, Federal Republic of Germany

Is the CANDU 300 design already the basis of a plant in construction or operation ?

R.S. HART, Canada

The CANDU 300 utilizes proven systems and components throughout. All the components (steam generators, heat transport system, coolant pumps, pressure tubes, fuelling machine, fuel, etc.) are identical to those proven in service on the CANDU 600, however, in most cases only half as many are used in the Nuclear Steam Plant. Similarly, system parameters (heat transport system pressures, temperatures, steam quality for example) are identical to those of the CANDU 600.

The principal changes incorporated in CANDU 300 are in the areas of station layout, building layouts, and construction methods. Sale of the first CANDU 300 is expected during 1987.

V.J. STREICHER, Federal Republic of Germany

Have there been any major influences of the Chernobyl accident ?

R.S. HART, Canada

There has been no need identified for any significant design changes to any CANDU power station, including the CANDU 300, as a result of the comprehension review of the Chernobyl accident by AECL, the CANDU operators, and the regulatory authorities.

R. COMINI, Italy

Could Mr. Stang indicate the forecast cost for decommissioning Gundremingen NPP ?

W. STANG, Federal Republic of Germany

Cost of decommissioning will not be more than 10 per cent of the cost of construction on the same price base. This has been proved until now by decommissioning of the systems in our turbine hall.

P.R. PARKMAN, United Kingdom

Could the last 4 speakers identify in what respect the experience from operational problems is thought to be of specific relevance to plant life extension ?

R.S. HART, Canada

There is extensive experience in Canada relative to plant life extension. This experience includes the decommissioning of two prototype reactors (Douglas Point and Gentilly 1), and the refurbishing of Pickering units 1 and 2. The latter work included pressure tube replacement.

We have learned a lot from these projects, particularly with respect to the removal and replacement of components. This knowledge has been applied to the CANDU 300. We have found that in some cases modest changes - in component design and for building layout - can reduce replacement time for a component considerably. We have also found that incorporation of life extension features does not increase initial cost, and often reduces it.

C.J. MARCHESE, United Kingdom

U.K. experience leads the CEGB not to regard design pressure and temperature as fixed quantities. Life extension can be economic at different values for these parameters; it is a question of optimising the work to be done against the electric output to be achieved. Secondly we find that in addition to very significant planning of the industrial workforce the technical task of producing safety cases and assessments also need careful planning. Finally there is a need we have learned for continuous liaison with regulatory authorities throughout the outage period.

A. RAYNAL, France

L'expérience acquise par EDF sur les réacteurs à gaz de CHINON, dans le domaine des gros composants sous pression, est importante.

Pour ce qui concerne les contrôles non destructifs, et plus particulièrement les contrôles par ultra-sons, les équipes spécialisées d'EDF se sont familiarisées aux méthodes, à leur mise en oeuvre en milieu actif, et surtout à leur délicate interprétation, depuis 1969. On sait le développement pris par ces techniques dix années plus tard.

Dans le domaine du calcul des structures, les méthodes actuelles (éléments finis, mécanique de la rupture ...) ont été appliquées dès 1973 aux composants pour justifier leur tenue.

Enfin, le remplacement de gros composants des circuits primaires ou des échangeurs de chaleur a apporté une connaissance des travaux en milieu contaminé à ceux qui allaient intervenir, dix ans plus tard, dans les réacteurs à eau.

V.J. STREICHER, Federal Republic of Germany

What kind of life time prediction is required for licensing by authorities ?

R.S. HART, Canada

In Canada, the regulatory authority (AECB) continuously monitors station operation, and grants operating licence extensions for relatively short periods (1 or 2 years). If a need is determined, based on new information (research or experience of Canadian or other utilities), for modifications or additions to plant hardware and for operating procedures, the AECB imposes these modifications or additions as a basis for licence extension.

This approach is not expected to change with time, irrespective of the operating life of the station. It is expected that extension of licence will be granted for as long as safety of operation is demonstrated by the owner. This demonstration may, however, become more demanding with time.

N.R. McDONALD, NEA

Comments were made on the need for consideration of the approach adopted by regulatory authorities to life extension.

In response, I draw attention to points made in my written paper 2.2. There is not only a need for economic and technical assessments but, in the latter case, the question of the continued safety of operation of the plant or component must be satisfied. The approach to this will be specific to each country, depending on its laws, regulations and procedures. It is also likely in many cases to be plant and component specific. In all cases, however, the degree of conservatism that regulatory authorities will adopt in assessing the safety case will depend significantly on the confidence in the available data and the assessment methodologies used. A hierarchy of the information required is given in my paper. A number of Symposium papers and interventions in the discussions have highlighted the particular attention that must be given to monitoring of performance, operating parameters and component condition. To be useful, however, this data must be available and applicable to the assessment of the future ability of the component to perform its function with requisite safety margins being maintained. This requires predictive models and validation of the relevance of available integrity assessment methodologies to real structures over the relevant time frame. It also means that in setting up the information collection systems attention must be given to what end use is to be made of the data.

Differences between the regulatory approaches adopted in different countries will not be removed, but there should at least be a large measure of uniformity in the underlying technical basis for safety assessments and regulatory decisions. There should also be a strong trend towards removing technical conservatism in assessments where understanding and reliable data permit this. For example, there is not much point in developing more refined and accurate measurements of crack size (using non-destructive examination) or of the fatigue usage factor (through monitoring systems) if use is not eventually made of the better information in regulatory and safety decision making. As a step forward we plan in the NEA to try to improve mutual understanding of issues in the integrity assessment area by bringing together non-destructive examination, fracture mechanics and regulatory experts in a workshop environment.

One other important need is to obtain information from the inspection and testing of decommissioned components to provide benchmarks against which properties and structural condition estimated via surveillance, in-service inspection (ISI) and operating data can be checked. International cooperative efforts would be beneficial in this regard.

SESSION III

PROJECTS OF PLANT LIFE EXTENSION

SEANCE III

PROJETS DE PROLONGATION DE LA DUREE DE VIE DES CENTRALES

Chairman – Président

D.R. HOSTETLER

(United States)

EPRI/DOE NUCLEAR PLANT LIFE
EXTENSION OVERVIEW

John J. Carey
Melvin E. Lapides
Electric Power Research Institute
USA
Dennis Harrison
Art DuCharme
Department of Energy
USA

ABSTRACT

Recognizing the major investment in current U.S. nuclear capacity and the excellent prospects that these units have a useful life substantially in excess of their 40 year license term, EPRI and DOE have jointly undertaken a comprehensive, multiyear, nuclear plant life extension program. The program, which has its antecedents in EPRI studies of 1978-9, aims to support U.S. utilities, first in verifying the requirements of extended operation and then in implementing a plan for achieving extended service and license renewal. The effort, begun in 1985, has already yielded numerous benefits and is expected to further aid in improving near-term performance of nuclear units.

A Utility LWR Plant Life Extension Committee has been established to provide overview and guidance to the DOE/EPRI research and development activities and also to develop and integrate utility responses to licensing and codes and standards issues.

Pilot study projects, performed by Virginia Power and Northern States Power, were the initial EPRI/DOE focus. This base has gradually expanded to incorporate other utilities and generating units, as well as a broad base of technology support. The latter includes: a) economic and financial analysis methods applicable at the unit, region and national level, b) long-term materials deterioration analysis and sampling, c) component life prediction methods and d) refurbishment and repair evaluations. This paper presents the history and status of the overall EPRI/DOE program.

ETUDE EPRI/DOE SUR LA PROLONGATION DE LA DUREE DE VIE DES CENTRALES NUCLEAIRES

RESUME

Conscients des investissements considérables que représentent les centrales nucléaires américaines actuelles et des excellentes perspectives qu'offrent ces tranches d'atteindre une durée de vie utile sensiblement supérieure aux quarante années prévues dans l'autorisation d'exploitation, l'Institut de recherche sur l'énergie électrique (EPRI) et le ministère de l'Energie (DOE) ont lancé en commun un vaste programme pluriannuel de prolongation de la durée de vie des centrales nucléaires. Ce programme, qui s'appuie sur les études d'EPRI datant de 1978-79, vise à aider les compagnies d'électricité américaines à vérifier dans un premier temps les dispositions à prendre pour prolonger l'exploitation de leurs centrales, puis à mettre en oeuvre un programme destiné à prolonger effectivement leur durée de vie utile et à obtenir le renouvellement de l'autorisation d'exploitation. Cet effort, amorcé en 1985, a déjà porté de nombreux fruits et devrait aussi contribuer à améliorer les résultats des centrales nucléaires à court terme.

Un comité sur la prolongation de la durée de vie des centrales nucléaires équipées de réacteurs à eau ordinaire (REO), composé de représentants de compagnies d'électricité, a été constitué pour passer en revue les activités de recherche et de développement de DOE/EPRI, donner des orientations générales et définir de façon cohérente la position des compagnies d'électricité face aux questions d'autorisation ainsi que de codes et normes.

EPRI et DOE ont axé leur attention tout d'abord sur les projets d'études pilotes réalisés par les compagnies Virginia Power et Northern States Power. Cette base a été progressivement étendue à d'autres compagnies et à d'autres unités de production et est devenue un élement important d'aide technologique. Elle comprend : a) les méthodes d'analyse économiques et financières applicables au niveau des centrales, des régions et de l'Etat, b) le prélèvement d'échantillons de matériaux et l'analyse de la dégradation des matériaux à long terme, c) les méthodes de prévision de la durée de vie des composants et d) l'évaluation de la rénovation et des réparations de composants. Ce rapport présente l'historique et l'état d'avancement de l'ensemble du programme EPRI/DOE.

The chronology of U.S. Nuclear Plant Life Extension (NUPLEX) efforts involving DOE and EPRI which lead to the program shown in Figure 1 is summarized in Figure 2. What is illustrated is an orderly progression which came into sharpened focus when business uncertainties fostered utility interest in better definition of the useful life of existing generating units.

Any maintained system, be it an automobile or a nuclear power plant can be operated for virtually any period of service. Retirement normally occurs when the costs of output maintenance exceed the costs of output from alternative sources. Many alternatives to nuclear power exist which are perceived to have lower capital costs or higher thermal efficiency, but few offer lower net fuel costs. Even fewer appear to be attractive alternatives when the comparison is between purchasing new capacity and refurbishing older nuclear capacity--even for substantial levels of refurbishment. All of these observations have focused attention on NUPLEX.

NUPLEX has taken on the connotation of 'post 40 year service' since the United States licenses nuclear power plants for 40 year terms. However, this and perhaps the term 'life extension' itself, are somewhat misleading. There is comparatively little to suggest that LWR units were intentionally designed for a 40 year limitation. Many major components are expected to have a substantially longer useful life; many have already shown that they must be refurbished well before 40 years. Most governing safety requirements and design proscriptions do not consider time as a variable; accident initiation scenarios appear to bound any age deterioration phenomena which can be realistically conceived. Unfortunately, the basis for these lifetime judgements is not as sound as desired. Currently, the reference experience behind modern power plant design probably spans about 20 service years and is benchmarked by service experience which averages less than 15 service years. So, it is probably more convenient to think of NUPLEX in two phases.

The first NUPLEX phase, sometimes referred to as "Life Assurance" aims at long-range forecasting of unit maintenance and refurbishment requirements. It is coupled with predictive efforts to reduce both of these items and thus improve performance. The second is a perturbation of the first which starts when management is interested in determining whether the existing unit should be replaced by an alternative source of power. In the U.S., that management decision is most likely to occur in the 25th-30th service year of a unit. Looking at statistics, 60 U.S. units will have been through the decision cycle before the year 2010 and the remainder after that. The year 2010 is significant since it is at that time that the industry will have an average experience base of 30-40 service years. The management decision process for these 60 units is the second element of NUPLEX in the EPRI/DOE R&D Plan. Because it involves license renewal it is probably a true case of life extension.

The second NUPLEX phase poses unique timing requirements for research considered within the R&D Plan. Obviously, comparatively few truly long range research efforts can be of consequence to the management decisions of interest. Phenomenological analyses of long-term deterioration processes are inadequate. Each must be examined in terms of consequences, if any, so that management can decide on well-focused inspection and perhaps physical sampling plan for the unit in question--or alternately, decide to eliminate the uncertainty by component replacement.

It is clearly not possible to describe the DOE/EPRI work in detail in this paper. It is hoped that this will be accomplished by other presenters at this Symposium and that this description of scope and definition is beneficial to participants.

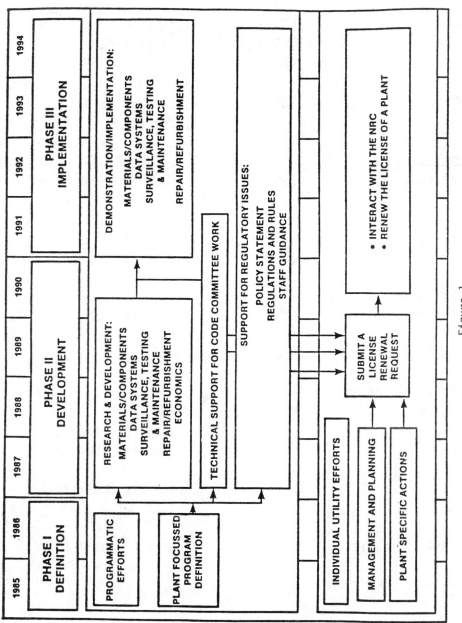

Figure 1
OVERALL FLOW OF LIFE EXTENSION RESEARCH

EPRI	1978-1984	FEASIBLIILTY STUDIES
DOE/EPRI	1984	CO-FUNDING
	1985	JOINT PLAN R&D
	1986	MOU
VP/NSP	1985	PILOT STUDIES WITH EPRI/DOE
LWR UTILITY STEERING COMMITTEE	1985	• R&D RECOMMENDATIONS TO DOE/EPRI
		• NRC R&D INTERFACE
AIF	1985-6	REGULATORY STUDY
ASME SECTION XI SPECIAL SUBCOMMITTEE	1985	REQUIREMENTS EVALUATION
IEEE SUBCOMMITTEE	1986	EVALUATION
LWR UTILITY STEERING COMMITTEE	1986	EXPANSION: LICENSING, TECHNICAL CODES & STANDARDS SUBCOMMITTEES
NRC	1986	POLICY AND ORGANIZATION STUDY
ADDITIONAL UTILITIES	1987	PILOT AND VARIATIONS STUDIES WITH EPRI/DOE
EPRI/DOE	1987	EXTENDED R&D

CHRONOLOGY
FIGURE 2

THE MONTICELLO NUCLEAR GENERATING PLANT
LIFE EXTENSION PILOT STUDY

G. H. Neils
Northern States Power Company
Minneapolis, MN (USA)

O. E. Gray III
Electric Power Research Institute
Palo Alto, CA (USA)

F. E. Gregor
Multiple Dynamics Corporation
Southfield, MI (USA)

ABSTRACT

In 1983, Northern States Power Company management directed a life extension feasibility study be conducted for its nuclear generating plants. The motivation for this initiative was a recognition of the continuing value to the company of the three nuclear units in providing low cost generation in a safe and environmentally acceptable manner and in the absence of substantial improvements in generation technology, would likely remain the case for the foreseeable future.

In Autumn 1984, Multiple Dynamics Corporation of Southfield, Michigan in conjunction with the General Electric Company was selected to perform a life extension evaluation for the Monticello plant. This program was selected by EPRI and the US Department of Energy for funding assistance along with a similar program being conducted on a pressurized water reactor plant by Virginia Power Corporation.

The Monticello Pilot PLEX Study consists of the following major steps:

a. Determination of critical plant components

b. In-depth evaluation of critical components with recommendations for follow-up activities

c. Study of selected non-critical components with recommendations for follow-up activities

d. Completion of detailed cost-benefit studies

e. Development of financial and project management plans

Critical components were identified using a Delphi method with independent evaluation teams from Multiple Dynamics Corporation, General Electric Company, and Northern States Power Company.

Detailed evaluations of each of the 12 components groups were conducted by Multiple Dynamics Corporation and the General Electric Company. Results of these evaluations were presented in a series of project topical reports. Each evaluation included a detailed design review, comparison of original codes, standards, and regulations to current requirements, assessment of equipment qualifications, review of equipment design basis, evaluation of maintenance and operation history, evaluation of debilitating effects, assessment of monitoring and inspection programs, and identification of potential modifications and improvements. Each evaluation concluded with a life prediction (if possible) and recommendations for follow-on activities.

The major lesson learned to date from the Monticello Pilot PLEX study are:

a. A 70-year plant life appears technically achievable. There are no big surprises.

b. Some components cannot last for the current licensed life of 40 years without some action being taken.

c. Some key preventive maintenance actions are needed now.

d. A PLEX records management systems is needed.

e. Significant generic research remains to be done to provide needed assurance in some areas.

f. Improved operational methods, maintenance, inspection, and diagnostics are important.

ETUDE PILOTE SUR LA PROLONGATION DE LA DUREE DE VIE
DE LA CENTRALE NUCLEAIRE DE MONTICELLO

RESUME

En 1983, la Direction de Northern States Power Company demanda la réalisation d'une étude de faisabilité portant sur la prolongation de la durée de vie de ses centrales nucléaires. Cette demande était motivée par le fait que ses trois centrales nucléaires continuaient de produire de l'énergie à un faible coût dans des conditions sûres et acceptables pour l'environnement et qu'en l'absence de progrès sensibles des techniques de production d'électricité, cette situation ne se modifiera probablement pas dans un avenir prévisible.

A l'automne de 1984, l'évaluation de la prolongation de la durée de vie de la centrale de Monticello fut confiée conjointement aux sociétés Multiple Dynamics Corporation de Southfield dans le Michigan et General Electric Company. L'Institut de recherche sur l'énergie électrique (EPRI) et le ministère de l'Energie (DOE) sélectionnèrent, pour les faire bénéficier d'une aide, ce programme ainsi qu'un programme similaire de la Virginia Power Corporation portant sur une centrale équipée d'un réacteur à eau sous pression (REP).

L'étude pilote PLEX de la centrale Monticello comprend les grandes étapes suivantes :

a. détermination des composants critiques de la centrale,
b. évaluation méticuleuse des composants critiques et recommandations d'activités de suivi,
c. étude de composants non critiques sélectionnés et recommandations d'activités de suivi,
d. réalisation d'analyses détaillées coûts-avantages,
e. établissement de programmes de gestion financière et de gestion de projet.

Les composants critiques ont été mis en évidence par la technique Delphi en interrogeant des équipes d'évaluations indépendantes appartenant à Multiple Dynamics Corporation, General Electric Company et Northern States Power Company.

Multiple Dynamics Corporation et General Electric Company ont réalisé les évaluations détaillées de chacun des douze groupes de composants. Les résultats de ces évaluations ont été présentés dans une série de rapports de projets spécifiques. Chaque évaluation comprenait une étude détaillée de la conception des composants, une comparaison des codes, des normes et des règles en vigueur lors de leur mise en service par rapport aux dispositions actuelles, une évaluation de la qualification des équipements, un examen des critères de conception des équipements, une évaluation du dossier d'entretien et d'exploitation de ces équipements, une évaluation des effets préjudiciables aux matériels, une évaluation des programmes de contrôle et d'inspection et un recensement des modifications et améliorations possibles. Chaque évaluation s'achevait par une estimation de la durée de vie utile (dans la mesure du possible) et par des recommandations d'activités de suivi.

Les principaux enseignements tirés de l'étude pilote PLEX de la centrale Monticello sont les suivants :

a. Il apparaît qu'une durée de vie utile de 70 ans est techniquement réalisable. On n'a noté aucune surprise majeure.

b. Un certain nombre de composants ne pourront pas atteindre la durée de vie de 40 ans actuellement autorisée si des mesures ne sont pas prises.

c. Il faut prendre dès à présent quelques mesures essentielles d'entretien préventif.

d. Un système de gestion des enregistrements PLEX est nécessaire.

e. Il convient de consacrer encore d'importants efforts à la recherche générique pour avoir les garanties nécessaires dans certains domaines.

f. L'amélioration des méthodes d'exploitation, d'entretien, d'inspection et de diagnostic est importante.

Determination of Critical Plant Components. The initial program step of the BWR plant life extension project was to prioritize plant components for the purpose of identifying those major plant elements which could force eventual retirement or present substantial technical obstacles to extended operation. These components were defined as "Critical Plant Elements" and were prioritized for further detailed evaluation.

The resultant prioritization determined the degree to which the various components were assessed. The most highly ranked plant elements, the critical components, received an intensive and thorough treatment and were addressed in topical reports. The noncritical components received less intensive treatment.

A complete criteria screening or evaluation of all of the structural and hardware items or types in the plant would have been a major undertaking. Therefore, a pre-selection process or pre-screening was performed to generate a reasonable listing of items to be evaluated.

The first step in this process was the identification and categorization of the structures and components in the plant. The screening guidelines applied in defining the candidate components were:

- Fundamental or key plant structure or component
- Major replacement cost and outage impact
- Significant impact on plant safety or availability
- Known history of regulatory concern
- Harsh operating and/or environmental conditions
- Safety margin assessment
- Historical troublesome performance

A total of 120 individual components and generic commodities were finally selected for detailed prioritization. These items were arranged in thirteen groupings as follows:

Group Number	Candidate Component Grouping
1	Reactor Vessel Components
2	Primary Containment Components
3	Primary Concrete Structures
4	Primary Steel Structures
5	Secondary and Outbuilding Structures
6	Pressure Retaining Components - Pumps and Turbines
7	Pressure Retaining Components - Tanks and Heat Exchangers
8	Pressure Retaining Components - Piping Systems
9	Pressure Retaining Components - Valves
10	Other Major Mechanical Equipment and Components
11	Primary Electrical Equipment and Components
12	Major Electrical Motors
13	Primary I&C Equipment and Components

The selection of plant structural and hardware components which are critical to plant life extension was accomplished by comparing candidate components to a common set of weighted evaluation criteria. The six categories of criteria are general criteria, service conditions, regulatory factors, service history, potential for service life extensions, and reliability considerations.

Following completion of the evaluation by the three scoring teams, the team scores were combined by simple averaging to provide the evaluation results.

The critical components were then grouped and evaluated in topical reports.

Topical Report	Critical Component
1	Reactor vessel pressure boundary, including head, flange, and stub tubes
2	Reactor pedestal, drywell foundation, biological shield, fuel pool slabs and walls, Reactor Building basemate, sacrificial shield wall, Reactor Building floor slabs and walls, and turbine pedestal
3	Drywell metal shell
4	Suppression chamber and supports, vent lines and bellows, and vent headers and downcomers
5	Reactor vessel support
6	Administration Building, including control room
7	DRD housings and guide tubes, not including stub tubes
8	Shroud, shroud ledge, core support plate, core top guide, and jet pumps
9	Emergency diesel generators
10	Reactor recirculation lines
11	Nozzle safe ends
12	ECCS, main steam, and feedwater piping inside primary containment

Critical component evaluation of the critical components was the principal focus of Phase I of the pilot plant study. The evaluations are a first order level of assessment of potentially life limiting effects. The intent of the evaluation was to scope the major technical issues and identify those which could significantly inpact a plant life extension decision or lead to early plant retirement. Preliminary physical life predications were made where possible on the basis of existing data, simplified failure models, and engineering judgement. Primary outputs of the evaluations include recommendations for improved life predictions and future research and development objectives.

The critical component evaluations are documented in topical reports. The following provides an overview of various aspects addressed in the topical reports.

The component is described to define the scope of the evaluation. Where applicable, a comparison is made to a number of other plants, noting other plants with essentially the same component design. Unique aspects of the pilot plant component are identified.

Codes, standards, and regulations considered in the original design are listed. New codes, standards, and regulations that may have to be considered for modifications or replacements are identified, and the significant differences highlighted.

Safety issues, pre-operational test requirements, surveillance testing, acceptability of refurbished equipment, requalification and in service inspection requirements for ASME code components are identified. Methods to demonstrate and maintain continued integrity are discussed for both ASME and non-ASME components. Environmental qualification is covered, if applicable.

Detailed information on vendor specifications, materials, performance ratings, and other pertinent data necessary to evaluate design adequacy was reviewed and evaluated.

For some components, an assessment of the excess margin provided in the design was performed which could help justify extended operations, i.e., to identify conservatisms in addition to those provided by code. For example, comparison of specified loading conditions to actual loading conditions and comparison of calculated maximum stress intensity values to code allowables was performed.

The margin assessment is not intended to revise the design basis. However, used in conjunction with the operational record, the margin assessment provides evidence of continued design adequacy.

An operating and maintenance history review of necessary repairs, repair frequency, replacement frequency, and any chronic maintenance problem was conducted. Comparison was made to industry performance where possible. Use of an availability of spare parts, repair and replacement technology and spare or redundant capacity of components was investigated.

Transients, environmental effects, fatigue, wear, or any other effect or event that causes degradation of the component's ability to perform its function is addressed. Specific areas and material that will be affected were determined from operation experience and industry reports.

Data currently being collected that measures transients, environmental conditions, and performance degradation were assessed to determine if it provides the information necessary to monitor the component for life assessment. The need for additional a data collection, by on-line monitoring, surveillance, inspection, diagnostics, testing, or other method was addressed.

The life prediction methodology consists of two basic elements. A qualitative assessment of the historical operating period is made from actual plant records and performance data to determine the rate at which the component life is used. This rate is then projected at a constant slope to the 40-year design life to assess whether the slope is above or below the original life line. This information provides an initial indication of life limiting degradation mechanisms. The second element of life assessment is a predictive exercise of anticipated future operations, needed changes, preventive actions and technology advancement. The available techniques for predicting the remaining life of the component are discussed, and a suitable method identified to predict the remaining component life or replacement schedule, as appropriate. For some degradation parameters, including those having technical uncertainties, more than one method was explored. The resulting life prediction was frequently compared to the original design life, and actual operating experience at other plants.

Potential improvements to operating and maintenance procedures are evaluated on the basis of experience on other plants. In many cases, these recommendations will potentially contribute to a longer service life and improved availability.

Capital improvements are evaluated where the probability exists that cost effective gains in plant or component life can be made. Technical feasibility and associated licensing aspects are explored and suggested timing of implementation is discussed.

The estimated cost of re-engineering, redesign, additional monitoring, changes in operating and maintenance procedures, and capital improvements was compared with the resulting gain in overall plant service life.

Historic and ongoing research and development that has a bearing on the component life is cited. The need for additional research and development is identified, as well as suggested objectives. These recommendations are viewed as a key input to prioritizing future necessary in the area of life extension which may be undertaken by EPRI, DOE, NRC and the utility industry.

The service life of the critical components was evaluated on the basis of key debilitating parameters. These potentially life threatening parameters were identified and categorized according the their severity and overall threat to plant life extension. In general, life predictions were based on design codes and specifications. Historical failures of similar components within the industry were considered. Due to lack of component operational history, life predictions for a few components were based on the consensus of opinion of a number of knowledgeable engineers. In a few cases, an ultimate life estimate was not ventured. The approaches used to evaluate various failure modes are described below. Each of the failure mechanism is complex, and synergism and combined effects will likely be present in many cases. The prediction methods are simplified, but these techniques do provide a scoping assessment of the key debilitating parameters. Actual trend data gathered as part of life extension program will help to confirm the predictions. Items evaluated included fatigue, stress corrosion cracking, irradiation, concrete aging, and wear.

Testing and surveillance activities were recommended based on condition assessments. Three findings were of special interest - drywell shell corrosion at the concrete floor interface, oil spillage on the reactor building floor slabs, and vent lines interior corrosion.

The drywell metal shell and interior concrete floor interface is protected by an area of flexible joint sealant which allows for the differential thermal expansion of the shell and floor. Removal of an area of concrete and joint sealant exposed the drywell metal shell, which exhibited an approximate 2" wide band of corroded material. The visual state of the corrosion indicated that the oxidation process at the shell had initiated several years ago. Ultrasonic wall thickness measurements indicated that material loss was not substantial and that the drywell shell thickness was still in excess of design requirements. Continued propagation of corrosion at this location without repairs/preventive measures could produce significantly reduced wall thickness within this critical section of the drywell shell.

Visual inspection of the concrete floor slab within the MG sets room produced findings of oil spillage and subsequent seepage into the concrete at multiple locations surrounding each MG sets pedestal. No significant cracking or spalling of the concrete slab due to this condition has occurred to date. Continued oil seepage into the slab, however, will eventually produce degradation of the concrete and possibly of the reinforcing steel. Performance of concrete core sampling from this slab an subsequent testing to verify adequacy of the current condition was scheduled.

Visual inspection of the interior surfaces of the vent lines, vent header, and downcomers that comprise the containment vent system indicated that there are localized areas of paint loss and material corrosion within each vent line (near centerline) and downcomer (submerged portions) lines.

Additional maintenance, inspection and monitoring activities were recommended for the critical components. Data currently collected for transients, environmental conditions, operating parameters and performance degradation was assessed. Most of the recommended activities will also benefit plant operations for the 40-year design life, even if plant life is not extended.

Noncritical Component Charaterization. The 93 noncritical components are listed below for which topical reports on life extension characteristics were not prepared. A brief evaluation for each of these noncritical components was deemed necessary in order to establish expected components lifetimes, summarize component aging mechanisms and identify potential actions to monitor aging and to ensure

component functionality throughout the life extension period. The technical
evaluations of noncritical components is currently in progress.

The 93 noncritical components involve a variety of mechanical and electrical
equipment and commodity items and substantial number of structural items.

Component Type	Number of Noncritical Components
Structural (S)	21
Piping (P)	15
Machinery (M)	15
Vessels/Tanks/Heat Exchangers (VHE)	13
Electrical Equipment (EE)	10
Instrumental/Control (IC)	9
Electrical Commodities (EC)	6
Other Mechanical Equipment (OME)	4
Total	93

The important life assessment parameters and potential life extension activities
vary considerably with component type. Many of the structural components are
massive concrete structures and major structural steel supports which make
replacement or significant refurbishment extremely difficult. For most of the
mechanical components (M, VTE, OME), partial or complete replacement is
possible. Many of the commodity components contained in the P, IC, EC, groupings
(valves, instrument tubing, cable) are currently replaced at Monticello
individually upon failure or on a regular preventive maintenance schedule.
However, the need for replacement of a significant portion of such items due to
aging is a life extension consideration.

    The cost benefit analysis is an economic assessment of the Monticello life
extension program. The goal is to quantify the assumed economic advantages of
cost-benefit life extension and provide a sensitivity analysis for the significant
parameters. The analysis is an incremental cost/benefit approach and a present
value format. The life extension alternative is compared with a replacement plant
as defined below.

Replacement Plant Alternative - Retire Monticello when its current operating
license expires and replace it with a conventional coal fired generating facility
of equal capacity.

PLEX Alternative - Extend the life of Monticello for thirty years beyond its
current operating license and then replace it with a conventional coal fired
generating facility of equal capacity.

The Monticello PLEX program has a very long duration from and economic evaluation
viewpoint (up to 54 years if life is extended until year 2040). Long duration
economic studies are subject to significant uncertainties regardless of efforts
made to incorporate in detail all aspects of expenditures and revenues. Over the
long term, technological developments are difficult to predict, business
conditions and government policies are less certain and unforeseen events are more
likely to occur. Recognizing these inherent uncertainties, a relatively simple
economic model was developed for the cost benefit analysis; and the net present
value and discounted benefit cost ratio for the PLEX base case was determined.
The sensitivity analysis evaluated life extension economics for a most optimistic
and a most pessimistic case.

Activity costs include the estimated costs for PLEX activities identified for the critical plant components, appropriately factored to account for life extension activities required for the remained of the plant components. Extended outage and have an estimated duration greater than 42 days (normal refueling outage). The projected outage durations have not been optimized from an outage planning viewpoint.

The expenditure deferment benefits are the result of a significant delay in capital expenditures for the construction of the replacement coal fired facility and for the decommissioning of the Monticello plant. The economic benefit is based on the assumed positive differential between the discount (or interest) rate and the inflation rate in the United States. The replacement plant operating benefit is obtained because the variable unit electrical generation costs for Monticello are projected to be lower than the variable unit electrical generation costs for the replacement coal fired facility. The availability benefit is based on the fact the PLEX activities are expected to reduce forced outagers and have a positive impact on component reliability and availability. The results of the cost benefit analysis provide strong evidence that a Monticello life extension strategy is economically attractive. The base case net present value is $313 million and discounted benefit cost ratio is 3.93. The sensitivity analysis indicates that Monticello life extension provides some economic benefits even for the most pessimistic case and very large benefits for the optimistic case. The base case shows that the present value of Monticello life extension costs is $107 million or about $200 per installed kilowatt.

Development of financial and project management plans. Plant Cycle Management Charts have been developed as a convenient summary of program findings for life extension planning and implementation. These charts are histograms of the costs in money, outage time, and number of activities versus the year in which the costs are incurred.

The Plant Cycle Management Charts are a "first look" at potential costs and associated outage impact. The expenditures and outage scheduling all have some flexibility in respect to implementation times. Using the charts, expenditure and outage scheduling can be optimized according to the specific needs of the utility. In order to maintain their effectiveness, the charts will require updating as more information becomes available.

THE SURRY I PLANT LIFE EXTENSION PILOT STUDY

David R. Hostetler
Virginia Power
Richmond, Virginia USA

ABSTRACT

Virginia Power's nuclear units represent a large, low cost segment of its total generating capability. Interest in extending the operating lives of those units is, as a result, very high.

With the support of the Electric Power Research Institute, the U. S. Department of Energy and others, Virginia Power is evaluating the feasibility of extending the operating life of its Surry 1 nuclear unit. The pilot study, which is being conducted by Virginia Power, Grove Engineering, Westinghouse and Stone & Webster, represents a necessary first step in the development of a comprehensive, integrated life extension program.

The primary objectives of the pilot study are: 1) identifying potential major obstacles to life extension, 2) identifying actions which will maintain the option to life extend, 3) developing a model approach to life extension which others can follow and 4) identifying R&D activities that are required to support life extension.

Potential critical plant elements, i.e. components, structures or systems which individually or collectively could impact the feasibility of life extension, were identified, prioritized and evaluated. The five highest priority elements were the reactor pressure vessel (RPV), containment, RPV support, reactor coolant piping and steam generators. None of the evaluations of these and other elements performed to date cast serious doubts as to the feasibility of extending the operating life of Surry Unit 1.

Improved monitoring and record keeping and identifying and implementing programs to mitigate age related degradation are activities to maintain the option to life extend that can be implemented quickly and relatively inexpensively. Prompt implementation of activities such as RPV fluence reduction and transient monitoring is important to maximize benefits. Since these activities also enhance current operations, they are beneficial regardless of the ultimate decision with respect to license renewal.

R&D recommendations are primarily concerned with materials properties, analytical methods and inspection techniques.

LA DUREE DE VIE DES CENTRALES : SURRY I ETUDE

RESUME

Une part importante de la puissance installée totale de la compagnie Virginia Power est constituée par des tranches nucléaires produisant de l'énergie à faible coût. Il est par conséquent particulièrement intéressant de prolonger la durée de vie utile de ces tranches.

Avec l'aide de l'Institut de recherche sur l'énergie électrique (EPRI), du ministère de l'Energie des Etats-Unis (DOE) et d'autres organismes, Virginia Power examine la possibilité de prolonger la durée de vie utile de la tranche Surry 1. L'étude pilote menée par Virginia Power, Grove Engineering, Westinghouse et Stone & Webster, représente une première étape nécessaire en vue de l'établissement d'un vaste programme intégré de prolongation de la durée de vie des centrales nucléaires.

Les grands objectifs de l'étude pilote sont : 1) la mise en évidence des principaux obstacles potentiels à la prolongation de la durée de vie, 2) la détermination des actions permettant de sauvegarder l'option de prolongation de la durée de vie, 3) la mise au point d'un système modélisé de prolongation de la durée de vie applicable à d'autres tranches et 4) la définition des activités de recherche et de développement nécessaires à l'appui de la prolongation de la durée de vie.

Les éléments de l'installation susceptibles de jouer un rôle critique, c'est-à-dire les composants, les structures ou les systèmes qui peuvent influer, individuellement ou collectivement, sur la faisabilité de la prolongation de la durée de vie, ont été recensés, classés par ordre de priorité et évalués. Les cinq éléments présentant le degré de priorité le plus élevé sont la cuve du réacteur, l'enceinte de confinement, les supportages de la cuve, les tuyauteries primaires et les générateurs de vapeur. Les évaluations de ces éléments et d'un certain nombre d'autres n'ont, jusqu'à présent, pas sérieusement mis en doute la faisabilité de la prolongation de la durée de vie utile de la tranche Surry 1.

Une amélioration du contrôle et des enregistrements, d'une part, l'établissement et la réalisation de programmes destinés à atténuer la dégradation par vieillissement, d'autre part, constituent des activités de nature à sauvegarder l'option de la prolongation de la durée de vie et qui peuvent être réalisées rapidement et à un coût relativement peu élevé. La mise en oeuvre rapide d'activités telles que la réduction du phénomène de fluence dans la cuve et le contrôle des transitoires est importante pour obtenir les avantages maxima. Etant donné que ces activités favorisent également l'exploitation courante, elles sont avantageuses quelle que puisse être la décision ultime concernant le renouvellement de l'autorisation d'exploitation.

Les recommandations en matière de recherche et de développement portent essentiellement sur les propriétés des matériaux, les méthodes d'analyse et les techniques d'inspection.

The initiative for addressing life extension of nuclear units is based upon two principal objectives:

o   Maximize the useful life of the material system for these major capital investments.

o   Plan and support efforts to maintain the life extension option in an acceptable regulatory climate.

With most nuclear plant licenses expiring well beyond the year 2000, many in the U. S. nuclear industry had questioned the need to begin life extension activities now. The need to begin to develop the license renewal process promptly was addressed in the recently published report entitled "Regulatory Considerations for Extending the Life of Nuclear Power Plants" (AIF/NESP-040, December 1986). For example, Virginia Power would need to know with reasonable certainty by the year 2000 whether or not the NRC would renew the Surry Unit 1 operating license so that planning for and construction of replacement capacity could begin if the renewal request were denied. Other reactors with earlier license expiration could need a decision as early as the mid 1990's.

Furthermore, no utility wants to spend large sums of money on life extension modifications without assurance that the license of its nuclear unit will be renewed. Such commitments cannot be made until regulatory criteria for license renewal have been established. However, in the meantime, the option should be maintained.

In addition, certain actions have the potential to maintain and to enhance the option to life extend, and those actions should be implemented as soon as possible. The current strategy is to perform those activities necessary to maintain the option while devoting the requisite resources for continuing to maintain the plant in a condition that safely and reliably supports life extension. It is clear that many of these activities will provide potential near-term benefits in plant performance, which accordingly further justifies support of these programmatic activities.

With those preliminary thoughts as background, I will briefly describe Virginia Power and the Surry Life Extension Pilot Study.

Virginia Power is an investor owned electric utility serving Northern, central and Eastern Virginia and Eastern North Carolina. A profile of the Company is provided in Table I. Virginia Power owns and operates four Westinghouse 3 loop pressurized water nuclear units at two generating stations. Key parameters for these units are given in Table II.

In early 1984, Virginia Power performed an in-house study to evaluate the life extension option. This effort resulted in a corporate commitment to develop and implement the necessary programs for its facilities to maintain the life extension option. As a result of this commitment, Virginia Power was pleased to respond to the LWR Pilot Plant Life Extension RFP from EPRI in the Fall of 1984.

The Surry Unit 1 Pilot Study is sponsored by Virginia Power, the U. S. Department of Energy (DOE), the Electric Power Research Institute

(EPRI), and the Westinghouse Owners' Group. Electricite de France has provided financial and technical support, and a broad utility perspective is provided by a utility working group associated with the project. The project team comprises Virginia Power, Westinghouse (which has provided expertise on the NSSS), Stone & Webster (which has concentrated on the balance of plant), and Grove Engineering (which has provided overall coordination and staff support to Virginia Power).

The primary objective of Phase 1 of the Surry pilot study, which represented a necessary first step in the development of a comprehensive, integrated life extension program, were: 1) identifying and evaluating plant components and systems that may have a major influence on life extension decisions; 2) uncovering potential obstacles to life extension; 3) developing a model approach to life extension which other utilities can follow; and 4) recommending to EPRI/DOE and the industry R&D activities that are required to support life extension. Phase 1 is essentially complete and Phase II, the implementation phase, is beginning.

The first task of the pilot study was to identify potential official plant elements (i.e., structures, components, or systems) which individually or collectively could impact the feasibility of life extension, and to prioritize them for further evaluation. Hundreds of components, structures, and systems were categorized according to their potential impact on life extension according to the following categories.

Category 1 - Plant Life non-limiting, Justification required (e.g. containment)

Category 2 - Long Life with High Potential Impact on Life Extension (e.g. reactor vessel)

Category 3 - Long Life with nominal impact on Life Extension (e.g. pumps, major piping, large valves)

Category 4 - Nominal Life with Repair or Replacement Feasible, Low Impact on Low Extension (e.g. cranes, motors)

Category 5 - Limited Life with Recurring Replacement or Refurbishment, no Impact on Life Extension (e.g. routinely replaced items)

Because of funding and scheduling constraints it was necessary to limit the review to elements in Categories 1, 2 and 3 and to prioritize those elements according to their potential impact on life extension. A set of 11 prioritization criteria were developed and assigned importance weighting by members of the project team. The criteria, in decreasing order of importance, were:

o   Consequence of Failure on Plant Safety
o   Regulatory Importance
o   Impact on Plant Availability
o   Consequence of Failure on Plant Operations
o   Cost to Refurbish or Replace
o   Modifications Required to Support Life Extension

o   Dose to Refurbishment or Replace
o   Consequence of Failure on Surry Unit 2
o   Mode of Failure
o   Replacement Precedent
o   Generic Applicability

Members of the project team applied the criteria to 34 selected elements in the first three categories. Based on this effort, the "potentially critical components" were evaluated and grouped into the following components and systems which were selected for further review.

o   Reactor Pressure Vessel (RPV)
o   Containment (including basemat)
o   RPV Supports and Neutron Shield Tank (NST)
o   Reactor Coolant Piping
o   Steam Generators (SGs)
o   Emergency Diesel Generators (EDGs)
o   RPV Internals (upper and lower)
o   Reactor Coolant Pumps (RCPs)
o   Pressurizer
o   Control Rod Drive Mechanisms (CRDMs)
o   Spent Fuel Pool/Transfer Canal
o   Main Turbine Generator
o   Structures
o   Cable in Containment
o   Intake/Discharge Structures
o   Containment Penetrations
o   Primary Shield Coolers
o   Station Transformers
o   Accumulator
o   Intake/Discharge Canal
o   NSSS Supports
o   Cable Outside Containment
o   Containment Subsurface Drainage
o   Control Room Equipment
o   Major Piping (other than RCS)

These 25 potentially critical components were evaluated in the second task of Phase I, which constituted well over half of the total Phase I effort. The results of the evaluations of these and other elements are documented in project topical reports (PTRs).

To date, based on the evaluations of these structures, components, and systems, nothing that has been identified casts serious doubts regarding the feasibility of extending the operating life of Surry Unit 1 well beyond the initial 40 year license period. Enhanced monitoring and recordkeeping and further analyses will obviously be required to fully justify life extension, and certain components (such as the RPV supports) may require supporting R&D.

Task 3 of Phase 1 dealt with reviewing the monitoring and recordkeeping practices at Surry, retrieving data required in support of the PTRs, comparing actual recordkeeping practices with needs to support life extension identified in the PTRs, and recommending appropriate changes in current practices. The conclusions are that life extension will impose additional monitoring and recordkeeping requirements, but that those additional requirements are not likely to be excessive.

Task 4 involved comparing actual operations and maintenance (O&M) practices at Surry with life extension enhancement practices recommended in the PTRs, and consolidating those recommendations with potential hardware modifications, also recommended in the PTRs. While a number of recommendations have been made, none appear to limit life extension feasibility.

One of the primary goals in the development of each PTR was the identification of R&D needed to support life extension. These recommendations were consolidated in Task 5. As might be expected, recommendations are primarily in the areas of materials, analytical methods, and inspection techniques. Some of the higher priority R&D activities are listed below:

o   Effect of Neutron Irradiation of Neutron Shield Tank Materials at Low Temperatures

o   Development of a Monitoring Program for Reactor Internals

o   Weld Repair Methods for Vessel and Internals

o   Development of Mechanistic Models for the Effects of Irradiation of Reactor Vessel Materials

o   Containment Testing Frequency

o   Fracture Toughness of Reactor Vessel Internals

o   Fatigue and Transient Analysis

o   NDE Techniques to Assess Fatigue Damage

o   Development and Application of Advanced Ultrasonic Detection and Sizing Techniques

o   Annealing Demonstration

o   Power and Instrument Cable Insulation and Jacket Materials

All of the evaluations, conclusions and recommendations will be presented in the Phase I final report, which will be issued in early 1987. A feature of this report will be a proposed life extension implementation plan for, Surry Unit 1. This plan, augmented by unit-specific evaluations, can be used as a model by other utilities.

Some of the insights and key findings gleaned from these activities are summarized below:

Two categories of life extension enhancing activities that can be implemented quickly and relatively inexpensively are improved monitoring and recordkeeping and the identification and implementation of age-related degradation mitigation programs. These efforts should be of value to near term operation regardless of the ultimate license renewal decision.

During the Surry pilot study it has become evident that we do not have readily available all the records needed to characterize plant age-related degradation such that the material condition of the plant can be easily ascertained. Much of the information is in the files, but it is not in the form or detail needed or it could not readily be found during the time of the study. Other data were monitored but not recorded because they were not thought to be important at the time. This is likely to be true at most other reactors placed in service during the early to mid 1970s, or even later. Another area of concern is the degradation of existing records such as microfiche and radiographs of components and systems. We are reviewing data storage and retrieval systems which will facilitate long term retention of such records.

Operating transient data are an important example in this category. If transients actually experienced by the reactor system are less severe or less frequent (or both) than those assumed in the design bases and those transients have been characterized accurately, the ability of the affected component to safely operate during the license renewal period can be proved analytically. Unless those transients are 1) recorded in a systematic manner as they occur, or 2) can be reconstructed from strip charts and operating logs, the opportunity will be lost forever. Data gathered in support of the PTR development and subsequent evaluations have indicated that transients are indeed less frequent and less severe than the design basis. For example, in about 13 years 63 plant heatups at about 20° per hour had actually occurred versus a lifetime design basis of 200 heatups at 100°/hour.

Additional monitoring to quantify age-related degradation or to detect the existence and magnitude of factors which contribute to age-related degradation should be identified and implemented in a timely manner. A very simple example of a recommendation at Surry is the monitoring of ground water from under the containment for constituents that could cause concrete degradation. In many cases, such as the containment, the justification for life extension will be a demonstration that no significant degradation mechanisms exist or that the onset and status of age related degradation can be detected in a timely fashion and repairs can be implemented.

While monitoring and recordkeeping will not guarantee life extension, weaknesses in this area will certainly make the burden of proof more difficult and could preclude life extension.

Mitigation has tremendous potential benefits in a number of areas. The most notable of these is the use of low-leakage core configurations to reduce the fast neutron fluence on the reactor pressure vessel. Surry 1 has operated with low leakage cores since the late 1970s, and the vessel fluence has been reduced accordingly. However, in one cycle the placement of a fuel assembly resulted in a fast flux level in the critical weld nearly as high as would have occurred with one of the earlier high leakage core configurations. That cycle was not designed with vessel fluence as a criterion. In current cycle designs care is taken to ensure that the fast flux at the critical weld is minimized.

An obvious corollary to mitigation is that the sooner it is implemented, the better. Once fluence has been accumulated or a severe transient has been experienced, the impact on plant age-related degradation cannot easily be undone. Undoing, if it can be done at all, will be much more costly than prevention. Ideally, planning for life extension should begin the first day of operation.

Proposed modifications to hardware and O&M practices focus on components of the reactor vessel, emergency diesel generators, control rod drive mechanisms, reactor coolant pumps, steam generators and reactor internals.

Specific Phase 2 activities now or soon to be underway include:

o Proposing a program to resolve issues arising out of potential neutron embrittlement of the reactor vessel support.

o Reviewing and recommending state of the art data storage and retrieval systems.

o Revising and/or developing operating procedures recommended in Phase 1 of the Pilot Study.

o Developing a set of inspection procedures for reinforced concrete structures.

o Validation and characterization of system transients.

o Reviewing the technical worth of Type A containment leak tests.

o Characterization of temperature and radiation effects on cables in containment.

o Characterization of the temperature of control rod drives.

o Evaluating the impact of life extension recommendations on outage critical paths.

o Economic evaluations of life extension.

o Feed and condensate system life cycle evaluation.

o Reactor coolant system life cycle evaluation.

While many of the current project efforts are focused on the future, an important anticipated near-term benefit of life extension evaluation and planning is improved reliability. It is clear that through these efforts the plant staff will become more knowledgeable about the material condition of the plant and better prepared to deal with age-related degradation. Condition monitoring and strategic maintenance have the potential for reducing forced outages. For example, if during life extension evaluations it becomes apparent that a component is degrading more rapidly than originally anticipated, corrective action can be planned. Had an active life extension program been in effect at Surry, the recent pipe erosion induced tragedy would likely have been averted. In addition, repair vs. replace decisions can and should be made in a life extension context. As the nominal end of life extension approaches, different decisions can be justified if it is known that the unit will operate substantially longer.

Nuclear plant life extension is of enormous potential benefit to utilities and their customers, truly a win-win situation. We have the opportunity to maximize the benefits and to provide for implementation if we act know. Virginia Power feels this is a prudent and necessary step to maximize the worth of these nuclear assets and to preserve the life extension option. We recommend that every utility take advantage of the results of these pilot studies and put them to use in its plants.

TABLE I

A PROFILE OF VIRGINIA POWER

| Peak Loads | Summer (July 1986) | 10358 MW |
| | Winter (January 1987) | 10640 MW |

| Load Growth | Summer Peak Load Growth | 3.0%/Year |
| | Winter Peak Load Growth | 3.6%/Year |

Capacity Mix	Nuclear	26.9%
	Coal	32.2%
	Oil Steam	17.3%
	Hydro (Conventional)	2.6%
	Hydro (Pumped Storage)	10.2%
	Combustion Turbines	4.4%
	Purchases	6.3%

Generation Mix	Nuclear	42.7%
(through June 1986)	Coal	44.7%
	Oil	2.2%
	Hydro (Conventional)	0.9%
	Hydro (Pumped Storage)	2.7%
	Purchases & Interchanges	10.7%
	Other	0.2%
	Pumping Energy	(3.5)%

TABLE II

NUCLEAR UNITS

	Capacity MWe Net	CP Date	OL Date	License Expires
Surry 1*	788	1968	1972	2012
Surry 2*	788	1968	1973	2013
North Anna 1	915	1971	1978	2018
North Anna 2	915	1971	1980	2020

*First Units in U.S. to be licensed for Dry Cask Spent Fuel Storage

DUREE DE VIE DES CENTRALES REP
LE PROJET E.D.F.

R. Noël - L. Reynes - J.P. Mercier

RESUME

Les centrales nucléaires d'EDF fournissent aujourd'hui 70 % de
la consommation française d'électricité. Cette production est
assurée essentiellement par les tranches REP récentes. Cette
situation justifie qu'un effort particulier soit consacré à la
durée de vie de ces unités. La longévité des REP semble devoir
bénéficier de conditions techniques et économiques particulièrement favorables.

Le "Projet durée de vie" EDF comporte un programme de travail
de 4 ans. Après une synthèse, en cours, de tous les éléments du
problème disponibles, des travaux complémentaires seront définis
et exécutés en tant que de besoin.

Les premières conclusions des études sont que les REP sont
capables de fournir un service très long, sous réserve d'une
surveillance et d'une maintenance appropriées.

ABSTRACT

Operating a very large number of standardized PWR units which
supply today 70 % of French power generation, Electricité de
France is highly interested in getting the best estimate of the
safe and economical life of these plants. An extensive program
of work has been undertaken in this respect.

The studies have first to go through all available data on
aging process, survey and maintenance of a limited number of
major components. This review will lead to recommendation of
complementary work in these fields.

The first conclusions are that these units are able to perform
a long service time, under provision of careful survey and
maintenance.

I. INTRODUCTION

Il suffit de porter le regard sur la part des centrales nucléaires REP dans l'équipement thermique d'EDF (fig.1) et dans la production de l'établissement (fig.2) pour prendre conscience de la dimension nouvelle des problèmes de maintenance, de durée de vie, de remplacement futur de ces unités très homogènes et encore très jeunes.

Dans le passé de la production thermique, le problème ne s'était jamais posé avec la même acuité : La rapidité du progrès (fig.3), et les bouleversements du marché des combustibles, ont souvent conduit à déclasser des centrales dont l'exploitation aurait pu, techniquement, être prolongée.

Les REP semblent devoir posséder un potentiel de longévité plus grand que les équipements antérieurs :

- stabilité relative des puissances unitaires et caractéristiques,
- coût de combustible à l'abri de bouleversements du genre "choc pétroliers",
- absence de filière concurrente dans les 2 ou 3 décennies à venir,
- stabilité des règles de sûreté fondamentales, et politique EDF de mise à jour systématique de toutes les tranches en service,
- longévité intrinsèque du REP, fonctionnant à des températures modérées (pas de fluage, peu de fatigue) et dont les chaudières nucléaires bénéficient de méthodes modernes de conception mécanique.

Le SPT et la DE ont donc décidé de consacrer de grands efforts pour mieux apprécier et exploiter ce potentiel de durée de vie des REP. C'est le "Projet durée de vie".

2. LIGNES DIRECTRICES DU PROJET

a) Il faut s'efforcer d'abord de poser convenablement le problème à résoudre :

Dans l'absolu, il n'existe pas de limite évidente à la durée de vie d'une centrale REP. Les matériels principaux ont été étudiés pour un service de 40 ans (durée de vie de "conception"), mais on peut à la limite les remplacer tous, sauf sans doute le génie civil. Le problème qui se pose est donc celui d'une optimisation économique de la durée de vie

Pour le schématiser, on peut dire qu'un allongement de la durée d'utilisation d'un REP se traduira par une réduction du coût d'investissement imputé au kWh, mais que le coût de maintenance, après une période de stabilité plus ou moins longue, devrait croître à long terme de façon inacceptable lorsque l'usure de certains "matériels sensibles" nécessitera des remplacements ou réparations très coûteux (fig.4).

Le "Projet durée de vie" se propose de cerner les éléments technico-économiques de cette optimisation.

b) On a donc dressé une liste de ces "matériels sensibles", ceux dont le remplacement ne peut être prévu dans le cadre des programmes de maintenance normaux, et sur lesquels les "interventions lourdes" sont les plus difficiles et coûteuses :

- matériels principaux de la chaudière nucléaire
- enceinte de confinement
- contrôle commande
- installation électrique (câbles)
- groupe turbo-alternateur

Pour chacun de ces "matériels sensibles", on va :

- rassembler tous les éléments accessibles de la prévision de durée de vie (études, fabrication, essais spéciaux, retour d'expérience national et international),

- engager, lorsqu'une durée de vie suffisante (jusqu'à 50 ans) ne peut être assurée aujourd'hui, les études visant à assurer un meilleur suivi du vieillissement, améliorer la maintenance, réparer ou remplacer - y compris coûts et durée prévisibles de ces opérations,

- au moyen de tous ces éléments, rassembler ou
développer, mettre au point des outils d'aide à la
décision, permettant aux responsables, lorsque les
tranches en service auront pris de l'âge, de choisir
à bon escient entre leur maintien en service et
leur remplacement.

On fixe a priori à l'étude une limite inférieure
de 25 ans - c'est la durée de l'amortissement comptable -
et une limite supérieure de 50 ans, car il paraitrait peu
sérieux de prétendre à des projections plus lointaines.

3. TACHES PRINCIPALES ET PLANNING DU PROJET

Le projet comporte 3 phases

- une première, qui est achevée, de préparation
et d'organisation,

- une seconde, en cours d'inventaire et synthèse des
nombreuses données déjà disponibles ou accessibles
sur la durée de vie des matériels sensibles,
complétée par une réflexion sur l'influence des
modes d'exploitation, et sur les problèmes d'ordre
réglementaires (tâches 1 à 3 - figure 5).

- une troisième phase, au cours de laquelle seront
engagés et exécutés les travaux d'études techniques
et industrielles, de chiffrement, de R et D, qui
pourront s'avérer nécessaires au vu de ces "constats". Il s'agira de travaux complémentaires car,
bien entendu, ceux dont la nécessité était la plus
évidente auront déjà été engagés dans le cadre
normal des études de maintenance : mises au point
de méthodes de contrôle non destructif, ou étude
de changement de générateur de vapeur, pour nous
limiter à ces deux exemples.

La deuxième phase occupe les années 1986 et 1987

La troisième phase pourra durer jusqu'à la fin
de 1989, sinon plus tard.

(fig. 6 - planning)

4. ORGANISATION

La phase préparatoire a été assurée par le membres
du comité directeur du projet, qui appartiennent aux états
majors des services centraux de la DE et du SPT.

La phase en cours repose essentiellement sur des ingénieurs du SEPTEN et du SPT : ceux-là mêmes qui gèrent les dossiers des matériels sensibles dans nos services.

La troisième phase d'actions complémentaires, études techniques, technico-économiques, industrielles, actions de R et D, fera davantage appel à des moyens extérieurs : constructeurs, organismes de recherche.

5. CONCLUSIONS

A ce stade d'avancement du projet, ses conclusions ne peuvent être que très préliminaires. Quelques enseignements capitaux se dégagent cependant concernant en premier lieu deux matériels sensibles entre tous :

On ne discerne pas en première analyse de limite pratique à la durée de vie des structures principales de confinement (expérience des caissons en béton précontraint de la filière gaz graphite).

Les cuves des réacteurs REP semblent également devoir présenter une longévité particulièrement grande grâce à la faiblesse prévue - et constatée - du décalage sous irradiation de la température de transition de fragilité des matériaux (fig. 7).

La garantie de résistance à la fatigue des composants principaux des chaudières nucléaires est par ailleurs très satisfaisante dans l'ensemble : La "comptabilisation des situations" montre que la "consommation" des transitoires pris en compte à la conception est plus faible qu'il n'était prévu.

Le bilan ne sera pourtant pas aussi agréable à coup sûr sur toute la ligne. Il n'est pas certain que tous les modes de dégradation des structures par corrosion, vieillissement, ou fatigue, aient été aussi bien appréciés sur tous les matériels sensibles. Qu'il s'agisse donc de faisceaux tubulaires de générateurs de vapeur ou de rotors de turbines, on ne saurait donc aujourd'hui exclure la perspective de "mauvaises surprises" dans les coûts de maintenance qui pourraient rendre le palier inférieur de ces coûts moins "paisible" que la perspective idéale de la figure 4.

Un objectif essentiel du projet, qui se confond ici avec les études de maintenance à long terme, sera également de fournir des éléments d'une bonne maîtrise de ces aléas, à défaut de laquelle la disponibilité moyenne du parc risquerait de présenter des fluctuations aussi désagréables que le montre la figure 8. On ne saurait faire abstraction de ce risque lorsqu'on cherche à évaluer l'adéquation future de nos moyens de production aux besoins de la consommation.

Quant à la prospective des actions de R et D que la projet durée de vie pourra susciter, il est a fortiori trop tôt pour l'aborder.

Tout au plus peut-on augurer, d'une manière générale, qu'il ne s'agira pas du défrichage d'un terrain vierge, car de multiples travaux visant à améliorer le suivi des matériels en service et la connaissance de leurs modes de dégradation figurent déjà dans nos programmes.

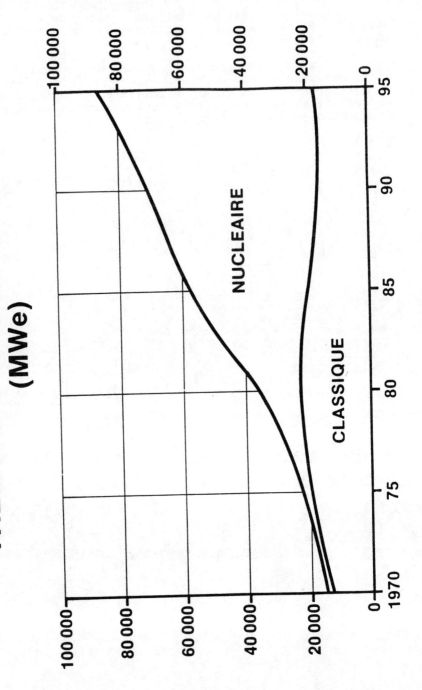

FIGURE 1

PUISSANCE THERMIQUE INSTALLEE EDF (MWe)

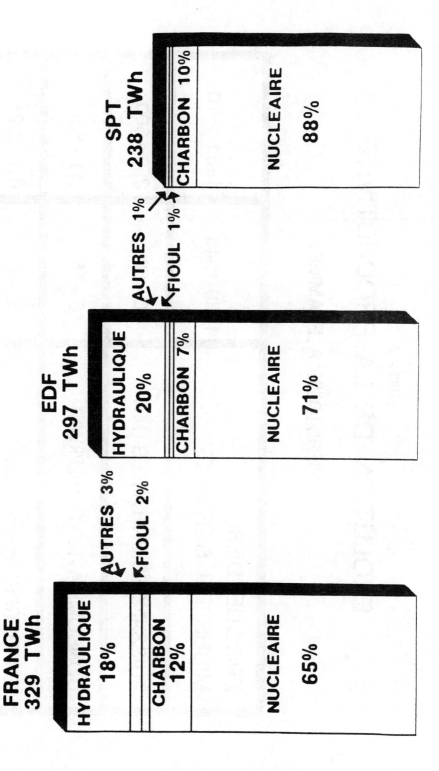

FIGURE 2

PRINCIPAUX RESULTATS 1985

FIGURE 3

EVOLUTION DE LA PRODUCTIVITE

(THERMIQUE A FLAMME)

EPOQUE DES MISES EN SERVICE	1930-1940	1960-1970
PUISSANCES UNITAIRES (MW)	20 - 50	250 - 600
CONSOMMATIONS (MJ/kWh)	16 - 15	11 - 9,5
EFFECTIFS (agents/MW)	5 - 3	0,3 - 0,2

FIGURE 4

EVOLUTION DU COUT DE LA MAINTENANCE

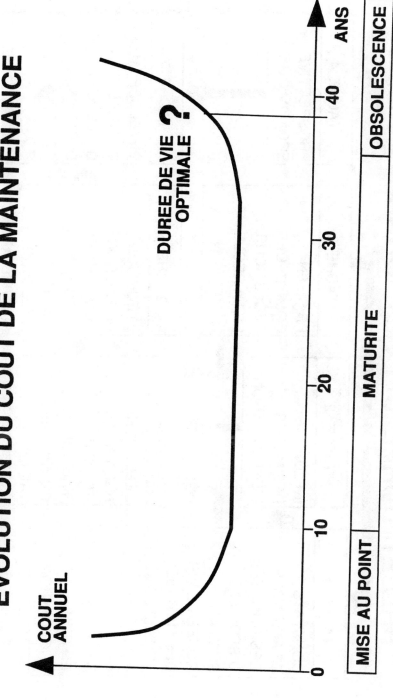

FIGURE 5

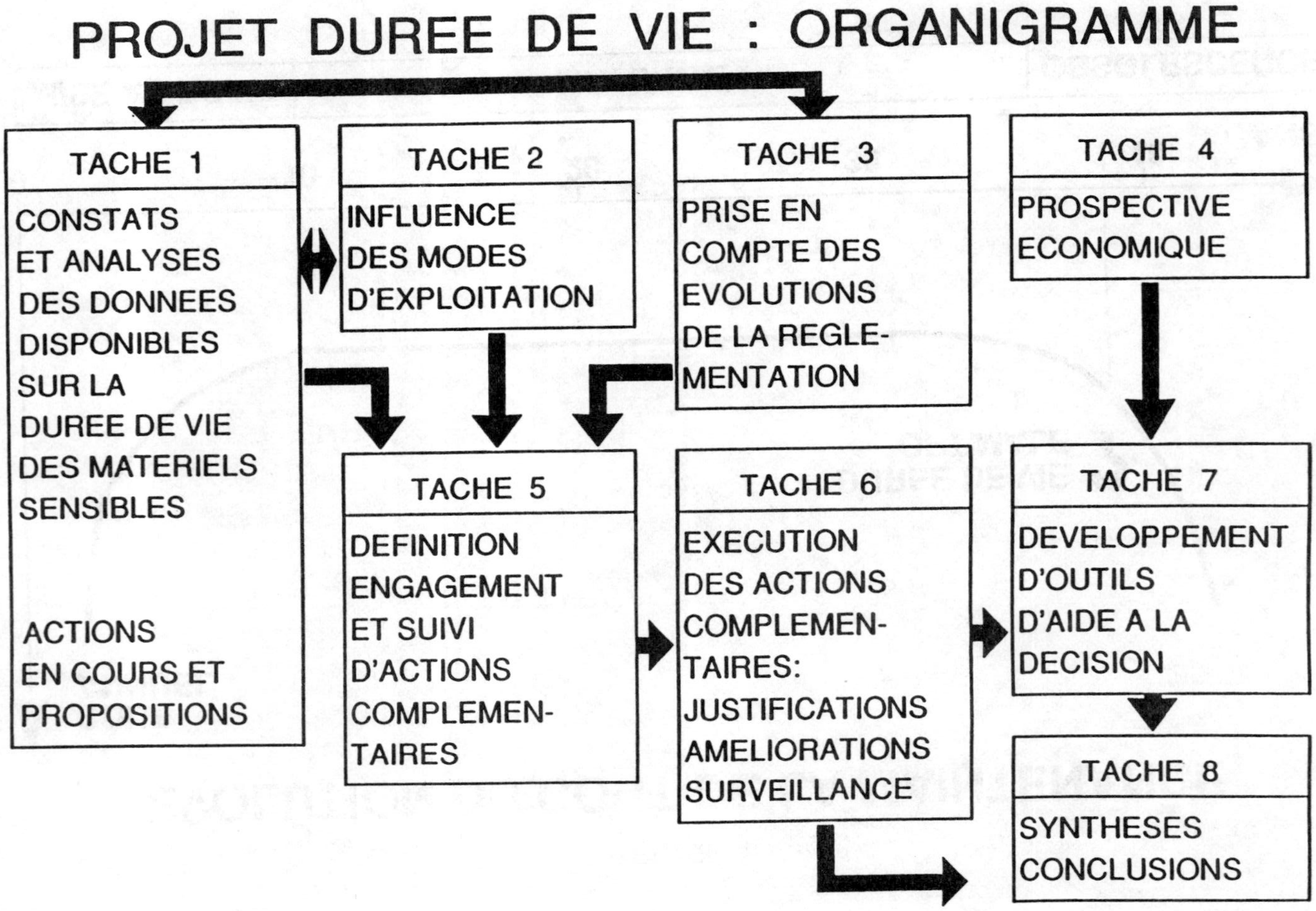
PROJET DUREE DE VIE : ORGANIGRAMME
TACHE 1
CONSTATS ET ANALYSES DES DONNEES DISPONIBLES SUR LA DUREE DE VIE DES MATERIELS SENSIBLES
ACTIONS EN COURS ET PROPOSITIONS
TACHE 2
INFLUENCE DES MODES D'EXPLOITATION
TACHE 3
PRISE EN COMPTE DES EVOLUTIONS DE LA REGLE-MENTATION
TACHE 4
PROSPECTIVE ECONOMIQUE
TACHE 5
DEFINITION ENGAGEMENT ET SUIVI D'ACTIONS COMPLEMEN-TAIRES
TACHE 6
EXECUTION DES ACTIONS COMPLEMEN-TAIRES: JUSTIFICATIONS AMELIORATIONS SURVEILLANCE
TACHE 7
DEVELOPPEMENT D'OUTILS D'AIDE A LA DECISION
TACHE 8
SYNTHESES CONCLUSIONS

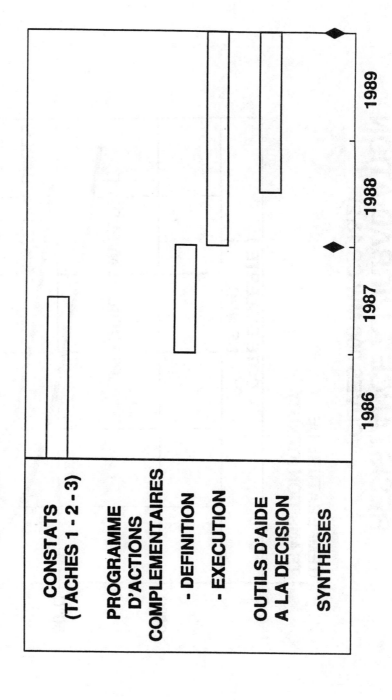

FIGURE 6

PROJET DUREE DE VIE : PLANNING

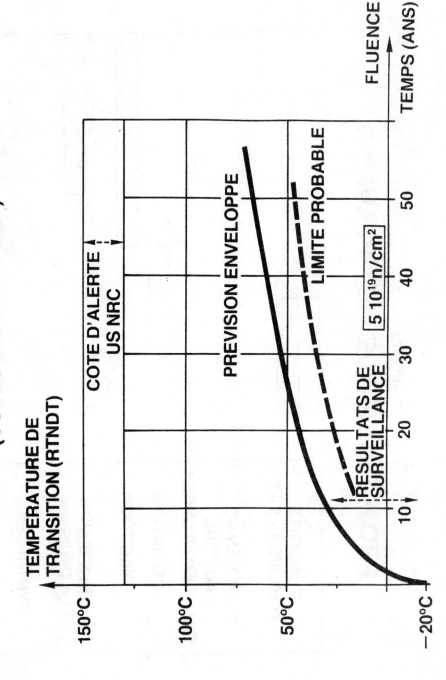

FIGURE 7

RESISTANCE A L'IRRADIATION
(CUVES 900 MW CP 1&2)

TEMPERATURE DE
TRANSITION (RTNDT)

150°C

100°C

50°C

−20°C

COTE D'ALERTE
US NRC

PREVISION ENVELOPPE

LIMITE PROBABLE

RESULTATS DE
SURVEILLANCE

$5 \cdot 10^{19} n/cm^2$

10   20   30   40   50   FLUENCE

TEMPS (ANS)

FIGURE 8

EVOLUTION DE LA DISPONIBILITE
(PARC NUCLEAIRE REP 900 MW)

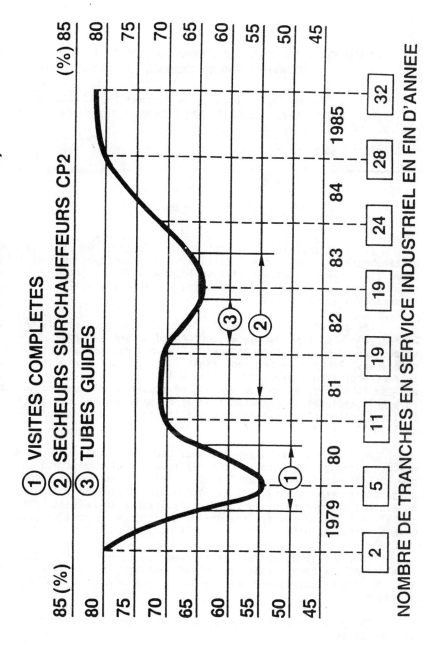

IMPROVEMENTS TO TRINO – E. FERMI – NPP TO UP-DATE SAFETY TO MODERN STANDARDS AND TO INCREASE LIFE EXPECTANCY

A. Buono, R. Comini, G. Filippelli, A. Giuriato

ENEL – ENTE NAZIONALE PER L'ENERGIA ELETTRICA – ITALIA

SUMMARY

Trino Vercellese – E. Fermi – plant is equipped with a 870 MWt, Westinghouse type PWR; first criticality was achieved on June 1964 and commercial operation was started on 1 January 1965. Trino is a nuclear power plant of the very first generation and for some years it was the largest PWR in operation in the world.

The operation of the plant presented some problems at the end of the first cycle when some damage was evidenced on the internals and on the thermal shield caused by vibration induced by the primary coolant flow. The thermal shield was permanently removed, eight fuel assemblies were replaced by dummies to reduce neutron flux on the vessel walls and internals were repaired: it was the first very extensive example of repair works carried out under water on highly radioactive components in a nuclear power plant. During subsequent fuel cycles the plant operation was quite regular with a very satisfactory availability factor.

In June 1979 the plant was shut down to instal new ECCS and new emergency diesel generators; the plant was started up again in March 1984. A new ECCS is not the only backfit of the plant; during shut down extensive up-gradings were carried out, particularly seismic and "post TMI". Recently an evaluation concerning containment resistance in case of increase of containment pressure above the design limit (severe accident) was conducted with positive results.

In conclusion, to reach the scheduled life and, if possible, extend it, Trino plant has been treated as a "live entity", it has therefore been changed and upgraded regularly and extensively in line with the most up-to-date safety standards.

The paper describes the major changes and outlines the implementation of such changes.

RENOVATION DE LA CENTRALE TRINO VERCELLESE - E. FERMI -
EN VUE DE SA MISE EN CONFORMITE AUX NORMES DE SURETE ACTUELLES
DE LA PROLONGATION DE SA DUREE DE VIE

RESUME

La centrale Trino Vercellese est équipée d'un réacteur REP de type Westinghouse d'une puissance thermique de 870 MW. Elle a divergé en juin 1964 et sa mise en service industrielle a eu lieu le 1er janvier 1965.

Cette centrale nucléaire de la toute première génération a été, pendant quelques années, la plus puissante unité de la filière à eau sous pression en service dans le monde. Le fonctionnement de la centrale souleva quelques problèmes à la fin de la première campagne parce que des vibrations dues à l'écoulement du réfrigérant primaire avaient quelque peu détérioré les structures internes et l'écran thermique.

L'écran thermique fut définitivement retiré, huit assemblages combustibles furent remplacés par des assemblages factices pour réduire le flux neutronique sur les parois de la cuve et les structures internes furent réparées. Ce fut là le premier exemple de réparations de grande envergure effectuées sous eau sur des composants fortement radioactifs d'une centrale nucléaire.

Pendant les campagnes suivantes, la centrale fonctionna tout à fait normalement avec un coefficient de disponibilité très satisfaisant.

La centrale a été arrêtée en juin 1979 pour mettre en place un nouveau circuit de refroidissement de secours et de nouveaux groupes diesel de secours, puis remise en service en mars 1984.

L'installation d'un nouveau circuit de refroidissement de secours n'est pas la seule mesure de mise en conformité prise dans la centrale. Pendant l'arrêt, de nombreuses améliorations ont été apportées, en particulier sur le plan sismique et dans le cadre des mesures "post TMI".

Récemment, une évaluation portant sur la résistance de l'enceinte de confinement à une augmentation de la pression au-delà de la limite de conception (accident sévère) a donné de bons résultats.

En conclusion, afin que la centrale nucléaire de Trino Vercellese atteigne sa durée de vie prévue, voire la dépasse, on l'a traitée comme une "entité vivante". Elle a donc évolué et s'est améliorée de façon régulière et notable pour se conformer aux normes de sûreté les plus récentes.

La communication décrit les principales modifications apportées et leur mise en oeuvre.

1 GENERAL

The E. Fermi Nuclear Power Plant, owned by ENEL, is located on the Po river near the Trino's town.

The plant is equipped with a four-loops pressurized water reactor and with two turbogenerators rated respectively at 220 MVA and at 110 MVA. The reactor, designed and built by Westinghouse, has been the first in the world to be ordered by a utility for commercial purposes and for several years it was also the largest PWR in the world.

First criticality was reached on June 21, 1964 and the plant was connected to the grid with the 220 MVA turbogenerator on October 22, the same year. The 110 MVA turbogenerator was phased to the grid on July 20, 1965. This turbogenerator was ordered later due to the uprating of the reactor power from the initial contractual value of 615 MWt to 825 MWt.

Commercial operation at 615 MWt started on Jannuary 1, 1965, while the nominal power at 825 MWt was reached on November 26, 1965.

During cycle 4, the reactor nominal power was increased up to 870 MWt. Presently the plant is in operation for completing its ninth fuel cycle.

Since initial commercial operation, the plant total gross generation was 24.854 GWh as of December 31, 1986. During the same period the plant cumulated 3845 EFPD, equal to 10,5 EFPY.

Table 1 presents the plant performance data for the nine fuel cycles while figure 1 presents the plant load diagram during the same period.

During the time span of almost twenty-two years with the plant operation, ENEL commitment was constantly aimed at verifying the adequacy of the safety systems to face the postulated accidents according to the current criteria.

Most of the modification works were implemented during two long plant outages. The modifications were necessary both to correct design inadequacies or to upgrade the plant systems to the most recent safety criteria.

2 REPAIR WORKS

The first plant long outage took place at the end of the first fuel cycle, from may 1, 1967 to may 1, 1970. The plant outage was necessary to repair several failures on the reactor internals that were discovered during the refuelling shut-down. The failures were mainly due to fatigue stresses caused by fluid dynamic forces.

The repair required extensive investigation to clarify the failure mechanism involved and the development of special tools for underwater works.

The repair works required:
- the removal of the thermal shield;
- the replacement of several screws, studs and nuts on the lower package;
- the installation of a secondary core support;
- the removal of eight corner fuel assemblies and their replacement with eight dummies;
- the removal of the neutron flux mapping system (aeroball);
- the removal of the temperature measuring system at the fuel outlet channels;
- the development of a new reactor vessel material surveillance program;
- the development of a loose parts monitoring system;
- the development of a nuclear noise technique for monitoring the movements of the reactor internals.

Periodic inspections to the reactor internals carried out during subsequent refuelling shut-downs indicated that the repair works were adequate.

Extensive lessons were learned from the Trino reactor internals failures and repair works which were beneficial to the reactor technology development.

As reported in table I, during the subsequent fuel cycles the plant operated quite satisfactorly and regularly achieving high utilization factors.

3 BACKFITTING ACTIONS

The second plant long outage occurred during cycle 8 and took place from June 21, 1979 to march 30, 1984.

The plant outage was initially planned on request of the Licensing Authority for replacing the existing ECCS, as well as the electric emergency power supply with new ones.

During the plant outage, however, a number of requestes were put forward by the Licencing Authority which compelled ENEL to carry out an extensive backfitting plan for the plant.

The additional requestes derived mainly from:
- the post TMI-2 review plan;
- the sistematic evaluation program issued by the Licencing Authority after ten years of plant operation, according to the plant licence.

3.1 NEW ECCS

The modifications for the new ECCS concerned exstensive works in the mechanical, in the electrical and in civil areas. The existing ECCS were removed and new systems were installed to meet the plant functional requirements both during normal plant operation and during accident conditions.

The replacement of the ECCS resulted in installing:
- a new low pressure safety injection system,
- a new high pressure safety injection system,
- an high pressure accumulators injection system,
- a bottom containment recirculation system,
- a new spray system, inside the containment, with borated water,
- a cooling system for the new ECCS,
- two 3KV diesel generators for supplying power to the new ECCS. The two existing 380 V diesel generators were devoted to emergency auxiliary functions.
- a building for installing the new diesel generators,

and in replacing the two refuelling water storage tanks with new ones seismically qualified.

The new ECCS satisfy:
- the single failure criterion, for any active component, either mechanical or electrical,
- the redundancy criterion,
- the physical and electrical segregation criterion,
- the seismic design criteria for mechanical components,
- the seismic design criteria for the electrical components of class 1E.

In the same framework, the following systems were upgraded:
- the auxiliary feed water system by installing a new motor-driven pump;
- the main steam lines isolation system, replacing the existing stop valves with new quick-closing ones;
- the main steam and the main feedwater lines by inspecting all the welded joints and remaking all the weldments with unacceptable indications.

3.2 POST TMI-2

The post TMI-2 review plan resulted in the following actions:
- modification of the plant containment isolation system installing several new valves and improving the electric circuitry;
- installation of a reactor coolant margin-to-saturation-monitoring-system;
- installation of new lines for actuating the hot leg recirculation in the post-accident long term actions;
- installation, inside the plant containment, of enviromentally qualified instrumentation for post-accident conditions;

- installation of seismic instrumentation, both for protection and supervision purposes.

3.3 SISTEMATIC EVALUATION PROGRAM

The sistematic evaluation program, after ten year of plant operation, resulted in the following actions:
- extensive seismic requalification works of the reactor auxiliary building, of the fuel building, of the fans building and of the turbines building;
- extensive seismic requalification works of the mechanical systems and components;
- extensive modification of the electrical systems with continuity requirements;
- extensive modifications of the control-room ventilation system;
- extensive modifications of the fire fighting system;
- replacement of over 40 electrical penetrations of the plant containment;
- replacement of all the cables performing safety functions with qualified ones and shielded with protecting conduits.

Because of the extensive works to be carried out, a priority plan was set-up to implement the works during two refuelling outages, respectively at the end of cycle 8 and 9.

During the same plant outage, several analytical studies and inspections were requested by the Licencing Authority for evaluating the reactor vessel conditions.

Precautionary actions were enforced both through administrative controls and hardware modifications.

To take care of any fracture toughness decrease of the reactor vessel material, the following actions were implemented:
- adoption of a criticality limit,
- installation of an over-pressure protection system to avoid undue cold over-pressurization of the primary system;
- increase of the borated water temperature, both in the accumulators and in the refuelling water storage tanks, up to 60°C.

A special ISI of the reactor vessel was also carried out, at the end of cycle 8, to investigate for any reportable indication in the undercladding and in the base metal of the beltline region.

At last, a cross check was performed, with two different ISI service companies, on the base material of the reactor vessel.

4 PLANNED BACKFITTING ACTIONS

Since safety can be improved also by replacing the existing components with improved or more reliable ones, during the next refuelling shut-downs, ENEL planned to carry out the following special maintenance actions:

- replacement of the two emergency, 380 V, diesel generators with new ones;
- replacement of the pressurizer safety valves;
- replacement of the let-down regulating valves;
- replacement of the butterfly valves on the containment ventilation ducts;
- installation of a mitigating system for the anticipated transients without scram.

Along with the hardware modifications, analytical studies and investigations, are presently being carried-out concerning the following aspects:
- evaluation of the plant containment for the beyond design basis accidents (BDBA),
- investigation of some plant areas using the probabilistic approach.

As for are licensing aspects, a licence has been issued by the Ministry of Industry for operating the plant for a five years period, from 1985 to 1990.

By that date ENEL has been requested to submit a report reviewing the plant safety status according to the on-going safety criteria.

5 GENERAL REMARKS

It is wortwhile to make few general remarks on Trino concerning same peculiar features of the plant, whose vintage goes back to the early sixties. Some of these features indeed, are being reconsidered for the design of future generation reactors.

First of all, the primary system components, say steam generators, pressurizer, etc., are designed for a thermal power rating of 1000 MWt, while the plant has always been operated at a maximum thermal power of 870 MWt.

The loops of the primary system are equipped with by-pass lines and isolation valves which allow operation of the reactor coolant pumps through the steam generators without affecting the reactor vessel (figure 2). This feature resulted very useful both for operational and maintenance purposes. The valves could also result very usefull for emergency condition caused by steam generators' tube failure. Adopting periodic preventive maintenance, the valves performance was quite satisfactory.

The reactor coolant pumps are of the canned rotor type: their performance is excellent.

Since a back-up pump is available at the plant, and each pump is interchangeble with the others, at each refuelling outage a pre-assembled pump is replaced in a loop, while the removed pump is overhauled after the refuelling and stored for the next maintenance outage.

The fuel is stainless steel cladded and no failure or leakage has ever been experienced during the plant life, even after long storage periods both in the reactor vessel and in the spent fuel pit.

Steam generator tube-bundle material is stainless steel and no leaking tube has ever been experienced during the plant life. So far only 6 tubes were plugged over the 6648 existing tubes in the four steam generators.

Tube plugging was carried out as a preventive maintenance action because of point-defect indication, evidenced in the antivibration bars zones, through eddy-current examination.

We believe that this satisfactory performance of the steam generators is mainly due to a combination of the material utilized for the tube-bundle and the scrupulous maintenance of a correct water chemistry both for the primary and the secondary systems.

As for water chemistry aspects, it has to be reported that since the very beginning of the plant life an AVT water chemistry was adopted and, as a rule, the plant was never operated with raw water inleakage from the turbines' condensers.

As for the radiological aspects, it is to be reported that:
- because of the fuel cladding and steam generators tube-bundles excellent behavior, primary and secondary systems are very "clean";
- the average value of the collective dose, over the 22 years of the plant commercial operation, both to the plant personnel and to the external workers, is below 85 man rem/year and the general trend is decreasing;
- during the same period, the doses to the critical group of the population are less than 0,1 millirem/year.

Trino is operated by ENEL as a base-load plant. As reported in table 1, the plant performance indicators (availabilty and utilization factors) are high throughout the plant life.

6 CONCLUSIONS

All the abovementioned backfitting actions were carried out by ENEL mainly aiming at a safe operation of the plant and at updating, during the time, its standard of safety with evolving and more stringent criteria, therefore to-day, the plant is substantially safer than when it started commercial operation in 1965.

Plant backfitting is carried-out through a continuos interaction between ENEL, safety authority the and manufacturers and is based upon a constant information exchange with the other utilities.

So far, no constraint has been identified which would prevent an extention of the plant life beyond that originally forseen.

Besides appropiate backfitting, ENEL believes that a well planned and carefully executed preventive maintenance program plays an important role in keeping a high standard of safety and in assuring a life of the plant longer than expected.

TABLE 1
TRINO NPP PERFORMANCE DATA DURING THE FUEL CYCLES

FUEL CYCLE Nº	FUEL CYCLE DURATION (days)	GROSS GENERATION (MWh)	PLANT AVAILABILITY FACTOR (%)	PLANT UTILIZATION FACTOR (%)	REACTOR AVAILABILITY FACTOR (%)	REMARKS
1	848,0	3.387.899	73,1	68,8	92,7	CYCLE STRETCH OUT 13 DAYS
2	415,8	2.243.967	91,2	90,7	99,3	
3	508,8	2.719.186	88,8	85,8	98,7	CYCLE STRETCH OUT 40 DAYS
4	409,7	2.381.359	96,4	92,9	99,2	CYCLE STRETCH OUT 80 DAYS (1)
5	528,8	3.031.877	95,7	90,1	99,8	CYCLE STRETCH OUT 95 DAYS
6	321,6	2.050.024	98,3	98,2	99,8	
7	535,8	3.216.681	94,9	91,1	97,8	CYCLE STRETCH OUT 42,7 DAYS
8	474,4	2.853.995	98,8	92,9	99,9	CYCLE STRETCH OUT 105 DAYS (2)
9	518,2	2.968.901	91,8	88,6	94,9	(3)

(1) Continuos Operation of 322 days of which 214 at full power

(2) Cycle 8 was interrupped from 21/6/1979 to 7/4/1984 after 102 days of operation for carrying out modifications both to the ECCS and to the emergency power supply

(3) Plant in stretch out condition since 28/10/1986

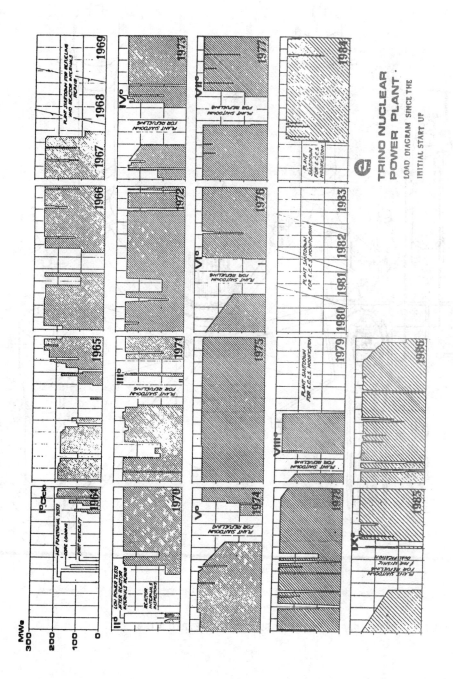

TRINO NUCLEAR POWER PLANT.
LOAD DIAGRAM SINCE THE INITIAL START UP

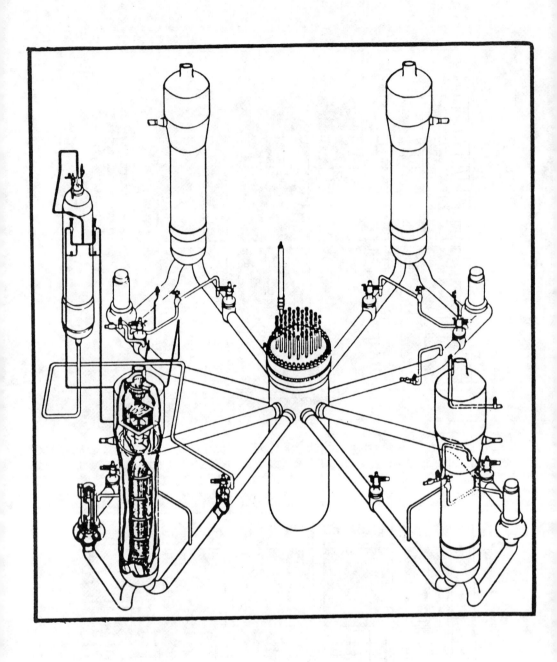

FIGURE 2: TRINO NPP – PRIMARY SYSTEM ISOMETRIC VIEW

DISCUSSION

R. COMINI, Italy

Could Mr. Carlson say whether the NUPLEX program includes also NPP of the first generation ?

D.D. CARLSON, United States

40 year licensed lifetime applies to all US nuclear power plants including the earliest ones. Representatives from these older plants are actively involved in the activities of the Nuclear Utility Plant Life Extension Steering Committee.

J. OLASO, Spain

Is there any provision for foreign participation in the DOE-EPRI project ?

D.D. CARLSON, United States

EDF is an active participant in the program. Interest from other countries is welcome.

H. ALDER, Switzerland

How many years beyond 40 is the new time limit for the life extension program ?

D.D. CARLSON, United States

The pilot plant studies suggest an additional life of 20 or more years may well be possible. In general, no conclusion can be made ; the situation depends upon the particular operating history and design of each particular plant. Each plant must make its own technical and economic assessment to ascertain the life appropriate for the plant.

D.L. HARRISON, United States

The objective of the US research activities is to develop sufficient technology and information so that regulatory criteria can be established which will give the utility decision makers the flexibility to operate their plant 1, 5, 10, 20, up to 40 or more years if it is economical. In summary, our efforts are directed at developing the technology and recommending the regulatory framework for life extension and license renewal decisions.

M. IBANEZ, Spain

1.   What has been the human effort for the implementation of Phase I of the US project ?

2.   What is the actual cost investment in the United States for the installation of a new nuclear kilowatt ?

D.L. HARRISON, United States

1.   Including Electric Power Research Institute (EPRI), US Government (DOE and NRC), Utilities, AIF, and cost sharing by consultants (NSSS, AE, etc.) the estimated cost is $ 4-6 millions for the US total.

2.   Units comming on line over the past few year average $\simeq$ 2,500-3500 $/KW. For future units, under the Advanced LWR program sponsored by Government and Industry the cost objective is about $ 2000/KW. The actual cost will be influenced by the NRC's final requirements for standard plants.

G. ECKERT, Federal Republic of Germany

Do you use specific inspection and testing equipment and programs for Phase II (which I see as analysis and inspection rather than implementation) or rely on existing operational equipment and records ?

D.R. HOSTETLER, United States

Anything done now is with existing testing equipment and programs. These are not necessarily adequate for life extension. Existing records are not adequate.

G. ECKERT, Federal Republic of Germany

When will the real implementation phase begin ? How long will it last ? A major problem will be convincing regulatory authorities to accept your recommendations.

D.R. HOSTETLER, United States

Implementation begins, in our view, with preserving the option of life extension and includes gathering information to support an application for license renewal. We would not anticipate undertaking major modifications until we were reasonably certain that the license would be renewed otherwise the investment would be too risky. In Mr. Eckert's terms implementation would begin once license renewal was granted. This renewal would have to be based on a life extension implementation plan.

R.S. HART, Canada

Current and previous speakers have indicated that plant life extension must begin at the earliest possible date.

My comment is that Canadian experience, including the refurbishing of Pickering A units 1 and 2 by Ontario Hydro, indicates that life extension should ideally begin at the design stage. My paper in Session II was intended to demonstrate the gains that are readily achievable in the area of life extension, at very low or negligible cost - in fact in some cases, with cost reduction - if long operating life is identified early as a design objective.

D.R. HOSTETLER, United States

I agree that changes can and should be made in the design stage to enhance maintability. However, this can be carried to extreme. Such considera-tion could make the design more complex and more expensive. Cost benefit eval-uation must be made.

R. COMINI, Italy

Could Mr. Noël speak about the area, if any, in which provision has been included by EDF in the design of latest generation PWR (P'4 and N4) taking account of the PLEX programme ?

R. NOEL, France

We cannot say now - when our life evaluation project is in its first phase - that this project has already influenced improvements in the design of future plants.

A list of such improvements, significant from the point of view of service life, would be difficult to supply immediately, since they are more or less related to all components and systems design in the fields of materials, construction, installation, improvement in access, removability, etc.

G. SCHÜCKTANZ, Federal Republic of Germany

I would like to comment on Mr. Noël's and Mr. Hostetler's statement that actual transients are usually less severe than the design transients. If that is true how could one explain the occurrence of fatigue cracks in feed water lines and charging lines ? We know from experience and from extensive measurements in operating units that there are components whose transients are more severe than the specified ones. They just cannot be monitored as the normal plant instrumentation is not designed for monitoring such transients. I feel that fatigue of such components has to be looked at very carefully, either by modification of design or the mode of operation or by extensive ISI or by some kind of monitoring. I feel we cannot afford an attitude such as "what I do not know does not worry me".

R. NOEL, France

It is quite obvious that the guarantee obtained from the design analysis is valuable only if the user verifies very carefully that the operating parameters remain permanently within the design hypothesis.

Such a verification is very strictly required in France by our "Arrêté du 26 février 1974", which is the basic regulatory text for construction and operation of nuclear pressure systems. It initiated what we call "transient monitoring" or "transient bookkeeping" which has been a current practice for 10 years.

The experience of this surveillance led to important modification in system regulation, to lighten so far as possible transients on pressurizer surge line and feed and bleed lines.

Our general conclusion on the fatigue behaviour of main primary and secondary system is that the prospective situation of the heaviest components (vessels and piping) is very good. However, the margins are smaller on some auxiliary systems and piping, which need further work. Anyhow, the eventual repairs involved would not lead to prohibitive expenses.

D.D. CARLSON, United States

Both the Surry and Monticello pilot plant studies have identified the need to better understand age-related degradation of vessel internals. Is this a concern in other countries ? Are efforts underway to inspect or examine vessel internals in other countries ?

R. COMINI, Italy

In 1968 and 1970 repairs were carried out with extensive use of Inconel for screws and bolts. Evidence of degradation was found so that at the end of cycle 8 further work was done to replace all the Inconel X-750 bolts and screws installed at the end of cycle 1.

J. BOYER, France

Les matériels électriques et câbles ayant une fonction de sûreté subissent des programmes de qualification extrêmement sévères concernant la tenue sous irradiation, vieillissement, irradiation, LOCA.

Dans le cadre d'un prolongement de la durée de vie (en particulier au-delà de 40 ans) faudra-t-il reprendre ces programmes de qualification notamment concernant le vieillissement thermique et l'irradiation ? Ou bien l'expérience acquise permet-elle d'extrapoler ?

D.D. CARLSON, United States

In-containment cabling is currently being further investigated. In particular, work is ongoing to better define the environment (temperature, humidity, radiation) experienced by the cabling to better understand the actual experience in contrast to that for which the cabling was designed. Replacement of a few cables would not represent a significant life extension concern. Replacement of all in-containment cabling would, however, be a major undertaking.

D.R. HOSTETLER, United States

Cables are designed to function in an accident environment to the end of 40 year life. We do not know how much longer these cables can operate past 40 years. By demonstrations that the actual temperature and radiation environments experienced by the cable are less severe than in tests, additional life can hopefully be demonstrated.

J.W. HARROW, United Kingdom

There are many uncertainties in extrapolating damage predictions for time dependent phenomena. In extending plant lives to about 60 years there is a real danger that factors of safety incorporated into the original design are diminished unknowingly. This, combined with a lack of long term operating experience, increases the risk of unpredicted failure.

What account is taken of this increased risk in the economic evaluation of the Surry and Monticello plant ?

D.R. HOSTETLER, United States

We recognize that there are unknowns. As a result we will not proceed blindly. We will monitor the status of critical equipment so that an acceptable safety margin is maintained. The utility and regulators need this assurance during the first 40 years.

The economic evaluation takes into account (in the form of risk analysis) the possibility that a failure will require shutdown prior to completion of the extended life period.

UN CHANTIER ROBOTISE POUR LA REPARATION DU REACTEUR CHINON A3
L'OPERATION I.S.I.S.
A ROBOT-AUTOMATED WORK SITE FOR REPAIR OF THE CHINON A3 REACTOR

A. RAYNAL

RESUME

C'est l'évolution des détériorations dues à la corrosion des aciers doux par le gaz carbonique qui conduisit l'exploitant à décider de la réparation de certaines structures supérieures du réacteur CHINON A3 en 1982. Il fallait consolider les dispositifs de supportage de la thermométrie et des prélèvements d'analyse de gaz en posant environ 200 pièces de réparation par campagne. Le recours à la robotisation s'est revelé indispensable.

Deux robots approvisionnés de l'extérieur en têtes-outils puis en pièces de réparation constituent avec leurs serveurs un véritable chantier coordonné par un ordinateur central et surveillé par caméras vidéo. Chaque réparation est exécutée après un apprentissage sur maquette échelle 1 conformée au mieux à la réalité d'après les relevés dimensionnels effectués par télémétrie.

Opérationnels depuis juin 1986, les robots cumulent plus de 20 000 heures de fonctionnement. Soixante dix pièces ont été soudées en réacteur. Pour réduire le temps d'apprentissage une méthode de création des grandes trajectoires par CAO 3D et simulation du robot a été adaptée.

ABSTRACT

In 1982, following degradation due to corrosion of low-carbon steel by carbon dioxide gas, the utility undertook to repair some of the support structures at Chinon A3. This involved consolidation and reinforcing thermocouples and gas monitor pipeworks supports. A welding process was selected and the use of robots became indispensible because of the large number of components to be replaced (200 per outage).

Two robots, supplied with tool heads and replacement components from outside the reactor were used. The robots and their servers were coordinated by a central computer and monitored by a closed circuit television system. Each repair operation was performed after "training" on a full-scale mockup of the top of the reactor reconstructed from telemetry of the real reactor dimensions.

Since becoming operational in June 1986, the robots have accumulated over 20 000 hours of operation and seventy parts have been welded to the reactor. A 3D CAD system has been adapted to simulate the robots and analyze long trajectories in order to reduce robot learning time.

SESSION IV

REFURBISHMENT EXPERIENCE AND MONITORING

SEANCE IV

EXPERIENCE ET CONTROLE DES TRAVAUX DE RENOVATION

Chairman – Président

G. SCHÜCKTANZ

(Federal Republic of Germany)

LE PROBLEME (figures 1 et 2)

Après 80 000 heures de fonctionnement, il était devenu nécessaire, pour assurer la disponibilité de la tranche de 400 MW, de procéder au renforcement de certaines structures internes du réacteur situées en partie supérieure du coeur.

Les dégradations pouvant survenir ne mettent pas en jeu la sûreté d'exploitation de l'installation mais sa disponibilité de production à terme. L'unité CHINON A3, couplée au réseau en 1966, totalise environ 90 000 heures de fonctionnement. Les plus gros composants, échangeurs de chaleur et circuit primaire, ont déjà été remplacés en 1969 et 1974. Une utilisation complémentaire de 40 à 50 000 heures est attendue de cette réparation qui a été décidée en 1982 compte tenu du bilan économique aux conditions de cette époque.

Le réacteur CHINON A3, de la filière uranium naturel modéré au graphite est refroidi au gaz carbonique sous pression à 25 bar. Il comporte un caisson en béton précontraint de forte épaisseur (4 à 7 mètres) relié par un circuit primaire externe aux échangeurs de chaleur. Le gaz circule de bas en haut dans le coeur constitué de 3 200 canaux chargés de 15 éléments et groupés en cellules de 33 canaux.

En partie supérieure du réacteur (à la température moyenne la plus élevée, 365°C) se trouve un ensemble de structures en acier doux supportant la thermométrie et les prélèvements d'analyse du gaz (800 tuyauteries). La tenue de ces assemblages boulonnés et soudés s'est dégradée du fait de l'oxydation des aciers doux par le gaz carbonique chaud (au-delà de 350°C).

LES CONTRAINTES D'OPERATION

Il s'agit donc de reconstituer, à distance, un squelette mécanique capable de reprendre des efforts de supportage et d'assurer le confinement des pièces existantes risquant de se désolidariser.

1 - Au premier plan des contraintes d'opération apparaît immédiatement l'hostilité constituée par la géométrie naturelle du milieu dans lequel doit avoir lieu l'intervention :

. taille réduite des accès possibles pour les outils et les pièces = puits verticaux de 24 cm de diamètre et de 7 mètres de long ; ils sont, par contre, nombreux à desservir une zone d'intervention donnée (aux sommets et au centre d'un réseau hexagonal de pas 1,3 mètre) ;

. masse des pièces à poser de l'ordre de 10 à 20 kilogrammes ;

. intervention jusqu'à des distances de l'axe vertical du robot de l'ordre de 2 mètres, soit à près de 12 mètres de l'extérieur ;

. cible des outils située dans des zones très encombrées et dont les positions sont imprécises à plusieurs centimètres près. C'est ce point qui constitue la difficulté majeure.

2 - Le déplacement des outils dans ce milieu ne doit pas donner lieu à des collisions susceptibles d'engendrer des détériorations des structures en place.

3 - Tout dysfonctionnement des outils doit être solutionné "à distance" par les moyens intrinsèques du robot ou à l'aide d'un outillage complémentaire. Nous verrons par la suite le poids de cette contrainte dans la mise au point des systèmes.

4 - Le volume des travaux constitue en lui-même un élément influençant la méthode retenue par le nombre important d'opérations élémentaires à effectuer et, par conséquent, la durée d'intervention. Quinze pièces de réparation sont en moyenne nécessaire à la réparation d'une structure. Quinze structures à réparer constituent une campagne qui conduit donc à la pose de plus de 200 pièces en réacteur (figure 3).

5 - L'agressivité de l'ambiance de travail est, par contre, relativement peu contraignante = air à la température maximale de 120°C et ambiance de rayonnement γ de l'ordre de 100 R/h.

6 - Le dimensionnement mécanique des pièces de réparation ne représente pas non plus une difficulté notable compte tenu des chargements modestes (quelques centaines de daN au plus) et des conditions de fonctionnement du réacteur.

LES OPTIONS RETENUES

Pour faire face aux contraintes d'opérations exposées précédemment, des options fondamentales concernant les méthodes et les outils ont été prises d'un commun accord entre le titulaire du marché (HISPANO-SUIZA) et E.D.F.

1 - Options générales d'opération

Il a été réalisé un examen préalable, le plus exhaustif possible, de l'ensemble des avaries pouvant survenir aux structures et des moyens pour y faire face. Toute méthode de réparation imaginée doit pouvoir être mise en oeuvre par les outils à concevoir. La morphologie générale du robot (bras articulé à 6 degrés de liberté associé à 2 degrés complémentaires) résulte de cet examen.

En l'absence d'adaptation d'outils existants, il n'est pas prévu de démontages systématiques de pièces existantes. La réparation consiste à substituer aux anciennes structures une chaîne de pièces adaptées cas par cas (mais pré-formées) pour le reprise des efforts et le confinement des pièces détériorées.

Compte tenu des multiples difficultés d'environnement et de la lenteur des procédés de télémanipulation sous surveillance visuelle lorsqu'on cherche une certaine précision la méthode globale de réparation choisie est la suivante :

- apprentissage préalable de toutes les tâches en maquette 1/1 avec des outils parfaitement identiques aux outils d'intervention,

- exécution des tâches (différée d'une durée quelconque) en mode robot autonome séquentiel contrôlé par opérateur disposant de grandeurs physiques caractéristiques (déplacements, forces,...),

- possibilité de reprise manuelle de la conduite en mode séquentiel ou télémanipulateur à tout moment,
- surveillance vidéo indépendante permanente.

Une organisation de la qualité d'ensemble de l'opération est mise en place. Un dossier de fin de réparation est associé à chaque opération.

2 - Options spécifiques ou technologiques (figure 4)

Les fonctions "porteur" et "outils" sont totalement séparées sur le plan des servitudes et des liaisons de contrôle-commande. Le porteur reste positionné de façon stable pendant toute l'opération de réparation et il est "alimenté" en tête-outils ou en pièces de réparation par des outils annexes indépendants. Une tête de préhension universelle assure la connexion porteur-outils de façon autonome.

Le mode d'assemblage des pièces retenu est le soudage des goujons par opposition aux modes mécaniques envisageables, pour des questions de rapidité d'exécution, notamment lorsque la pièce est positionnée (quelques secondes suffisent). Une redondance 2/1 de ces goujons (diamètre 12mm ou 8mm) permet d'espérer une sécurité d'assemblage suffisante. Aucun contrôle non destructif a postériori n'étant possible c'est un contrôle de bon déroulement de l'opération de soudage (intensité - tension - pénétration) qui permet de valider l'opération. Néanmoins un appareil de test de traction in situ peut être mis en oeuvre dans certains cas litigieux.

Les opérations de métrologie en réacteur et d'aide à la reconstitution conforme de la maquette dans les tolérances prévues sont réalisées avec un appareil reversible associé à un porteur normal pour s'affranchir au mieux des erreurs inhérentes à la flexibilité des outils ou à leur non-identité.

Pour disposer des informations nécessaires au suivi par les opérateurs en situation normale ou au diagnostic en situation incidentelle, il a été décidé d'équiper l'extrêmité du bras articulé, à l'interface avec les tête-outils, d'un capteur d'effort tri-dimensionnel interactif ainsi que de revêtir le corps du robot d'éléments sensibles aux contacts eux-mêmes interactifs.

Compte tenu des efforts mécaniques à développer et des encombrements disponibles, une technologie d'actionneurs à huile sous haute pression a été retenue.

LES OUTILS - CARACTERISTIQUES - PERFORMANCE

1 - Le "porteur" ISIS (figure 5)

Le robot possède 8 degrés de liberté, un diamètre hors tout de 0,22m. Il se compose d'un mât de 7,5 m avec mouvement linéaire (ascenseur) télescopique de 3,20 m et d'un système de bras articulés d'une longueur de 2,5 m. Son poids total est de 3,8 tonnes environ. Sa capacité est de 70 kg à 2,5 m de l'axe du mât et de 150 kg à 1 m de l'axe du mât.

Ces degrés de liberté sont les suivants (cf. figure) :

- rotation du mât - mouvements électriques
- ascenseur   mât - mouvements électriques

			pression
- coude bras 1	- bras 2 (185°)	)	270 b
- poignet bras 2	(370)°	)	165 b
- coude bras 2	- bras 3 (185°)	)	270 b
- poignet bras 3	(370°)	) Mouvements	165 b
- coude bras 4	- bras 5 (115°)	) hydrauliques	165 b
- poignet bras 5	(360°)	)	165 b

La position des différents degrés de liberté est mesurée par des résolvers. La précision de positionnement de l'extrêmité du robot est de l'ordre du 1/10ème de millimètre.

Le bras articulé est équipé, sur toute sa longueur, de peaux anti-collision entre robot et environnement et provoquant l'arrêt instantané de l'évolution.

En extrêmité du bras articulé se trouvent :

- un capteur d'effort permettant de mesurer le torseur des efforts exercés en extrêmité sur le robot,

- un interface universel permettant la connection d'une tête-outils.

Le robot est introduit en réacteur sans tête-outil à son extrêmité. C'est à l'intérieur du réacteur qu'il saisit (ou dépose) automatiquement la tête-outil nécessaire à l'opération en cours et qui lui est présentée par un puits de chargement voisin, au bout d'un serveur d'outils.

2 - Les têtes-outils

La connection entre le robot et une tête-outil est purement mécanique. La tête-outil est équipée d'un toron ombilical par lequel passent tous les fluides et les informations nécessaires à son bon fonctionnement. Ce toron ombilical emprunte le puits de chargement occupé par le serveur d'outils.

- tête de télémétrie-recopie :

Cette tête dans sa version télémétrie présente un télémètre vidéo à coïncidence d'images permettant de repérer facilement et rapidement la position dans l'espace de points caractéristiques de la structure à réparer. La même tête fonctionnant de façon réversible avec un laser de faible puissance permet la restitution, en différé, sur maquette, des points visés en réacteur en matérialisant directement le point visé à l'intersection de deux faisceaux laser. La précision globale de cette recopie, variable de 1/2 à quelques millimètres dans les cas courants est suffisante pour une bonne mise en conformité de la maquette d'apprentissage.

- <u>tête de préhension et de soudage des pièces de réparation</u> :

Cette tête permet de prendre et de poser les pièces de réparations en réacteur, par soudage électrique de goujons de diamètre 12 mm, avec pilotage informatique des différentes séquences du soudage et enregistrement des paramètres caractéristiques (I, U, pénétration).

- <u>tête de picotage</u> :

Cette tête permet d'aller décaper les zones oxydées sur lesquelles on vient souder en réacteur. Ce décapage se fait par picotage à l'aide d'un pistolet à aiguilles pneumatiques.

- <u>tête test</u> :

Cette tête permet, en cas d'échec du soudage détecté grâce aux enregistrements des paramètres caractéristiques, d'aller effectuer une traction sur les goujons avec un effort de 13 KN. En cas de résistance des goujons, la soudure est acceptée avec dérogation.

- <u>tête de vissage</u> :

Cette tête permet de visser, en position, certaines pièces de réparation très spécifiques, qui ne sont pas soudées avec le procédé habituel des goujons.

- <u>tête de grignotage</u> :

Cette tête permet, par grignotage, de couper certaines parties des structures réacteur existantes constituant des obstacles pour la pose des nouvelles pièces de réparation.

3 - <u>Les outils annexes - le chantier de réparation</u> (figures 4 et 5)

Pour présenter au porteur principal en réacteur les têtes-outils nécessaires puis les pièces de réparation des serveurs (porte-tête et porte-pièces) ont été conçus et sont installés sur des puits d'accès voisins du robot principal. Ils sont coordonnés au robot principal par le calculateur général.

Un (ou plusieurs) robot porte-caméra vidéo de surveillance autonome, à 6 degrés liberté et à trajectoires programmées pendant l'apprentissage, permet d'assurer une surveillance visuelle détaillée des phases de travail.

La mise en oeuvre d'une réparation nécessite donc l'utilisation simultanée de plusieurs outils :

. 2 robots principaux assurant les tâches majeures de dextérité,

. 2 robots de surveillance auxquel 1 "serveur" d'outils et 2 serveurs de pièces de réparation apportent leur concours à certains moments.

Quoiqu'un mode "télémanipulation" soit possible à tout moment, les opérations de réparation proprement dites se déroulent normalement en "automatique" sous surveillance vidéo.

Le scénario global d'une réparation est constitué des phases suivantes

1 - métrologie de la structure à réparer et de son environnement en réacteur (120 points environ) ;

2 - construction de la maquette de cette structure et de son environnement "conforme" par recopie des 120 points acquis ;

3 - apprentissage de tous les gestes de réparation : prises et pose des têtes- outils et des pièces de réparation adaptées, trajectoires et accostages ;

4 - exécution de la pose des pièces en mode automatique séquentiel sur-veillé.

Le déroulement des phases successives de la réparation d'une structure comporte tantôt le travail coordonné de deux robots pour les 5 premières pièces notamment, tantôt le travail d'un seul robot si aucun maintien des structures n'est nécessaire.

1 - Structure du contrôle-commande

L'ensemble du contrôle-commande est hiérarchisé autour d'une unité centrale qui joue le rôle de chef d'orchestre. Elle communique avec un ensemble d'unités locales, calculateurs décentralisés au niveau de chaque matériel (robots, têtes-outils, pantin, serveur d'outils et serveurs de pièces). L'unité centrale élabore les consignes de déplacement des robots et synchronise les actions des différents matériels. Les unités locales gèrent chaque matériel (séquences, alarmes, compte rendus à l'unité centrale). Elles communiquent avec le central par des liaisons série, mais jamais directement entre elles.

La gestion des logiciels est assurée par un opérateur multitâches multiprogrammation en temps réel (RMX 86).

L'unité centrale fait appel à des microprocesseurs 16 bits INTEL et dispose d'une mémoire vive de 640 Ko, une mémoire morte de 64 Ko ainsi qu'une mémoire masse de 40 Mo. Trois robots et sept unités locales (têtes ou serveurs) peuvent être connectés sur une unité centrale.

Les grandeurs d'états ou commande des actionneurs spécifiques des têtes-outils transistent de façon indépendante des grandeurs spécifiques du robot.

2 - Modes d'exploitation du robot

   a) - Mode "manuel"

      . A partir de la console dialogue il permet d'exécuter directe-
ment chaque mouvement élémentaire articulation par articulation ou des
déplacements linéaires ou angulaire programmés dans le référentiel de la
tête outil.

      . A partir d'un pantin homothétique à l'échelle $\frac{2}{5}$ (syntaxeur)
muni d'une sensation d'effort une commande de type maître-esclave permet de
générer les déplacements recherchés de la tête-outil par mouvements simul-
tanés de six degrés de liberté. Un système particulier permet d'annihiler,
à la demande, certains degrés de liberté.

      Ces modes d'exploitation sont utilisés en phase d'apprentissage
et éventuellement en secours sur incident d'exploitation en mode automatique.

      Une commande de secours permet d'agir au plus près sur les
actionneurs hydrauliques.

   b) - Modes "automatique" ou d'optimisation

      Le robot exécute toute trajectoire apprise et enregistrée
sur disquette. A ce type de fonctionnement peuvent être rattachées les
opérations d'assemblages de trajectoires déjà apprises ou de réalisation
automatique de retour d'un point de l'espace à un point voisin d'une
trajectoire ou même d'exécution de retour inverse d'une trajectoire donnée.

   c) - Mode "interactif" : accostage automatique séquentiel

      Toutes les phases d'opération "au contact" sont exécutées
avec la participation des palpeurs inductifs sensibles au déplacement ou du
capteur d'effort tri-dimensionnel d'extrêmité d'outil.

      Le déroulement de la succession des séquences d'approche
avec interaction des palpeurs est défini à l'apprentissage. Il peut s'agir
de déplacements sur distance ou angulaire, d'approches sur un point, une
arête ou un plan, d'approches avec intervention du capteur d'effort en
retour d'asservissement (équilibrage d'effort).

      Le conducteur dispose pendant toutes ces phases des informa-
tions de sécurité (positions, contacts, efforts) qu'il a programmées lors
de l'apprentissage.

      Le robot effectue donc de façon autonome l'adaptation de sa posi-
tion finale de travail à l'environnement réel rencontré.

LES ENSEIGNEMENTS DE L'EXPLOITATION

Après plus de 20 000 heures de fonctionnement des robots et la pose d'environ 70 pièces en réacteur le bilan suivant peut être dressé.

1 - La méthode globale apprentissage sur maquette avant exécution, longue et coûteuse, n'est pas à remettre en cause tant que des capteurs de perception d'environnement et un logiciel associé (certainement très complexe) n'existent pas ;

2 - L'intervention de robots en milieu hostile inaccessible et encombré implique un travail d'analyse des situations incidentelles et des actions de repli consécutives pratiquement aussi important que celui de la conception des fonctions normales. Il doit être entrepris en même temps. L'illustration de cette remarque nous a été apportée par la résolution (a postériori) du problème des pertes de sources motrices conduisant à l'affaissement naturel du bras articulé" (équilibrage mécanique impossible faute de place).

3 - La résolution de la quasi-totalité des problèmes d'exploitation rencontrés a été menée à bien grâce à l'adaptabilité des logiciels de l'informatique associée et à l'utilisation plus fine des capteurs externes: palpeurs et surtout capteur d'effort. Ce dernier, dont l'usage initial était plutôt orienté vers la protection et la commande manuelle intervient de plus en plus dans les modes automatiques. Il s'avère fondamental dans les phases d'accostage où il permet d'interpréter les situations de contact, voire d'encastrement.

4 - La phase de travail critique en durée est celle de l'apprentissage. C'est donc vers elle qu'il a fallu concentrer les efforts d'amélioration en perfectionnant l'organisation générale et les méthodes de création et d'enchaînement des trajectoires.

L'évolution ultime et nécessaire est le pré-apprentissage informatique par modélisation CAO 3D afin de n'avoir à réaliser que des adaptations mineures en maquette.

5 - Une opération d'une telle complexité a nécessité un important travail d'organisation de la qualité pour coordonner et gérer les multiples phases successives quelquefois espacées dans le temps. L'informatique utilisée a apporté un concours puissant à la résolution de ce problème.

6 - L'accent sur la qualité de certaines technologies d'apparences secondaires : connectique, raccords hydrauliques etc... doit être un souci dès la conception car les répercussions sur le fonctionnement sont très pénalisantes pour la disponibilité des outils.

7 - Dans l'état actuel de la robotique en milieu hostile l'obtention de la qualité habituelle de certains gestes simples de l'homme au travail est encore lointaine. Le conducteur de robot devant son écran doit découvrir totalement ce nouvel univers où les sensations n'existent qu'au travers de capteurs sensitifs inhabituels et purement intellectuels. C'est un métier nouveau, générateur d'une tension nerveuse liée à l'appréhension et à la réflexion permanente que nous avons découvert au début de la mise en oeuvre. L'homme s'est adapté à ce nouvel outil et en a tiré plus que ce pourquoi il avait été conçu. Il s'est, peu à peu, "décontracté" par assimilation des situations et confiance dans les performances de ses outils.

Les axes de recherches, pour le développement de ce type d'outillages, doivent porter sur les capteurs extéroceptifs, les logiciels d'aide à la conduite qui y sont associés et la clarté du dialogue homme-machine associé.

UNE EVOLUTION IMPORTANTE - L'APPRENTISSAGE CAO 3D

La phase d'apprentissage des grandes trajectoires en maquette s'avérant être de durée critique compte tenu de leur nombre (aller et retour de chacune des pièces) une adaptation de la méthode de génération mise au point par l'INRIA a été développée avec le concours de la Direction des Etudes et Recherches d'E.D.F.

Elle consiste à modéliser l'environnement grâce à un logiciel CAO 3D hiérarchisé très souple disposant d'un catalogue d'objets suffisant. Le robot est modélisé de la même façon.

Un logiciel spécifique génère ensuite de façon autonome, sous contrôle de l'opérateur, la trajectoire optimale ; exempte de collision qui est conservée sur disquette et qui servira de base à la mise au point en maquette.

La génération de l'environnement d'une structure demande environ quinze heures, celle de la trajectoire quelques heures. Les trajectoires réelles ainsi réalisées sont de durée trois fois plus courtes que celles réalisées manuellement et leur élaboration se situe en temps masqué. Le système est actuellement opérationnel.

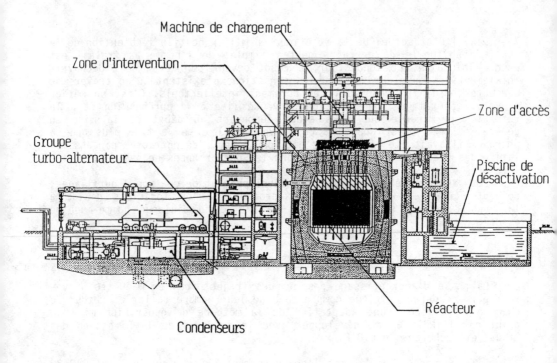

Machine de chargement

Zone d'intervention

Zone d'accès

Groupe
turbo-alternateur

Piscine de
désactivation

Condenseurs

Réacteur

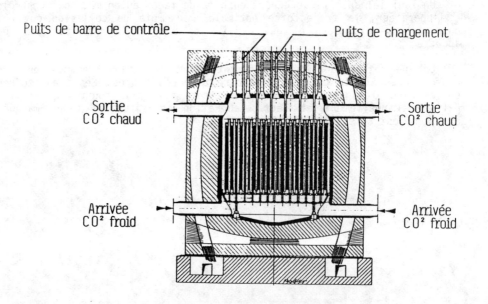

Puits de barre de contrôle

Puits de chargement

Sortie
CO_2 chaud

Sortie
CO_2 chaud

Arrivée
CO_2 froid

Arrivée
CO_2 froid

Figure 1 – Coupes de la tranche et du caisson **CHINON A3**

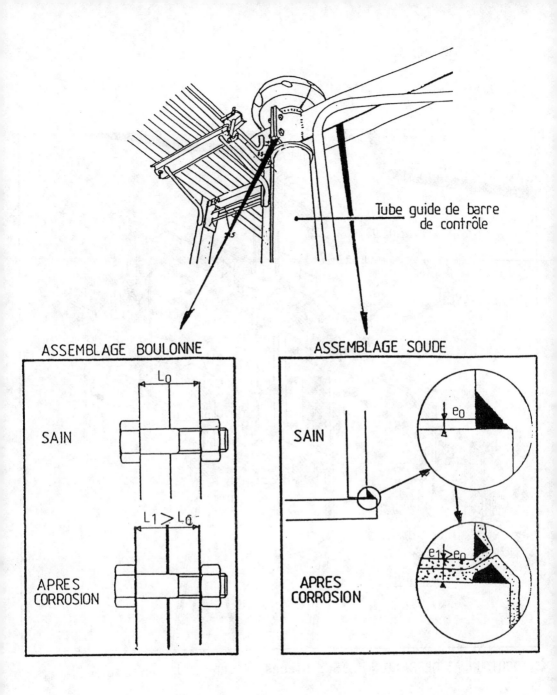

Tube guide de barre
de contrôle

ASSEMBLAGE BOULONNE

SAIN

L_0

APRES
CORROSION

$L_1 > L_0$

ASSEMBLAGE SOUDE

SAIN

e_0

APRES
CORROSION

$e_1 > e_0$

CHINON A 3
Corrosion des aciers non calmés par le CO_2

Figure 2

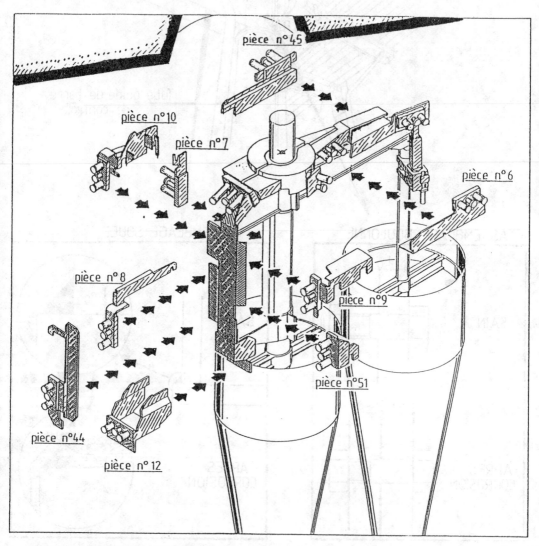

pièce n°45

pièce n°10

pièce n°7

pièce n°6

pièce n°8

pièce n°9

pièce n°51

pièce n°44

pièce n°12

CHINON A3 OPERATION ISIS : pièces de réparation – Figure 3

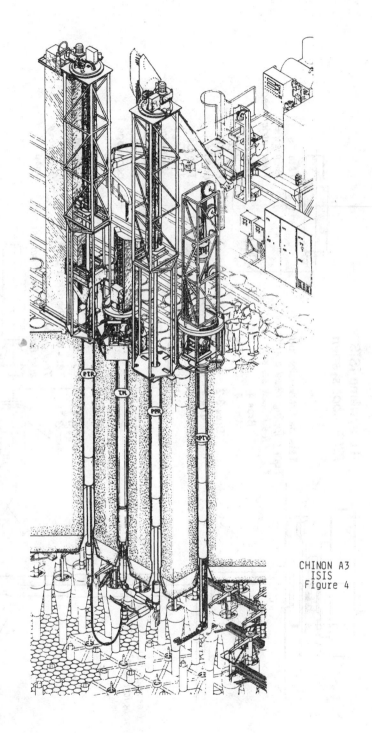

CHINON A3
ISIS
Figure 4

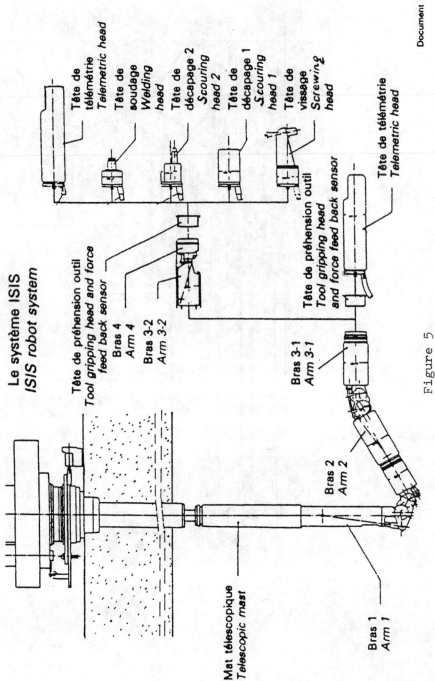

Le système ISIS
ISIS robot system

Tête de télémétrie
Telemetric head

Tête de soudage
Welding head

Tête de décapage 2
Scouring head 2

Tête de décapage 1
Scouring head 1

Tête de vissage
Screwing head

Tête de préhension outil
Tool gripping head and force feed back sensor

Bras 4
Arm 4

Bras 3-2
Arm 3-2

Tête de préhension outil
Tool gripping head and force feed back sensor

Tête de télémétrie
Telemetric head

Bras 3-1
Arm 3-1

Bras 2
Arm 2

Bras 1
Arm 1

Mat télescopique
Telescopic mast

Figure 5

REPLACEMENT OF STEAM GENERATORS AND RECIRCULATION PIPES IN LWR's AS LONGLASTING MEASURES TO EXTEND PLANT LIFETIME

G. Eckert
Kraftwerk Union Aktiengesellschaft
Offenbach, Federal Republic of Germany

ABSTRACT

Various types of corrosion attack led to severe operational impacts and availability losses at most LWR power plants after only a few years of their planned lifetime.

Several instant and also medium and long-term measures have recently been developed and implemented to ensure continued operation and prolong the lifetime of the by far most troublesome components, such as steam generators for PWRs and recirculation pipes for BWRs.

Since considerable experience is available in the use of steel grades which can resist such corrosion attack, and proven designs exist together with suitable installation methods, it would seem likely that power plant operators may plan to replace such components rather than perform repeated repairs during annual inspection or adopt questionable methods to ensure continued component operation.

The steel grades AISI 347 and INCOLOY 800 were used without corrosion problems in German BWRs and steam generator tubes of PWRs for more than 14 years. They have now been supplemented on the international market by the newly-developed grades 316 NG and INCONEL 690 to provide a greater variety.

The world-wide nuclear industry meanwhile has gained a fair amount of experience in handling large component replacement jobs in nuclear power plants under the associated special conditions such as :

- restricted working area and transport conditions,
- radiation exposure.

A large number of methods and remote-controlled special tools have been developed and proved to handle these jobs well while offering attractive low radiation exposure and short plant outage time.

For instance, with remote-controlled cutting devices and the so-called narrow gap welding device KWU has handled certain international replacement projects for steam generator and recirculation pipe replacement with plant outage times of as low as two months and radiation exposure in a 14-year old BWR as low as 800 manrems.

LE REMPLACEMENT DES GENERATEURS DE VAPEUR ET DES TUYAUTERIES DE RECIRCULATION SUR LES REACTEURS A EAU ORDINAIRE : MESURES A LONG TERME POUR PROLONGER LA DUREE DE VIE DES CENTRALES NUCLEAIRES

RESUME

Des attaques de corrosion de différents types ont eu des conséquences graves pour l''exploitation et occasionné de sérieuses pertes de disponibilité sur la plupart des centrales nucléaires équipées de réacteurs à eau ordinaire après quelques années de service seulement.

Plusieurs mesures immédiates, mais aussi à moyen et à long terme ont été récemment élaborées et mises en oeuvre pour poursuivre l'exploitation et prolonger la durée de vie des composants de loin les plus pénalisants pour l'exploitation comme les générateurs de vapeur sur les réacteurs à eau sous pression et les tuyauteries de recirculation sur les réacteurs à eau bouillante.

Etant donné que l'on dispose d'une très grande expérience d'utilisation de nuances d'acier capables de résister à de telles attaques de corrosion, de modèles éprouvés de composants et de méthodes d'installation appropriés, il est permis de penser que les exploitants de centrales nucléaires pourraient programmer le remplacement de ces composants plutôt que de procéder à des réparations à répétition au cours des inspections annuelles et d'utiliser des méthodes discutables pour maintenir les composants en service.

Les nuances d'acier AISI 347 et INCOLOY 800 sont utilisées en Allemagne sur les réacteurs à eau bouillante et pour les tubes des générateurs de vapeur des réacteurs à eau sous pression depuis plus de 14 ans sans connaître de problèmes de corrosion. Aujourd'hui, on trouve sur le marché international les nouvelles nuances 316NG et INCONEL690 qui élargissent le choix des matériaux disponibles.

Entre-temps, l'industrie nucléaire mondiale a acquis une expérience relativement importante pour les opérations de remplacement des gros composants de centrales nucléaires dans les conditions de travail spéciales suivantes :

- restrictions concernant les zones de travail et les conditions de transport,
- radio-exposition.

Toute une gamme de méthodes et d'outils spéciaux télécommandés ont été mis au point et on a démontré qu'ils permettaient de mener à bien ces opérations pour une faible radio-exposition et une brève durée d'arrêt de la centrale.

C'est ainsi, par exemple, qu'à l'aide de dispositifs de découpage télécommandés et de l'appareillage de soudage à chanfreins très étroits, KWU a réalisé certains projets internationaux de remplacement de générateurs de vapeur et de tuyauteries de recirculation en limitant la durée d'arrêt de la centrale à deux mois et la dose globale d'intervention à 800 hommes-rems dans un ancien réacteur à eau bouillante de 14 ans.

1. Introduction

The nuclear power plants' lifetime was planned by the technicians
to be 40 years. Under economic aspects most utilities counted 25
years as a minimum period to keep nuclear power plants in service.

Present utility plans for various reasons ask for technical measures to prolong lifetime of wear components. They aim at plant
operation beyond 40, at least 25 years.

In practice, however, many utilities must decide investment in
component life extension far earlier than after 15 years, in some
cases even earlier than 10 years of plant operation.

They make experience that major components are worn earlier than
predicted. Beside others, the most spectactular trouble-causing
components are steam generators for PWRs and the recirculation
piping for BWRs. In both cases the supply industry offers a variety of repair methods to keep the components running.

As it is primarily corrosion attack, cognizant engineers will confirm that predicted results of countermeasures are accompanied by
a quite bit of speculation as long as the defect-causing status is
not changed basically.

For a long-term promise it is mostly to exchange components completely, once they are identified to be weakened by intergranular
stress corrosion cracking (IGSCC).

However, I show understanding for utilities that are reluctant to
decide for the latter way and postpone the component exchange for
as long as possible, as it is a spectacular one-piece investment
with no guarantee that a new component, even with a proper design,
will last for the remaining plant lifetime. In that situation it
looks to be a good policy:

The longer you wait, the smaller is the risk that a new component
will fail again, perhaps even for some other reason of which you
are not yet aware.

This policy is acceptable as long as cost benefit calculations do not show better economics for the big splash instead of annual and inservice repairs with limited success. However, these calculations must compare, beside the actual repair costs, economical numbers for:

- plant outage costs

- prospective duration of repair success upon experience

- intermediate inspection costs

- experts' and licencing costs

- utilities' staff costs.

It may be worthwhile to pay attention to recent replacement activities in both problematic areas:

- steam generator replacement for PWRs

- recirculation piping replacement for BWRs

Technical information and working results show promising data and should be taken into account during any decision-making phase within a utililty, once a severe problem in either of the two areas has arisen.

It is my aim to present to the auditorium within my paper such information.

2. Steam Generator Replacement in PWRs

2.1 Replacement Steam Generators

Design Features to Minimize Corrosion

KWU presently has a total of 40 U-tube steam generators in operation which are essentially designed and manufactured in accordance with present KWU standards employing INCOLOY 800 tube materials. INCOLOY 800 tubing has been tested and shown to be highly corrosion-resistant (see Figure 1). Adoption of this tube material together with design improvements, as applied to these steam generators, has yielded an excellent reliability record:

- U-bend stress corrosion cracking has not occurred on the INCOLOY 800 tubing.

- Tube denting has been avoided by utilizing austenitic strip spacers which form an open grid with only linear contact to the tubes.

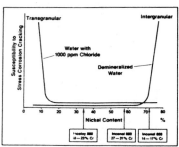

Fig.1 — Stress Corrosion Cracking in
660°F (350°C) Water.

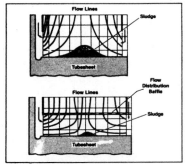

Fig. 2 — Flow Distribution and Sludge Deposits
in Hot Leg with and without Baffle.

- Tube wastage normally takes place at the tubesheet after
  corrosion products have formed sludge build-up. On top of
  a sludge pile a dry-wet zone appears with concentrated impurities. Avoiding sludge build- up would eliminate the problem.
  The design feature which has been adopted is a flow distribution baffle to minimize local tubesheet regions of low
  velocity flow where sludge typically would deposit (see
  Figure 2).

- Intergranular cracking in the tubesheet region has been eliminated by the material characteristics of INCOLOY 800 tubing.

Experience with Present Design

Experience has been gained since 1972 with the present steam generator design concept employing INCOLOY 800 tubing. The 662 MWe
Stade power plant has accumulated more than 90,000 service hours
with only one isolated tube leakage in 1980 which was attributed
to wastage at the hot side of the U-tube on top of the tubesheet.

The experience with all 40 steam generators of present design,
reveals only 0.4 percent tube failure in total. After 320 cumulative operating years inspection of these steam generators did not
reveal any indication of intergranular cracking from the inner
tube diameter, crevice corrosion or denting.

Conclusion

Controlling corrosion in steam generators is one of the greatest
concerns of the utility industry in trying to improve plant reliability. With the described steam generator design, corrosion-
assisted problems have been greatly eliminated. In addition, KWU
has gained extensive experience in the fabrication, start-up and
inservice inspection of total plants, or portions of them. This
overall experience has been utilized to achieve the outstanding
record of KWU pressurized nuclear power plants availability factor as illustrated in Figure 3.

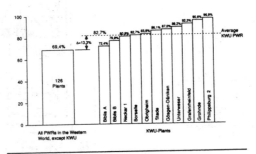

PWR Nuclear Power Plants in the Western World
Cumulative Time Availability Factors from Commercial Operation
up to December 1985   Fig. 3

2.2 Steam Generator Replacement

.2.2.1 The 345 MWe Obrigheim SG Replacement

Introduction

The two SGs of the 345 MWe Obrigheim power plant were built
in accordance with now obsolete design standards specifying
INCONEL 600 tubing. The plant went into operation in 1968.
After about 15 years of operation the stress corrosion problems
increased to a level that about 12 percent of the SG tubes had
to be plugged.

Project Planning

In mid 1982, it was decided to replace the two steam generators
during the next planned refueling in the summer of 1983. KWU was
responsible for the entire replacement project. A project team
was formed to schedule and manage the steam generator replacement.
Even though most of the actual site work was performed by KWU personnel, the administration and supervision of work performed by
subcontractors was also part of the replacement package. The reactor refueling and steam generator replacement schedule reveals 13
major steps from plant shut-down to restart. The actual schedule,
shown in Figure 4, indicates that from opening of the reactor vessel to the inspection of the vessel after the steam generator replacement, a period from June 6 to August 17, elapsed, which
amounts to a replacement time of 10 weeks. Even though there was
some delay in restarting the plant, the total refueling shut-down
took only 15 weeks from plant shut-down to restart up to full-
load operation.

Site Work

Since 1976 the new steam generators were stored at the site. It
was required to transport these 350,000 lb generators by flatbed
truck to the equipment hatch of the reactor building.

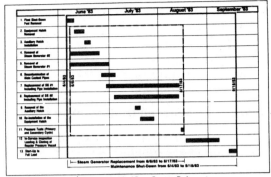

Fig. 4 – Actual Schedule of Steam Generator Replacement.

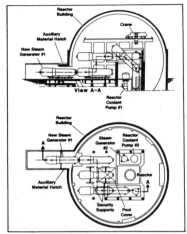

Fig. 5 – **Transportation of Completely Assembled Steam Generator #1 within the Reactor Building.**

The authorities demanded building an auxiliary hatch large enough to house an entire steam generator. The old, as well as the new steam generators were replaced in a fully assembled condition. A storage building was constructed for the two old steam generators. The transportation of the steam generator within the reactor building was even more difficult because lifting and tilting was involved, as shown in Figure 5. In addition, the steam generator No. 1 had to be moved over the fuel pool, requiring special security supports. For easy maneuvering of the steam generators, a special transportation clamping device with trunnions was mounted onto the steam generator shells near the center of gravity to minimize tilting forces.

Replacing the steam generators also involved pipe cutting, modification and field welding. To improve the new SG installation conditions and because the dimensions of the new SGs are slightly different, the existing pipe connections, such as those of the reactor coolant inlet and outlet, as well as the feedwater and main steam piping were cut out and replaced by new modified pipe sections. The old SG nozzles were closed by weldcaps to minimize contamination during transportation and storage into the newly constructed storage building. The new SGs were connected to the piping utilizing prefabricated pipe sections with two field weld connections. With the slightly larger overall dimensions of the two new 525 MWth steam generators, the heat transfer area could be increased by almost 10 percent. The overall thermal performance of the new steam generators has proven to be better, even though the INCOLOY 800 material has a smaller heat transfer coefficient than the old INCOLOY 600 tubing.

Decontamination of the remaining reactor coolant piping was necessary to reduce radiation levels at the open pipe ends. Electro-
polishing was used on the inner wall surfaces. Shielding plugs
were installed to minimize exposure from the reactor vessel and
coolant pumps. In addition, thermal plugs were utilized to avoid
contaminated airflow out of the piping during welding and heat
treatment procedures. A decontamination factor of 200 and more
was achieved. For example, the original radiation in the pump
elbow was 13 Rem/h and after the decontamination this level was
reduced to 0.05 Rem/h.

2.2.2 The Planning of 350 MWe Beznau (Switzerland) SG Replacement

The 350 MWe two-loop Beznau-1 power station went into operation
in 1969. KWU was asked in 1985 to plan the exchange of the lower
section of the steam generators.

The utility wanted to have all work prepared for an exchange of
the stored new components starting within only 3 months after
decision-making.

The typical standard concept which will be used in the case of
an exchange is based on the Obrigheim experience as well as on the
experience of large pipe exchange activities in BWRs, I will address to later on (Chapter 3)

Some Beznau-specific items must be taken care of. They are:

- Cutting and closing the reactor building wall for transport
  reasons of the components.

- Cutting and welding of steam generator vessels at site.

The scheduled outage time for the replacement will be as short as
11 weeks only.

3. Replacement of Recirculation Piping in BWRs

3.1 How to Avoid Intergranular Stress Corrosion Cracking

Intergranular Stress Corrosion Cracking in Recirculation Piping

During non-destructive examination of General Electric-designed
reactors, material defects were particularly found in the recirculation piping which had been caused by intergranular stress
corrosion cracking (IGSCC).

The defects start on the pipe inside surface in the heat-affected
zone of welds. Unless repairs are carried out or the recirculation
piping is replaced in whole or in part, leakages are bound to
occur.

The cause of the defects is possible sensitization of the heat-affected zone of welds, i.e. chromium-depleted grain boundaries in the unstabilized types of 304 and 316 steel, used in conjunction with stress and the corrosive action of the special BWR coolant which has a high oxygen content.

Low carbon 316 NG steel has to date been selected for replacement piping.

With one exception, KWU BWR plants do not have recirculation piping. Instead, recirculation pumps are installed inside the reactor pressure vessel. However, in all other austenitic piping systems KWU used X10CRNiNb189 stabilized austenitic steel (AISI 347 NG).

The advantages of this material, which has been successfully used for many years, are its high toughness, its resistance to IGSSC in media having a high oxygen content and its easy processing under the specific manufacturing conditions. Leakages due to IGSCC never have been identified.

Recirculation Pipe Exchange by Using IGSCC-Resistant Material

KWU has used stainless steel type 347 NG (following a restricted KWU specification) for 15 years in primary pipes for its operating BWRs without any indication of IGSCC.

316 NG, a recently developed stainless steel, also showed promising resistance to IGSCC, but has not yet been proven for such a long period under operating conditions of BWRs. However, KWU has shown the capability to handle both types of material.

We have done primary pipe replacement in KWU BWRs (ferritic steel) and recirculation piping replacement in GE BWRs using also 316 NG (see Figure 6).

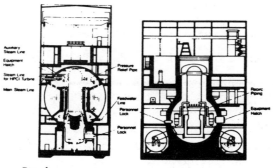

Fig. 6

KWU product-line 69   GE BWR-Mark 1

3.2 Replacement of Recirculation Piping in Santa Maria de Garona (Spain) and Mühleberg (Switzerland)

Introduction

The 440 MW NPP Santa Maria de Garona (Spain) went into operation in 1971. The 320 MW NPP Mühleberg (Switzerland) did so in 1972. Both are BWRs of the GE Mark-1 type with 2 external recirculation loops each.

The stainless steel material AISI-304 suffered from several IGSCC cracks and numerous ultrasonic indications. In 1984 and 1985 respectively, both utilities decided to replace the recirculation piping or at least major parts of it (Table 1).

Both utilities chose KWU as main contractor to do the replacement under turnkey responsibility employing national companies such as Nervion, Spain, and Sulzer AG, Switzerland, as subcontractors.

More details, especially about the Santa Maria de Garona replacement, from the utility's point of view will be presented to you by Sr. Olaso, who was the leading engineer bearing overall responsibility at the utility's site.

Project Planning And Replacement at Site

There is a concept in common for large replacement activities in NPPs which we have used successfully for any pipe replacement (Table 1) as well as for steam generator replacement.

Table 1

Scope of pipe replacement work in BWRs performed by KWU

Power plant	Pipe diameter /inches/	Pipe lengths /feet/	No. of elbows, bends, fittings	No. of welds	Dismantling time /weeks/	Erection time /weeks/	Radiation in working area/mrem/hr/
Philippsburg	3 - 4 [1)]	108	11	37	2	34	5
	8 - 22	719	101	236 [2)]			
Isar	3 - 4 [1)]	328	17	54	2.5	32	40
	8 - 22	961	83	141 [2)]			
Brunsbüttel	3 - 4 [1)]	541	62	16	3	32	40
	8 - 22	636	154	222 [2)]			
Würgassen	3 - 4 [1)]	460			3	33	50
	8 - 22	1378		275			
Santa Maria de Garona	18 - 24	85	14	26 [4)] (19) [5)]		10 [3)]	50 - 200
Mühleberg	3 - 6	72	6	10 [4)]	5	8	25 - 400
	8 - 18	295	28	48 [4)]			

1) Owing to the extensive replacement of large piping, between 5.000 and 10.000 ft of piping smaller than 2" in diameter had to be replaced in each plant
2) Including 20 welds using automatic welding equipment
3) Owing to partial system replacement, erection activities were performed in parallel with dismantling
4) Welds performed using automatic welding equipment
5) Overlay welds

This concept has been made up of the following steps:

- Feasibility study prior to preplanning and calculation of cost of the backfitting measure (which can be ordered separately from the backfitting measure itself).

- Detailed preplanning and calculation of cost with emphasis on following as far as possible the customer's request for fixed prices (our experience is that only unquantifiable items arising on site - such as concerning radiation levels or unknown space requirements - should be offered on a time-and-material basis using standard prices).

- Assembly of an engineering team to work out detailed job procedures for any engineer and shift member in advance, including alternative procedures in case of changing situation amd quality assurance.

- Representation of the entire activity in a manpower chart with a time schedule based on daily work.

- Preplanning of any mechanized activity such as remote-controlled cutting and welding to determine the optimum quantity of requisite equipment.

- Designing and manufacture of special tools, shielding and mockups for personnel training.

- Training of all cutters and welders on full-scale mockups.

- Formation of an on-site team to manage the activity at the plant in close cooperation with the customer's staff which is especially important for decision-making in unforeseen circumstances.

- Employment and supervision of national or regional pipe constructing companies.

- Usage of almost the same standard remote-controlled tools as shown in Fig. 7, Fig. 8, Fig. 9.

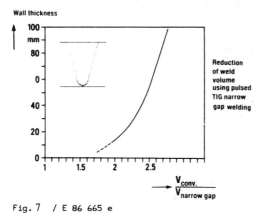

Wall thickness

Reduction of weld volume using pulsed TIG narrow gap welding

$\dfrac{V_{conv.}}{V_{narrow\ gap}}$

Fig. 7 / E 86 665 e

Narrow-gap welding

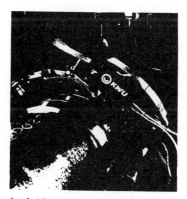

Fig. 8 / E 86 666 Ce

Gas tungsten arc narrow-gap orbital welding machine

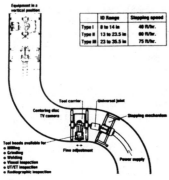

Fig. 9 / E 86 667 e

Remote controlled in-pipe multiple-task
manipulator

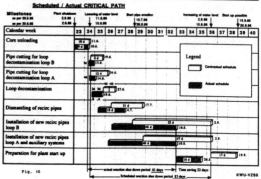

Muehleberg Recirculation Pipe Replacement
General Time Schedule

Fig. 10

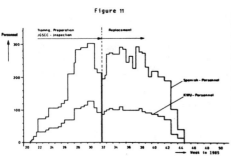

Figure 11

KWU-Manpower Chart for Workscope on Site
Santa Maria de Garona

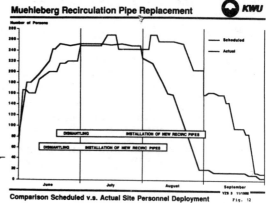

Muehleberg Recirculation Pipe Replacement

Comparison Scheduled v.s. Actual Site Personnel Deployment
Fig. 12

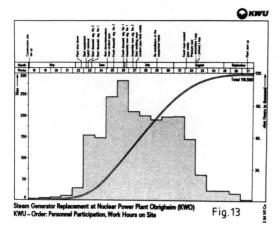

Steam Generator Replacement at Nuclear Power Plant Obrigheim (KWO)
KWU – Order: Personnel Participation, Work Hours on Site
Fig. 13

	Nominal	Actual
Santa Maria de Garona	720	575
Mühleberg	675	810

Table 2 – Accumulated Dose Rates Recirculation Piping
Replacement (manrem)

4. Conclusions to Be Drawn of for Future Steam Generator and Recirculation Piping Replacement Activities

Presently there are two philosophies to cure operating problems with steam generators or recirculation piping respectively, in LWRs as I already mentioned in my introduction. The component exchange has to be compared both on a technical and economical basis with a couple of measures which are used in total or selectively:

Steam Generator Problems

For technical and economical reasons the component replacement has to be compared with alternatives such as:

- Shot peening of heat tubes
- Plugging of heat tubes
- Sleeving of heat tubes
- Sludge lancing at tube sheet
- Chemical cleaning
- Annual inspection and non-destructive testing

For comparison of SG replacement with those repair methods or preventive measures including inevitable annual inspections on a technical and economical basis, the utility may count on:

- Heat tube material and design features available for steam generators with 15 years' secured operation and only 0.4 percent tubes plugged of some 150,000 which are in operation.

- Exchange of steam generators for 2-loop plants in 2.5 months. (Fig. 4)

- Partial SG replacement (lower section) and cutting transport hole into reactor building walls in practically the same outage period (2.5 months).

- ca. 45,000 manhours for the total planning of SG exchange. (2-loop plant)

- ca. 140,000 manhours for the total execution of work at site. (2-loop plant) (Fig. 13)

- ca. 700 manrem applicable total dose rate for SG exchange in a 2-loop nuclear power plant.

Recirculation Piping Replacement

Alternative measures to recirculation piping exchange are:

- Hydrogen injection into the reactor coolant water
- Overlay cladding of welds
- Annual non-destructive testing of welds
- Installation of on-line monitoring crack growth devices.

These measures have to be compared under technical and economical aspects by a decision-making utility with the reliable working results of both replacement jobs in Santa Maria de Garona and Mühleberg and the successful operating experience with stabilized stainless steel under the corrosion-activating typical BWR coolant ambient.

For comparison of partial or total recirculation piping replacement with state-of-the-art repair methods or preventive measures including inevitable annual inspections on an economical and technical basis, the utility may count on:

- Pipe material available with 15 years' secured operation without IGSCC under the typical corrosion-activating BWR coolant conditions.

- Exchange of 2 recirculation loops and 6 risers in 2.5 months (extended partial pipe replacement may be less attractive under the aspect of outage time). (Fig. 10)

- About 50,000 manhours necessary to preplan and to do all detailed planning for the replacement.

- 220,000 to 380,000 manhours necessary including training to execute the site activities. (Figures 11 and 12)

- 500 to 800 manrem applicable total dose rate by using remote-controlled tools at site. (Table 2)

Utilities Maintenance and Operating Philosophy and Plant Availability

For the nuclear power stations of Santa Maria de Garona as well as Obrigheim and Mühleberg the utilities decided to perform the large replacement projects in accordance with their operating and maintenance philosophy which led to an extraordinary successful operation record for this first generation of commercially operating plants. Their availability records show the benefit of a long-term investment policy.

The cumulative time availability factors - counting the period between the first commercial operation and ending December 1986 - range between 70 percent and 89 percent which are outstanding results. With their today's investment they aim at the next 25 years of successful operation.

PROLONGATION DE LA DUREE DE VIE DES GENERATEURS DE VAPEUR DE FRAMATOME

A. Remond
FRAMATOME, France

RESUME

1.   La ligne de produit "Générateur de Vapeur" FRAMATOME

Depuis 1975, FRAMATOME a developpé une importante ligne de produit
"Générateur de Vapeur" pour l'équipement des centrales neuves et, plus récemment pour le remplacement d'appareils.

Les premières améliorations ont été appliquées au modèle 68/19
(1 050 MWth, équipant les centrales "4 boucles" du palier français de
1 350 MWe comme Paluel). Les mêmes améliorations sont appliquées ensuite au
modèle 51B (950 MWth, équipant les centrales "3 boucles" du palier français
900 MWe) et au modèle 55/19 (1 000 MWth, équipant les centrales "Export",
comme Daya Bay en Chine Populaire). Plus récemment, FRAMATOME a créé le modèle
73/19 (avec économiseur axial à mélange, 1 100 MWth, pour le nouveau palier
"4 boucles" de 1 450 MWe comme Chooz B), et, dernièrement, différents modèles
de "remplacement" pour le marché français et étranger.

Les améliorations de conception, des matériaux et de fabrication seront
présentées.

2.   Extension de la durée de vie des Générateurs de Vapeurs

En présence de corrosion primaire ou secondaire des tubes du faisceau
tubulaire, et après plusieurs années de surveillance en exploitation et
l'application de solutions préventives, le choix ultime s'impose entre plusieurs méthodes de réparation et le remplacement. Ces différentes méthodes de
réparation (shotpeening ou rotopeening, traitement thermique local, nickelage
électrolytique, bouchon fixé mécaniquement ou par soudage) permettent de prolonger la vue du Générateur de Vapeur. La combinaison de plusieurs solutions
est possible mais il est très difficile de prédire de la durée de prolongation.

La décision d'une opération de remplacement doit être prise 3 ou 4 ans
avant l'opération elle-même, afin de concevoir et fabriquer les appareils et
préparer le site.

3.   Les Générateurs de Vapeur de "remplacement" FRAMATOME

Le remplacement d'un Générateur de Vapeur est l'occasion d'intégrer des
innovations permettant l'amélioration de la souplesse d'exploitation et de la
sûreté de la centrale. La première étape est la définition des :

    - points de fonctionnement (puissance thermique, surface d'échange,
       transitoires),

- dimensionnement du nouvel appareil,
- améliorations de conception facilitant l'opération de remplacement.

Cette étape nécessite la vérification des autorisations de fonctionnement tels que transitoires de fonctionnement, conception du bâtiment réacteur, comportement en situations accidentelles...

La dernière étape est le choix des matériaux, procédés de fabrication (pièces forgées plutôt que laminées), critères d'inspection en service...

L'auteur présente un panorama des modèles conçues pour les besoins du parc français ou étranger.

FRAMATOME STEAM GENERATOR UNITS FOR PLANT LIFE EXTENSION

ABSTRACT

1.-FRENCH SG's product line.
From 1975 up to now,FRAMATOME has developped a large SGs product line for new plants and, more recently, for replacement units.
All these equipments benefit from a continuous effort in design, materials and manufacturing areas, to improve the reliability, operation flexibility and especially tube bundle resistance.
First design and research effort was applied to 68/19 model(1050 MWth type, used in 4 loops 1350 MWe plant such as PALUEL plants).Improvements were backfitted on 51B model (950 MWth type used in 3 loops 950 MWe French plants and on 55/19 model (1000 MWth type used in 3 loops 1000 MWe plant such as Chinese Daya Bay nuclear Units). More recently FRA has designed the 73/19E model (with axial mixing preheater, 1100 MWth type for new 4 loops 1450 MWth plant such as CHOOZ B) and finally, different replacement models destined to foreign and domestic market.
Design, materials and manufacturing features will be presented.

2.-SGs life extension.
In case of tube bundle corrosion on primary or secondary side of the tube, and after some years of difficult operation with many inspection and plugging, the main choice appears between some various repair methods and the replacement operation. A short list of repair methods(shot peening or roto peening, local heat treatment, nickel electrolytic coating, mechanical or welded sleeving) gives many possibilities to extend SG units life. A combination of various repair methods is possible and the total life time extension is very difficult to predict. A replacement operation requires a decision to be taken 3 or 4 years before the replacement operation itself, for designing and manufacturing the units and for on site work preparation.

3.-FRAMATOME SGs replacement units.
A replacement unit permits to include features which improve performance, flexibility and reliability of the plant. First step is the definition of:
* functional requirements(thermal power,heat transfer area margin, transients capacity,
* overall dimensions of the new unit,
* design features which facilitate the replacement process. This step needs the verification of licensing issues such as operating transients, reactor building design, acceptable behaviour in faulted conditions....
Last step is the choice of materials, manufacturing process(forgings versus plates, inservice inspection features...

The author will present a general view of replacement units designed for French or foreign needs.

1.-INTRODUCTION

Quelle que soit la filière nucléaire considérée, le générateur de vapeur (GV) constitue un maillon sensible de la chaine de production d'énergie, tout spécialement pour les unités modernes de très forte puissance unitaire et fonctionnant à température élevée. Dans la filière à eau pressurisée (REP en français, PWR en anglais), le générateur de vapeur (GV) se caractérise par une haute puissance volumique (12 MW/m³),ce qui correspond à un avantage économique déterminant pour l'investissement initial, mais dont on trouve la contre partie dans la complexité de conception pour extraire dans des conditions fiables cette forte densité de puissance, pour éviter les problèmes de vibrations, d'assèchement localisé, de fatigue et chocs thermiques etc.... Il est maintenant bien connu que le générateur de vapeur REP est au premier chef menacé par des phénomènes multiples de corrosion tant par le fluide primaire que par le fluide secondaire, et comme le petit tube d'échange utilisé, épais de 1mm seulement,constitue 70 à 80% de la surface de la " seconde barrière de confinement " il n'est pas besoin d'insister davantage sur le souci constant de conception, fabrication, surveillance en exploitation qu'apporte le faisceau tubulaire du GV. La durée de vie d'une tranche nucléaire REP se trouve donc inévitablement associée au sort du générateur de vapeur, d'abord pour fiabiliser son fonctionnement et protéger sa santé, puis pour l'améliorer ou le réparer, enfin au stade ultime pour le remplacer en cas de nécessité. C'est précisément cette chaine d'expertise et de suivi que nous décrirons ici.

2.- LA LIGNE DE PRODUIT "GENERATEUR DE VAPEUR " DE FRAMATOME.

Avec 182 unités construites et 32 en cours de construction appartenant à 5 modèles de GV différents, avec plusieurs nouveaux modèles en avant-projet et projet, FRAMATOME bénéficie d'une très large expérience de conception, fabrication et règles d'exploitation des générateurs de vapeur a recirculation naturelle. La ligne de produit FRAMATOME présente depuis 1970 une continuité complète permettant d'assurer une parfaite maîtrise des problèmes posés, et de faire bénéficier les modèles les plus récents de toute la recherche, de l'amélioration continue des matériaux et procédés de fabrication, et du retour d'expérience des unités en fonctionnement, grâce à notre étroite collaboration avec Electricité de France. L'effort se poursuit non seulement pour améliorer encore la conception et la fabrication des nouvelles unités mais aussi pour développer et appliquer différentes techniques permettant d'allonger la durée de vie et de réparer les appareils en exploitation.

2.1.- Les différents modèles de la ligne GV de FRAMATOME (Tableau 1)

Issus d'une technologie sous licence américaine,les modèles de GV FRAMATOME ont adopté une conception propre à la fin de 1976, date de début de réalisation du palier " 4 boucles " français de 1350 MWe.
Le développement d'un modèle bouilleur de grandes dimensions (68/19) a été décidé en remplacement du modèle à préchauffeur croisé utilisé dans la centrale de référence américaine; puis les modifications étudiées à cette occasion ont été appliquées au modèle 51B, bouilleur du palier 3 boucles français de 900 MWe.
Cette même conception est également appliquée en 1983, au modèle 55/19; bouilleur de 1000 MWth, utilisé par FRAMATOME dans les chaudières nucléaires à l'exportation, telle DAYA BAY en CHINE populaire. Elle trouve enfin ses dernières applications dans les appareils dits " de remplacement " et notamment pour le tout dernier modèle en projet pour Electricité de France.

Une innovation est intervenue en 1981-84 avec la création du modèle 73/19E, appareil à économiseur axial à mélange, à faisceau tubulaire disposé au pas triangulaire et comportant 130 séparateurs centrifuges double étage.
Une boucle d'essais spéciale de 25 MWth a été construite à cet effet, en collaboration avec le Commissariat à l'Energie Atomique.

Les programmes expérimentaux de recherche, les théories et outils informatiques de conception, les équipes d'ingénieurs et techniciens constituent une base commune de savoir faire à partir de laquelle il est possible de concevoir et fabriquer n'importe quel produit spécifique au besoin bien particulier d'un client en matière d'appareil de remplacement et en faisant bénéficier celui-ci de toute l'expérience du Constructeur et du parc français.

2.2.- Les améliorations de conception

Thermohydraulique secondaire, fonctionnement en transitoire, efficacité des équipements de séparation séchage, tels sont les principaux domaines d'amélioration dans la conception des GV FRAMATOME, l'hydraulique primaire et les vibrations n'ayant jamais causé le moindre problème en FRANCE.
Le premier effort a porté historiquement sur l'amélioration des conditions de refroidissement secondaire du faisceau tubulaire et de l'écoulement sur la plaque tubulaire : augmentation du taux de recirculation, augmentation des vitesses de balayage de la plaque tubulaire, sous-saturation renforcée en branche chaude, purges de déconcentration renforcées dans les zones de basse vitesse, refroidissement amélioré du tube d'échange. Ces objectifs sont atteints par la diminution rigoureuse de tous les obstacles en boucle de recirculation, l'usage de plaques entretoises à ouvertures quadrifoliées ou trifoliées, la répartition de l'eau alimentaire, l'utilisation de nouveaux séparateurs, à profil amélioré et en nombre plus élevé pour plus d'homogénéité.
L'amélioration du fonctionnement en transitoire, c'est-à-dire la limitation des fluctuations de plan d'eau, la diminution du tassement, donc globalement l'élimination des risques d'arrêt d'urgence du réacteur liés au GV, est obtenue depuis 1977 par une répartition optimisée des masses d'eau liquide et d'émulsion dans la zone intermédiaire de l'appareil permettant de mieux compenser les variations de taux de vide dans la section d'échange.

L'amélioration de la qualité de vapeur en sortie de GV, malgré la diminution des pertes en charge en boucle de recirculation et le maintien du rendement de la section économiseur, a été obtenue par un important programme de recherche théorique et expérimentale en collaboration avec le CEA, aboutissant à deux nouveaux séparateurs utilisés pour le premier sur les GV 68/19, 55/19 et 51/19 et pour le second sur le GV 73/19E.

2.3.- Les améliorations de matériaux.

Le faisceau tubulaire étant le point sensible du composant, les recherches ont porté de tout temps sur l'optimisation du matériau constitutif. L'acier inoxydable austénitique utilisé sur les appareils les plus anciens du monde occidental et récemment encore dans les pays de l'Est a toujours manifesté un très bon comportement en service. Son utilisation a dû être interrompue en raison des augmentations de températures de fonctionnement des réacteurs, au profit de l'Inconel 600 (15 Ni Cr Fe) retenu initialement aux Etats-Unis. Cet alliage s'est lui-même montré sensible à la corrosion caustique sous contraintes ou à la corrosion par le fluide primaire, pour certains cas particuliers de composition chimique et procédé d'élaboration du tube d'échange. Cette susceptibilité occasionnelle a conduit au développement d'un traitement thermique complémentaire sous vide (720°C - 15 heures) utilisé en France depuis 1979, renforçant la résistance des joints de grains et éliminant les contraintes résiduelles de fabrication du tube.

Un nouvel alliage, l'Inconel 690 (30 Ni Cr Fe) vient d'atteindre le stade industriel en France, après un long développement en laboratoire de 1975 à 85. Il est actuellement d'usage généralisé par FRAMATOME (GV standards 68/19, GV de remplacement, GV 73/19E pour EdF, GV 55/19 pour la Chine, modèles spéciaux de remplacement à l'exportation) et constitue le meilleur choix actuel possible par rapport à l'Inconel 600 (sensible à la corrosion caustique ou au fluide primaire) ou à l'Incoloy 800 (sensible aux milieux chlorurés).

A côté de l'effort consacré au faisceau, une optimisation de la nuance constitutive des enceintes sous pression a été réalisée : après une première période utilisant exclusivement la nuance 16 MND5 (508 Cl3 et 533 GrB Cl1 pour l'ASME), puis une seconde période retenant le 20 MND5 (508 Cl3a et 533 GrB Cl2 pour l'ASME) pour l'enceinte secondaire, le choix s'est porté sur une nuance intermédiaire 18 MND5 offrant le meilleur compromis entre une résistance mécanique élevée, une bonne résilience, une fourchette industrielle confortable et un choix aisé de produits d'apport.

2.4.- Les améliorations de procédés de fabrication.

Le grand nombre d'appareils construits en France (200 en une décennie) a été l'élément essentiel d'amélioration des procédés d'élaboration et de fabrication : le nombre d'appareils de conception très voisine a autorisé les analyses fines et les investissements permettant d'optimiser les gammes et d'homogénéiser les produits; la répétitivité a permis d'augmenter la qualité et la fiabilité grâce à l'effet de série obligeant à un retour sur le passé à chaque défaut constaté; la standardisation a entraîné l'automatisation des procédés de fabrication, de contrôle, de suivi etc.... tous facteurs débouchant sur une fiabilité accrue.

Au titre des innovations et des automatisations, mentionnons plus particulièrement:
* l'augmentation des formats de tôles diminuant le nombre de joints circulaires soudés
* l'utilisation de fonds primaires forgés avec tubulures primaires forgées par poinçonnage
* la réalisation de joints circulaires soudés simultanément
* les contrôles automatiques par ultra-sons
* l'exécution d'assemblages bi-métalliques sur beurrages Inconel

D'autres exemples seront analysés plus loin tels que les revêtements, la méthode de tubage du faisceau par nappes successives, le dudgeonnage intégral des tubes par machine entièrement automatique sous surveillance informatique, tous procédés orientés vers la fiabilité, la reproductibilité en même temps que l'économie globale.

3.- EXTENSION DE LA DUREE DE VIE DES GENERATEURS DE VAPEUR.

3.1.- Connaissance du matériel et précautions d'emploi.

Le premier stade régissant la durée de vie d'un tel composant est bien sûr celui de la conception d'ensemble, du choix des matériaux, des marges adoptées, des procédés de fabrication et contrôles, tous sujets qui viennent d'être rapidement évoqués.Au delà du Constructeur il doit se prolonger chez l'Exploitant par une connaissance aussi approfondie que possible de ce même matériel: c'est en effet chaque jour que peut se manifester le péril d'une chimie mal contrôlée en fonction des matériaux utilisés, ou d'un régime de fonctionnement, même temporaire, inadapté à telle ou telle solution constructive.

Dans le GV REP, le facteur essentiel vient du respect scrupuleux des règles d'exploitation, tout spécialement dans le domaine des chimies primaires et secondaires, sans oublier les périodes d'arrêt, de stockage, de démarrage où il est souvent plus difficile de respecter la norme. On peut rappeler l'exemple malheureux de la striction des tubes par les plaques entretoises ferritiques (" denting ") où le non respect des consignes de chimie s'est amplifié d'une méconnaissance totale du risque, a conduit en deux ans seulement au remplacement de tous les GV de 4 tranches (Surry 1 et 2, Turkey Point 3 et 4).

Sans que les conséquences en soient aussi rapides et dramatiques, il en va de même de la connaissance des régimes limites de fonctionnement (vibrations, érosion, humidité de la vapeur), du respect des recommandations d'inspection et de nettoyage, et plus généralement de la connaissance et du respect des marges,seules garantes de la longévité du matériel.

3.2.- Surveillance en exploitation, inspection périodique, solutions préventives.

La durée de vie des GV passe par le suivi constant des conditions d'exploitation au jour le jour : surveillance de la chimie, respect des limitations de température et puissance en fonction du niveau de pollution accidentelle, pollution intégrée sur une longue période, comptabilisation des transitoires par types etc....Non seulement cette analyse est capitale pour l'appareil lui-même, mais elle permet surtout, traitée en large base de données, d'anticiper les programmes d'inspection et de prévention sur d'autres appareils. C'est cette politique qui est largement suivie par EdF et proposée conjointement par EdF et FRAMATOME en assistance à d'autres exploitants.

L'inspection périodique permet l'éveil de l'attention, le diagnostic précoce d'endommagement, la recherche des causes et le développement de remèdes .Nous retiendrons seulement à titre d'exemple deux diagnostics conduisant à des solutions préventives :
* le diagnostic de " denting " naissant qui incite à recourir à des modifications de chimie secondaire, à des modifications physiques du poste d'eau (type de condenseur, matériau d'échangeurs secondaires, installation de traitements des condensats), à des cycles de déséquestration d'espèces chimiques, à des traitements de lessivage secondaire;
* le diagnostic de corrosion primaire locale des tubes qui conduit soit au traitement thermique long ou court des tubes à petit rayon de cintrage, soit à des opérations de microbillage (shot peening) ou de micromartelage (roto peening) sur des zones à fortes contraintes résiduelles locales;

Généralement les premiers GV affectés ne peuvent profiter qu'imparfaitement des traitements préventifs qui au mieux limitent l'extension du dommage. L'application des procédés préventifs n'est parfaitement efficace que sur les appareils non encore affectés et les appareils les plus anciens doivent alors avoir recours à d'autres méthodes de réparation. Aussi, suite à l'apparition de la corrosion primaire dans les zones de transition de dudgeonnage et à la possibilité offerte par FRAMATOME de microbiller localement la paroi interne des tubes, EdF a fait choix de traiter en première priorité les GV équipés d'Inconel 600 hypertrempé les plus jeunes et n'ayant présenté encore aucun signe d'endommagement.

3.3.- Traitements de réparation.

Outre les méthodes de traitement thermique et de microbillage déjà citées, les réparations proprement dites comportent actuellement:
- la pose de manchettes, soit dans la plaque tubulaire, soit au droit de plaques entretoises, et ce, par différents procédés d'assemblage

- le remplacement des barres antivibratoires dans la zone cintrée

- les modifications des systèmes de distribution d'eau et les jeux tube/ support dans le cas particulier de certains types de préchauffeur,

- certains procédés en développement préindustriel comme le remplacement de toute une portion de tube ou le revêtement électrolytique local en paroi interne,

- tous les types de bouchons (fixés par soudage, à l'explosif, mécaniquement), les développements modernes étant tournés vers les bouchons aisément démontables et permettant la remise en service du tube.

Aux procédés appliqués au faisceau, il conviendrait d'ajouter ceux ayant trait à l'enceinte sous pression (réfection des ouvertures et de la goujonnerie, lutte contre la stratification, dispositifs anti coup de bélier etc...). La durée de vie d'un GV étant toujours associée à celle de son faisceau tubulaire, nous ne nous attarderons donc pas sur ce dernier aspect bien qu'il puisse peser lourdement aussi sur la disponibilité et la fiabilité des installations.

3.4.- Choix technico-économique.

Le diagnostic de santé est relativement aisé à faire chaque année. Le suivi d'année en année et la transposition de réacteur à réacteur sont déjà plus délicats, mais le choix le plus difficile reste celui d'une ou plusieurs opérations successives de réparation, et du remplacement d'une unité complète.
Ce choix dépend de la nature de l'endommagement, de son risque de généralisation, des solutions techniques de réparation partielle et de leur longévité potentielle, et,bien sur,des coûts d'intervention immédiats, directs et indirects.

Outre le fait que les méthodes de prévention les plus récentes n'ont pas encore de longues durées d'expérience, il est très souvent possible d'imaginer l'application successive de plusieurs d'entre elles. La difficulté est bien alors de définir l'optimum économique entre une ou plusieurs méthodes de réparation spécifiquement orientées vers un endommagement déterminé,plus le risque d'apparition ultérieure d'une seconde maladie, et la décision d'engager le remplacement par un appareil neuf.
Dans une perspective globale de prolongation de durée de vie pour une tranche complète, la décision homogène entre tous les systèmes et composants sensibles, restera sans doute difficile pendant de nombreuses années, d'autant plus que les solutions de réparations seront jeunes et nombreuses.

3.5.- Préparation des opérations de réparation et remplacement.

Quelle que soit la décision (mais surtout s'il s'agit du remplacement), l'anticipation et la préparation de l'opération sont des facteurs décisifs de succès. Des travaux préparatoires entrepris durant les arrêts programmés des années précédentes, peuvent raccourcir de plusieurs semaines le chemin critique de l'opération lourde.
Rappelons qu'en tout état de cause, la disponibilité de 3 ou 4 unités neuves nécessitera de l'ordre de 30 à 36 mois, surtout en cas d'exigences nouvelles et de produits non standardisés.

4. - LES GENERATEURS DE REMPLACEMENT PROPOSES PAR FRAMATOME.

Encore plus que dans le cas d'une chaudière nucléaire neuve, l'unité de Générateur de Vapeur de remplacement répond à un cahier des charges détaillé et précis émis par le client. Les astreintes sont multiples car elles cumulent habituellement:
- l'état de l'art mondial au moment de l'appel d'offre ou de la commande
- les exigences permettant de se prémunir des endommagements précédemment vécus (soit en propre, soit par expérience mondiale)
- la volonté d'utiliser au mieux les marges générales de la tranche et donc souvent d'augmenter un peu la puissance thermique du GV
- le désir de disposer de plus de marge de surface d'échange et de plus de souplesse d'exploitation (transitoires, ilotage, prolongement de cycle combustible)
- la volonté de rendre l'opération de remplacement la plus aisée et courte possible, ce qui très souvent est synonyme d'un contour extérieur et de limites géométriques quasi inchangés.

L'expérience des Constructeurs est prise en considération mais le poids des exigences imposées par le client est très marqué.
Nous évoquerons l'expérience de FRAMATOME à travers les appels d'offre internationaux et le projet en cours pour Electricité de France.

4.1.- L'augmentation de puissance et l'augmentation des marges.

Généralement, chaque matériel ou système, tant de l'îlot conventionnel que de l'îlot nucléaire, dispose d'une marge de conception de plusieurs pourcents qu'il n'est possible de quantifier qu'après démarrage de l'installation. Après avoir recensé et chiffré l'état réel de fonctionnement d'une tranche, il devient dès lors possible au moment d'une opération de maintenance lourde comme le remplacement de GV d'utiliser cette marge disponible en requerrant une nouvelle puissance thermique de GV, quitte à remplacer ou modifier en même temps quelques composants mineurs.
Il est ainsi envisagé en cas de remplacement de GV une augmentation de puissance de :
* 5% pour les tranches françaises du contrat pluriannuel 3 boucles
* 7% pour la tranche suédoise de Ringhals 2 par exemple
D'autres centrales ont actuellement le même projet à l'étude(**BEZNAU**...)

Cette première augmentation de performances permet de mieux rentabiliser l'opération de remplacement de GV. Elle est bien souvent prolongée par un accroissement de surface d'échange, bien au delà du strict nécessaire correspondant à l'augmentation de puissance, permettant alors d'exploiter la tranche à plus basse température primaire (d'où des marges sur l'exploitation du coeur, des possibilités accrues de prolongation de cycles combustible etc....) et de disposer pour l'avenir plus lointain d'une marge consommable de surface d'échange.

Toutes augmentations confondues, l'excédent de surface peut se trouver dans une gamme de + 10% à + 25% par rapport au GV d'origine. La définition de cette marge est de la responsabilité du constructeur et dépend, dans un volume d'origine défini et quasi immuable, des solutions techniques initialement utilisées telles que type et valeur du pas de construction, diamètre du tube d'échange.
Une marge accrue peut par exemple être obtenue en utilisant du tube de 19 mm au lieu de 22mm et en le disposant en pas triangulaire au lieu de carré, mais une telle modification n'est envisageable qu'après de très nombreuses vérifications portant sur la compatibilité globale de la tranche et sur les limites administratives d'exploitation dont elle dispose.

4.2.- L'Amélioration de la souplesse d'exploitation.

L'amélioration est recherchée tant pour le fonctionnement proprement dit que pour la période d'inspection et maintenance.
Durant le fonctionnement, les améliorations offertes par les GV de remplacement de FRAMATOME portent sur :
- l'absence de fluctuations de niveau d'eau et la fiabilité des mesures,
- le tassement faible du plan d'eau en raison d'une optimisation de masses relatives d'eau et de vapeur et de leur localisation dans l'appareil (ce paramètre étant essentiel à la réussite des transi-toires d'îlotage)
- l'absence d'impositions contraignantes dans la répartition de l'eau alimentaire à basse charge

Les améliorations liées à la maintenance sont plus classiques et nous citerons par exemple:
- l'augmentation du diamètre des trous d'homme primaire et secondaire
- le nombre et la disposition des ouvertures secondaires d'inspection et entretien
- le dégagement vertical important en périphérie de boite à eau primaire
- la présence de points d'ancrage et fixation à demeure dans l'appareil
- la possibilité de contrôler les joints soudés circulaires par dispositifs automatiques.

4.3.- Les solutions techniques évitant les risques déjà rencontrés ou connus.

Les solutions mises en jeu pour assurer la pérennité du faisceau tubulaire sont multiples, et pour certaines déjà bien connues, comme l'optimisation des conditions générales de refroidissement du faisceau tubulaire, l'amélioration du système de purge ou l'usage de plaques entretoises en alliage inoxydable, percées de trous brochés pour assurer le refroidissement local et le nettoyage hydraulique du tube.
Nous insisterons spécialement sur trois sujets : l'Inconel 690 TT comme matériau de tube, l'amélioration de la liaison tube-plaque tubulaire et le nouveau procédé de montage du faisceau.

L'Inconel 690, alliage de Nickel comportant 29% de chrome, est issu d'une optimisation systématique de la teneur en chrome pour lui assurer une parfaite résistance à la corrosion caustique et par le fluide primaire. Sa caractérisation et sa qualification sont intervenues entre 1980 et 85, et le stade industriel atteint en 1986.
Il est utilisé systématiquement depuis lors sur les GV FRAMATOME tant pour le parc français qu'à l'exportation.Rappelons son utilisation (tableau II) sur les tranches n°19 et 20 du palier 1350 MWe, dès la première tranche (CHOOZ B1) du palier 1450 MWe, sur les GV de rechange modèle 51 n° 4 à 6 pour EdF, les deux tranches de Daya Bay, et dans l'avenir sur les GV de Substitution d'EdF. Les appels d'offres internationaux (Suède, Belgique par exemple) sont très souvent lancés avec l'Inconel 690. Le tube subit également un traitement thermique final sous vide.

L'assemblage du tube dans la plaque tubulaire continue à bénéficier d'importants programmes de développement. Dans la technique du dudgeonnage mécanique capable d'assurer une étanchéité parfaite de l'interstice tube plaque, FRAMATOME utilise depuis maintenant une année, une nouvelle machine automatique où toutes les fonctions et paramètres sont contrôlés par ordinateur. Elle offre une grande fiabilité d'opération et une répétitivité excellente des formes géométriques (position spatiale de la fin de dudgeonnage, recouvrement des pas etc...). De plus il existe maintenant de nombreux procédés de contrôle de la profilométrie de l'assemblage réalisé(sondes à courants de Foucault par exemple). Les efforts se poursuivent à la fois dans la recherche d'un nouvel outil de dudgeonnage à profil progressif et dans la mise au point et qualification de l'expansion hydraulique à haute pression et double passe. Tous ces travaux ont pour objectifs la fiabilité accrue de l'opération, et la limitation des contraintes résiduelles notamment en peau externe.

Le nouveau procédé de montage du faisceau, dit de " tubage par nappes " utilisé tant en pas carré qu'en pas triangulaire consiste à monter les lits de tubes par nappes horizontales complètes alternativement avec les familles de barres antivibratoires. Cette technique nécessite des postes de travail et outillages spéciaux, ainsi surtout qu'un colisage très différent chez les tubistes, mais présente de nombreux avantages:
- la possibilité de réduire notablement le jeu statistique entre les tubes et les barres antivibratoires (et donc de réduire le degré de liberté global)
- la possibilité de contrôler le travail à l'avancement, et notamment d'éliminer tous les jeux forts ponctuels présentant le plus de risque d'usure
- la possibilité de contrôler la circularité des tubes et le jeu entre eux, sans risque de déformation à l'introduction des barres au stade final.

4.4.- L'état de l'art.

Il est délicat de synthétiser l'état de l'art; il serait même plus judicieux de parler d'équilibre entre le coût du matériel terminé et les précautions, innovations et contrôles qui ont été utilisés. L'expérience de fabrication accumulée dans la décennie passée chez tous les fournisseurs et constructeurs permet de disposer aujourd'hui à la fois de produits plus sûrs et performants, mais aussi de toutes les mises au point et gammes de contrôles optimisées à chaque stade de la fabrication. Le choix et le nombre de ces innovations dépendent des termes contractuels spécifiques à chaque affaire, mais globalement les GV fabriqués aujourd'hui sont profondément plus fiables que ceux d'hier.

Au delà des innovations déjà citées ou décrites et sur lesquelles nous ne reviendrons pas, voyons quelques exemples supplémentaires.

Concernant les enceintes ferritiques sous pression, les moyens industriels modernes permettent d'augmenter la taille et la précision des pièces unitaires, ces deux éléments réduisant d'une part le nombre de joints soudés et permettant d'autre part d'automatiser les contrôles non destructifs par ultra-sons soit en fabrication, soit en service. Il est également possible d'envisager de nouvelles pièces forgées comme le fond primaire de GV ou les éléments constitutifs de l'enceinte secondaire. A titre d'exemple, FRAMATOME utilise la même forme brute de forge pour constituer soit un fond hémisphérique de GV 73/19E, soit un fond cylindrico-sphérique de GV 51/19.
Dans le domaine des revêtements et beurrages, deux innovations importantes sont apparues: le revêtement par procédé plasma sous gaz permet de limiter la dilution en métal de base, la réalisation de beurrages inconel sur base ferritique améliore considérablement les propriétés de résilience des assemblages bimétalliques de tubulures sur les tuyauteries.
Les contrôles de fabrication ont également accompli de grand progrès :
- utilisation de machine et procédé automatiques de contrôle US des revêtements
- définition renforcée des radiographies par usage de source cobalt et écrans renforçateurs inoxydables
- contrôle par courants de Foucault de la profilométrie des dudgeonnages, des jeux entre support et tube etc....

4.5.- Le raccourcissement du temps de remplacement grâce au composant lui-même.

Indépendamment de la recherche opérationnelle proprement dite, il est possible de minimiser la durée d'indisponibilité de la tranche grâce au composant lui-même. Un tel gain n'est possible qu'en fonction de l'installation générale préexistante ou des procédés de remplacement mis en oeuvre.
Parmi les principaux gains possibles signalons:
- le GV complètement terminé et éprouvé en usine
- la réalisation de la visite complète initiale en usine
- l'amélioration du supportage sismique supérieur supprimant l'opération de réglage et calage à chaud
- la réalisation de traitements de passivation des surfaces évitant la phase correspondante lors des essais préliminaires.

Chaque situation est en fait un cas d'espèce; la seule recommandation générale consiste à réaliser un composant de remplacement géométriquement identique à celui d'origine et à replacer en usine le maximum possible de contrôles et traitements de préparation.

TABLEAU I

LIGNE DE PRODUIT " GENERATEUR DE VAPEUR " DE FRAMATOME

Année de conception	Modèles de GV				Client	Centrale typique	Années de Fabrication	Nombre d'Unités		
	Faible puissance 950 MWth Bouilleur	1000 MWth	1050 MWth	Économ. 1100 MWth				Livrées	En Constr.	Offertes
CENTRALES NEUVES										
1970 - 72	51A				EdF	Fessenheim	71 - 75	18		
74 - 75	51 M				"	Tricastin	75 - 83	60		
77 - 78	51 B				EdF	Paluel	78 - 88	68	12	
78 - 79			68/19 / 55/19		Escom	Blayais	80 - 86	24		
					Kepco	Koeberg	78 - 81	6		
						Uljin	82 - 85	6		
83 - 84					Chine	Daya Bay	86 - 89		6	
81 - 84				73/19E	EdF	Chooz B	85 - 88		8	
GV de REMPLACEMENT										
1978 + 84	51 R				EdF	"Remplacement"	84-87		6	
83	41/22T				Ebes	Doel 2	-			(2)
85	51/19T				SSPB	Ringhals 2	-			(3)
85	40/22				NYPA	Indian P3	-			(4)
1985 - 87		51/19			EdF	"Substitution"	87-90			3

TABLEAU II

AMELIORATIONS PRINCIPALES DE LA LIGNE DE PRODUIT GV FRA

Modèles GV	Tranches	CONCEPTION				MATERIAUX		FABRICATION	
		Nouveaux Séparateurs Centrifuges	Variation du niveau d'eau	Plaques Entret. 13%Cr Brochées	Fond primaire Forgé	Inconel 600 TT	Inconel 690 TT	Dudgeon. Autom.	Tubage par nappes
51B	EdF 950MW 16 à 20			x					
	21 à 28			x		x		(x)	
51B	Escom Koeberg	0		x					
51B	Kepco Uljin	0		x		x			
68/19	EdF 1350 n°1 à 18	x	x	x	(x)	x		(x)	
	19 à 20	x	x	x	x	x	x	x	x
73/19	EdF 1450 n°1 - 2	x	x	x	x		x	x	
55/19	Chine 1 - 2	x	x	x	x		x	x	
51R	EdF Rempl t 1 à 3	0		x		x	x	x	
	4 à 6	0		x			x	x	x
51/19	EdF Rempl t Standard	x	x	x	x		x	x	x

LEGENDE
x   en totalité
0   amélioration partielle
(x) sur certains GV

RECIRCULATION PIPING REPLACEMENT
AT SANTA MARIA DE GAROÑA NUCLEAR POWER STATION

J. Olaso López
Spain

As a result of the UT inspections performed on the recirculation system during 1983 and 1984, Nuclenor decided to partially replace the recirculation piping and install an H_2 injection system in the reactor feedwater.

This report describes the steps given by Nuclenor to accomplish the replacement work during the 1985 refuelling outage. It analyzes the decisions made during the preparation of the works and the coordination of these works during the performance of the replacement. It describes the sequence of activities and the time employed in each one, and gives a brief comment of Radiological Protection data such as dose rate, total dose and generated waste.

The performance of major replacement jobs that exceed the maintenance organization capacity demands the coordination of many different organizations, internal and external, the detailed planification of activities and an enormous utilization of human and material resources.

The experience obtained during the Santa María de Garoña replacement work shows the technical and economical viability of this type of major works.

REMPLACEMENT DE LA TYAUTERIE DE RECIRCULATION
A LA CENTRALE NUCLEAIRE SANTA MARIA DE GARONA

RESUME

A la suite des examens par ultrasons effectués sur le circuit de recirculation en 1983 et 1984, Nuclenor décida de remplacer une partie de la tuyauterie de recirculation et d'installer un système d'injection de H_2 dans l'eau du réacteur.

Le présent document décrit les étapes prévues par Nuclenor pour effectuer les travaux de remplacement pendant l'arrêt pour rechargement de 1985. Il analyse les décisions prises pendant la préparation des travaux et la coordination de ces travaux pendant les opérations de remplacement. Il décrit la séquence des activités et la durée de chacune d'entre elles et commente brièvement les données de radioprotection telles que les débits de dose, la dose globale et la production de déchets.

La réalisation d'importants travaux de remplacement qui dépassent la capacité d'organisation du service d'entretien exige la coordination d'un grand nombre d'organisations différentes, internes ou externes, la planification détaillée des activités et l'utilisation de ressources énormes en personnel et en matériel.

L'expérience acquise au cours des travaux de remplacement effectués à la centrale nucléaire Santa Maria de Garona met en évidence la faisabilité technique et économique de ce type de travaux de grande ampleur.

1. Introduction

Santa María de Garoña Nuclear Power Plant, located in the province of Burgos, is equiped with a General Electric forced circulation direct cycle Boiling Water Reactor (BWR-3) of 1380 Mwth (460 Mwe). Commercial operation began in May 1971 and up to December 1986, it has generated 39.788 Gwh with a capacity factor of 62.9%.

One of the features of this type of reactor is the re-circulation system that provides the hydraulic energy required to force coolant through the reactor core. The system consists of two external loops together with centrifugal pumps, jet pumps valves and piping.

The pump suction and discharge piping are 24 inches OD, and discharge high pressure flow into an 18 inch external header from which the 10 inch risers connect to the inlet safe-end of the vessel.

The two recirculation loops are almost identical and were interconnected by means of an equalizer line provided with two valves.

2. Condition of the recirculation system before replacement

During the 1983 refueling outage, Nuclenor carried out an ultrasonic inspection of a selected sample of welds in the stainless steel pipes inside the drywell following the inspection procedures developed specifically to detect intergranular stress corrosion cracks.

The result of the UT inspection was the detection of indications evaluated as intergranular stress corrossion cracking in thirteen (13) welds of the recirculation system (Fig. 1).

In September 1984 an intermediate outage was scheduled to carry out an ultrasonic inspection of those welds of the re-circulation system that had not been inspected and to inspect again those welds with indications, in order to check any variation of them. As a consequence of this ins-pection an structural weld overlay was performed.

Taking into account that the indications were located in the 24 inch lines and at the manifold ends with the rest of the lines completely clean, and the short time available to prepare the work that had to start in June 1985, and some other economic considerations, Nuclenor decided to replace only the recirculation system affected piping and install a H_2 injection system.

3. Work preparation

   3.1 Organization

   To plan, perform and manage all the activities of the project, Nuclenor formed up a project team made out of his own technical staff and hired personnel coming from several companies, but working together as a line (Fig. 2).

   Responsibilities of this team were:

   - Coordinating all the activities of the project.

   - Preparing the applicable design and installation specifications.

   - Performing the stress analysis of the system according to the new stress and seismic criteria.

   - Procuring the new piping and supports to be installed.

   - Designing and installing radiation shielding.

   - Dismantling and reinstaling drywell interferences.

   - Dismantling, procuring and reinstalling new insulation.

   - Planning and performing the final testing of the system.

   - Supervising all the activities and approving the installation documents.

   - Providing the adequate radiological protection of all the activities.

   Before performing the actual piping replacement all the activities were planned and personnel trained, such as provision of cutting and welding equipment, design of special equipment training and qualification of personnel and special procedures qualified, so that everything whould be ready for the outage.

   3.2 Scope of work and criteria definitions

   According to the results obtained from the ultrasonic inspections, the scope of the replacement would be (Fig. 3):

- The outlet safe-ends and upper elbows.

- All the elbows and spools connected to the recirculation pumps and valves.

- The caps of the header.

Also the two equalizer valves were removed and replaced with two caps.

To replace the affected piping, made out of type 304 stainless steel, it was decided to use the following main criteria:

- Seamless induction bent piping, made out of type 316 Nuclear Grade stainless steel, as recommended by GE and EPRI.

- Automatic gas tungsten arc welding with narrow gap bevels (Fig. 4).

- Existing piping with corrosion resistant cladding at the piping ends.

- Decontamination of piping and equipment free ends by electropolishing and flapper wheel.

4. Work description

Once the plant was shut down and before starting the refueling outage, all the welds on the lines of the reciculation system that had no indications were UT inspected to confirm that they were free of cracks. The inspection was performed by KWU using automatic and manual methods and confirmed the data from previous inspections so the scope of the replacement remained unchanged.

In parallel with the UT inspections, the drywell was conditioned for the replacement, dismantling site interferences, installing temporary supports, preparing equipment handling and installing radiation shielding to reduce radiation.

Once the inspections and the preparatory works were finished, the actual sequence was as follows:

The piping and components were securely anchored and then, in order to relief installation residual stresses, four plasma arc cuts were made, two in each loop at the suction and discharge of the pumps. The rest of the cuts were made by mechanical cutting machines. Waste pieces were moved to a temporary storage. The four 24" isolation valves were transferred to a machine shop attached to the reactor building for refurbishing before reuse.

To reduce the radiation levels at the free ends of piping, pumps and valves, a decontamination was performed before proceeding with weld end preparation machining. Electropolishing was used for pumps, valves and most of the piping.

Reactor vessel nozzles and one end of an specific piping spool were decontaminated by flapper wheel mounted on a machine specially designed for this application.

After decontamination of ends, special shield plugs were installed inside piping and equipment obtaining in this way a radiation level at the surface of the piping of the same magnitude as the average measured inside the drywell.

4.1 Machining and Welding

Reactor vessel nozzles were machined removing the old sensitized safe ends, leaving the austenitic build up with as much thickness as possible.

The austenitic 304 piping which would remain in the system was protected from potential future cracking by a weld deposit on the inside wall using a weld deposit inmune to stress corrosion.

First, piping inside wall was machined to a limited depth from the free end. Later the removed material area was filled up by depositing a corrosion inmune material as a buttering. Stiffening rings were placed on piping free ends in order to minimize shrinkage during this process of buttering (Fig. 5)

Once the welding was finished, the piping inside surface and weld end preparation were machined.

Optical measuring devices were used to determine the as built relative coordinates for finished weld end preparations. Based on these as built-data, new spools were cut, adding extra length for weld shrinkage wherever it was needed. This operation was performed on auxiliary machine shops.

Suction side valve was welded to suction elbow on auxiliary hot shop. Later, the assembly was moved into the drywell. Same operation was made on discharge side valve and spool.

New piping was moved into the drywell thus proceeding to alignment, tack welding and final weld in a pre--established sequence.

Plugs for purging during welding on 24" piping had a central guide fitted in order to permit weld radiography at different stages in panoramic exposure without re-

quiring purge removal. Those plugs were later removed
from other piping free ends or valve bodies having their
internals removed as stems were replaced with new ones.

4.2 Tests and inspections

After welds were completed, non destructive examinations
were performed, covering the liquid penetrant, radiography and ultrasonic inspection.

After performing and accepting all the non destructive
examinations, the reactor vessel was flooded up, and the
work came out of the refueling outage critical path.

The auxiliary systems were reset and the new insulation
was installed.

Simultaneously, transducers to monitor piping vibrations
and displacement were installed at selected spots of the
system. Those transducers during the plant start-up
would become part of the data acquisition system used to
check wether the vibrations and displacement of the
piping system were the calculated ones.

4.3 Planning

The main activities of the work and the duration of them
are shown in Fig. 6.

Decision to perform the piping replacement was taken by
November 84. At that time Nuclenor started the
negotiations with KWU as the main installer.

By April 85, after holding several meetings with the
Spanish Nuclear Regulatory Authorities and with the
Spanish Department of Energy about the scope of the replacement and the participating Spanish companies, the
contracts with all the involved companies were signed.

Along June and July, special procedures were qualified
and the personnel was trained and qualified.

On the 28th of June the plant was shutdown, and all the
preparatory works started.

First plasme arc cut was performed on the 3rd of August.

All the replacement, including the non destructive
examinations finished on the 16th of October.

5. Total dose received and waste generated

5.1 Total dose received

In Table 1 we can see for the different activities involved in the replacement work, the number of people participating, the duration of each activity (man-/hours), the average dose rate (Sv/h) and the total dose.

As you can see in Table 1, the activities performed under the title "Replacement of recirculation piping", represent 64% of the total dose. There are another half a dozen activities (scafolds in drywell, insullation, inspection of new and existing welds, shielding and pipe interferences), that represent 30% aproximately, and the last 6% is shared by the rest.

Taking into consideration the importance of the activity "Replacement of recirculation piping" we have subdivided it into several subactivities and the data is shown in Table 2. The subactivities called Machinning, Cutting and Welding Support and Automatic Welding, are responsible for 77% of the total dose. Also, the three subactivities represent 75% of the exposure time.

It is important to point out that the measured dose rate was much lower than predicted due basically to three reasons:

- The shut down of the plant was done in a very orderly manner avoiding to scram the reactor and to stir up the corrosion crud in the circuit.

- Due to a good decontamination of piping and equipment free ends and the installation of internal shielding in these locations, the radiation level in contact was of the same magnitude as the one measured inside the drywell.

- Finally, the systematic use of lead shielding over the recirculation system piping that was practically covered with 16 m.m. of lead, and the achievement of a good overlap between the shielding pieces, contributed to obtain a low and uniform radiation field in the work areas inside the drywell.

5.2 Generated waste.

The following types of waste were generated during the recirculation piping replacement activities:

- Waste from mechanical components (pipes, valves).

- Filters and electrolyte from the electro-polishing decontamination.

- Fungible material (gloves, overalls, etc.).

To calculate the total waste activity, we calculated first the specific activity of each type of waste and multiplied by the amount generated of such waste.

a) Mechanical components

A γ (total) = 1.88 Ci

A β (total) = 0.87 Ci

A α (total) = 6.78 x 10^{-3} Ci

b) Decontamination electrolyte

Two 80 litre lots were generated, as well as 63 litres of pickling acid, with the following activities:

Lot A = 8 x 10^{-2} Ci

Lot B = 9.92 x 10^{-2} Ci

Picling acid = 8.87 x 10^{-3} Ci

c) Electro-polishing filters

Three canisters were generated with the following activities:

canister 1 = 7.70 x 10^{-2} Ci

canister 2 = 6.42 x 10^{-2} Ci

canister 3 = 5.52 x 10^{-2} Ci

d) Fungible material

All the material was disposed in 220 litres canisters that were classified into three categories: Combustible, Non Combustible and Metallic.

Category	Number of canisters	Total activity (Ci)
Combustible	95	1.580
Non Combustible	30	0.164
Metallic	3	0.012

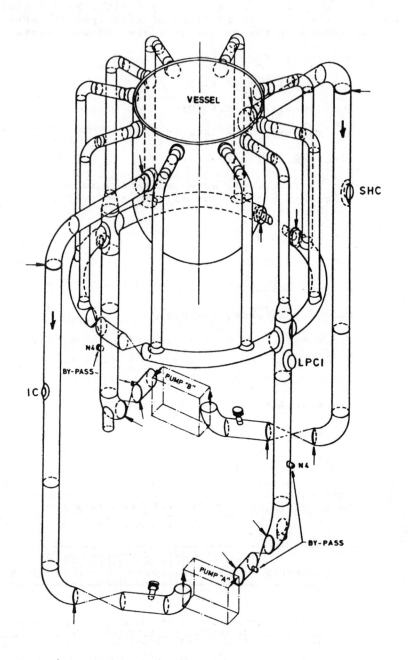

CRACK LOCATION

(Figure 1)

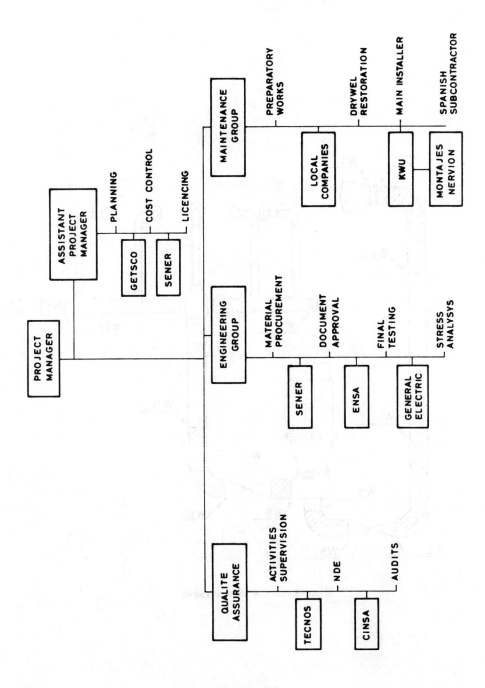

(Figure 2)

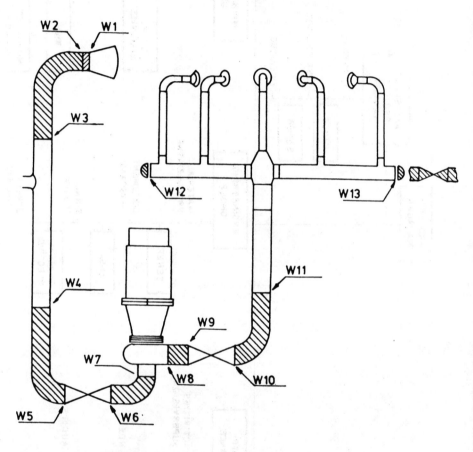

SCOPE OF THE REPLACEMENT

(Figure 3)

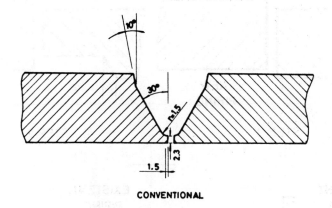

CONVENTIONAL

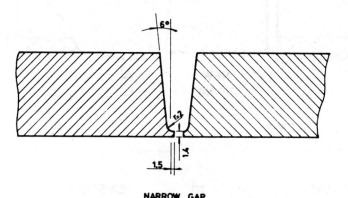

NARROW GAP

BEVEL GEOMETRY

(Figure 4)

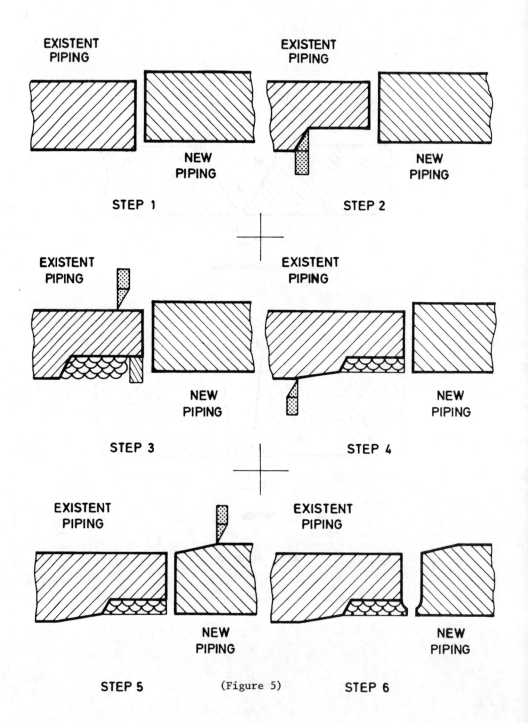

EXISTENT PIPING

NEW PIPING

STEP 1

EXISTENT PIPING

NEW PIPING

STEP 2

EXISTENT PIPING

NEW PIPING

STEP 3

EXISTENT PIPING

NEW PIPING

STEP 4

EXISTENT PIPING

NEW PIPING

STEP 5

(Figure 5)

EXISTENT PIPING

NEW PIPING

STEP 6

- 276 -

TIME / ACTIVITIES	1985 JANUARY	FEBRUARY	MARCH	APRIL	MAY	JUNE	JULY	AUGUST	SEPTEMBER	OCTOBER	NOVEMBER	DECEMBER	1986 JANUARY
DESING ANALISYS	DESING SPEC.			INSTALLATION SPEC.				STRESS ANALISYS	FINAL REPORT				
MATERIAL PROCUREMENT													
QUALIFICATION AND TRAINING													
PREPARATORY WORKS						PLANT SHUTDOWN							
PREVIOUS UT INSPECTION													
PIPING REPLACEMENT													
DRYWELL RESTORATION													
FINAL TESTING												PLANT START-UP	

(Figure 6)

TABLE I

FINAL DOSE REPORT FOR THE PARTIAL RECIRCULATION SYSTEM REPLACEMENT

TASK		NUMBER OF PERSONS	TIME CONSUMED (h. person)	AVERAGE DOSE (μ Sv/h)	TOTAL DOSE (μ Sv person)
SCAFFOLDING	Drywell	100	606.61	390	236,274
	Hot workshop	18	7.16	1,000	7,161
SHIELDING NOZZLES N-1 - N2		21	76.55	520	39,816
INSULATION		68	488.78	469	229,105
VENTILATION	Drywell	44	350.43	342	119,994
	Hot workshop	12	35.87	150	5,381
CLEANING	Drywell	85	288.6	270	77,769
	Hot workshop	1	19.99	100	1,999
INTERFERENCES - PIPING - OTHERS		247	1,574.40	295	465,091
INSTALLATION OF ARGON PIPING		3	18.37	297	5,446
ELECTRICAL INTERFERENCES		38	115.25	351	40,423
EXISTING WELD INSPECTION		225	791.2	599	473,785
NEW WELD INSPECTION		95	714.35	305	217,882
SHIELDING		126	500.98	522	261,318
DECONTAMINATION OF CUTS		87	481.63	365	175,647
RECIRCULATION PIPING	Drywell	763	8,921.90	380	3,394,511
REPLACEMENT	Hot workshop	158	1,494.97	491	733,716

TABLE II

PARTIAL WORKS FOR RECIRCULATION SYSTEM REPLACEMENT

TASK	TIME CONSUMED (h. person)	AVERAGE DOSE (μ Sv/h)	TOTAL DOSE (μ Sv person)
GENERAL ACTIVITIES	633.7	438.3	227,781
MACHINNING	2,804.0	491.7	1,378,784
CUTTING AND WELDING SUPPORT	2,927.7	345.2	1,010,547
AUTHOMATIC WELDING	2,031.6	391.2	794,832
SUPERVISION	35.1	301	10,564
MATERIAL TRANSPORTATION	561.5	301	168,982
ALIGNMENT	670.6	426	285,664
DISMANTLING SUPPORT INSTALLATION	744.5	333.4	248,180
MANUAL WELDING	8.3	348.5	2,893

LOOSE PARTS, VIBRATION AND LEAKAGE MONITORING METHODS AND SYSTEMS TO INCREASE AVAILABILITY, TRANSPARENCY AND LIFETIME OF POWER PLANTS.

V. Streicher, P. Jax, K. Ruthrof
Kraftwerk Union AG
Erlangen, Federal Republic of Germany

ABSTRACT

Monitoring Systems provide important information about the mechanical status of the surveyed plant or component. This paper deals with three stand-alone-systems as an aid to check the mechanical integrity of the primary circuit of nuclear power plants.

The main goals of these systems are early detection of faults and malfunctions, the facilitation of fault clearance, the avoidance of sequential damage and reduction of inspection time and cost.

Obviously the proper application of the systems as well as the measures they induce and make possible increase the availability of the plant and contribute to lifetime extension.

In order to detect, identify and pinpoint the changes in component structure such as
- loosened connections,
- broken parts or components,
- loose or loosened particles,
- fatigued materials,
- cracks and leaks,
specialized monitoring systems were developed by KWU (Kraftwerk Union AG) during the last ten years. For this development, two basic requirements had to be fulfilled:
- long term experience in erection, operation and service of nuclear power plants,
- systematic and determined research as well as extensive experience in the application and evaluation of monitoring systems.

Monitoring systems are classed as information systems and do not cause any automatic reaction of the reactor protection system, but acquire, process, store and document data and signals for a quick and safe fault analysis. The common technical concept provides for autonomous, modular, individual systems.

Requirements concerning vibration, loose parts and leakage monitoring are part of German guidelines and safety standards. Therefore systems for these applications are implemented in most of the nuclear power plants in Western Germany. This paper presents newly developed, microprocessor-based systems for loose parts monitoring, vibration monitoring and leakage monitoring and also includes specific case histories for the different topics.

METHODES DE CONTROLE DES CORPS MIGRANTS, DES VIBRATIONS ET DES FUITES ET SYSTEMES D'AMELIORATION DE LA DISPONIBILITE, DE LA TRANSPARENCE ET DE LA DUREE DE VIE DES CENTRALES ELECTRIQUES

RESUME

Les systèmes de contrôle donnent des informations précieuses sur l'état mécanique de l'installation ou du composant surveillé. Cette communication présente trois systèmes indépendants servant à contrôler l'intégrité mécanique du circuit primaire des centrales nucléaires.

Les principaux objectifs de ces systèmes sont de détecter rapidement les défauts et les anomalies de fonctionnement, de simplifier l'élimination des défauts, de prévenir les dommages induits, de réduire les temps et les coûts d'inspection.

Il est clair qu'une exploitation rationnelle des systèmes et les mesures qui en découlent accroissent la disponibilité des centrales et concourent à la prolongation de leur durée de vie.

Pour déceler, déterminer et localiser des variations dans l'état des composants comme

- le desserrage de raccords,
- la rupture de pièces ou de composants,
- la présence de corps migrants et de pièces desserrées,
- la fatigue des matériaux,
- l'existence de défauts et fuites,

la société KWU (Kraftwerkunion AG) a mis au point au cours des dix dernières années des systèmes de contrôle spécialisés. Deux conditions fondamentales devaient être remplies à cet effet :

- longue expérience de la construction, de l'exploitation et de l'entretien des centrales nucléaires,

- effort systématique et résolu de recherche et vaste expérience de l'application et de l'évaluation des systèmes de controle.

Les systèmes de contrôle sont considérés comme des systèmes d'information qui ne déclenchent aucune action automatique des dispositifs de protection des réacteurs, mais qui collectent, traitent, stockent et consignent des données et des signaux en vue d'une analyse rapide et sûre des défauts. Le concept technique de base prévoit des systèmes autonomes, modulaires et indépendants.

Les directives et normes de sûreté allemandes contiennent des prescriptions concernant le contrôle des vibrations, des corps migrants et des fuites. C'est pourquoi la plupart des centrales nucléaires de la République fédérale d'Allemagne sont munies de ce type de systèmes. Cette communication présente des systèmes à microprocesseurs récemment mis au point pour

- le contrôle des corps migrants,
- le contrôle des vibrations,
- le contrôle acoustique des fuites,

et quelques études de cas spécifiques relatifs à ces différents domaines.

1. Objectives [1, 2]

KWU's concept for development and construction of monitoring systems for nuclear power plants includes two important elements:
- the experience gained in years of construction, commissioning, operation and service of nuclear power plants and
- targeted research and development and also long years of implementation experience in the field of monitoring systems.

On this basis, an overall concept has been established for monitoring chiefly the primary loop which:
- assures primary system integrity,
- plays a vital role in enhancing the availability and service reliability of the plant.
- contributes to plant lifetime extension by avoiding incipient and sequential damage.

Monitoring systems are thus one of a number of measures implemented to protect the primary system, such as the "Basic Safety" general specification, pressure tests and in-service inspections.

Along with safety-related aspects, economic considerations play a major role in the implementation of monitoring systems. Important objectives, to name but a few, include:
- timely detection of faults and/or malfunctions and hence prevention of incipient damage; facilitation of damage correction and pinpointing of causes
- avoiding sequential damage
- reduction of inspection costs and radiation exposure.

Some examples for monitoring tasks and systems are enumerated below:
- loose parts monitoring
- vibration monitoring
- leakage monitoring
- crack monitoring (acoustic emission)
- fatigue monitoring (thermal stresses)
- seismic monitoring

2. System Concept [3, 4]

The monitoring systems presented are to be classified as information systems, i.e. their signals do not cause any automatic reaction of the reactor protection system, but may naturally lead to a decision to shut down the reactor, if a serious situation has been evaluated.

The functions of the monitoring system include acquisition, processing, storage and documentation of the necessary data and also provision of the other aids required for quick and reliable analysis.

The common technical concept, which is shown in Fig. 1, provides for autonomous modular individual systems based on the principle that identical functions (RMS generation, calibration, analog-digital conversion, filtering, etc.) are performed by identical modules. For analyses which exceed the capacity of their microprocessors, an option allows transferring compressed data records to a host computer or transferring in the form of remote data transmission. Another available option is the I & C interface which transfers analog and digital process data, from which operating modes can be recognized.

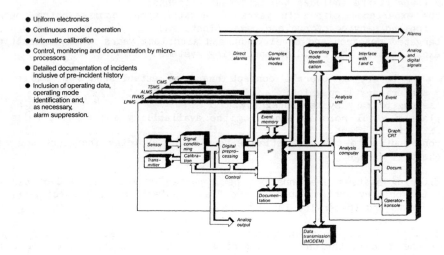

Figure 1: Monitoring Systems - Modular Design

The salient features of such a system concept are accentuated below:
(1) Continuous mode of operation
(2) Automatic calibration
(3) Control, monitoring and documentation by microprocessors
(4) Detailed documentation of events inclusive of pre-event history
(5) Differential complex alarm annunciation and/or suppression taking into account multiple input variables and process data
(6) Inclusion of operating data, operating mode identification

3. System Descriptions

Requirements concerning vibration, loose parts and leakage monitoring are part of German guidelines and safety standards. Therefore systems for these applications are implemented in most of the nuclear power plants in Western Germany.

KWU has developed a new generation of systems for these three tasks which are provided with modern microprocessor technology. They are designated as "Series '86" and described below.

3.1 Loose Parts Monitoring System (LPMS) [5, 6, 7]

The task of the LPMS is to detect loose parts entrained in or at least set in motion by the coolant. Such occurrences can neither be ruled out during the commissioning and starting up of new reactors nor during subsequent power operation.
For this reason, work on the development of loose parts monitoring systems began in the early 1970s. Our new microprocessor system, which became avail-

able in 1986, incorporates modern electronic technology and offers significant advantages over previously implemented systems, not only in monitoring
functions but also in data protection and analysis functions.

Binding requirements stipulating loose part monitoring systems have been
applicable to all German nuclear power plants for several years. KTA regulation 3204, with reference to DIN 25475 Part 1, forms the basis of these requirements [8].

This monitoring method detects and records structure-borne acoustic signals, which originate upon impact of parts on walls or internals, using appropriate sensors (typically piezoelectric accelerometers with sensitivity in
the range of audible sound).
Monitoring encompasses the primary system of pressurized water reactors, i.e.
the reactor pressure vessel (RPV), steam generators (SG), reactor coolant
lines (RCL) with a total of 14 sensors (1300 MWe plant).
Boiling water plants are monitored by 6 - 8 sensors at two levels in the
reactor pressure vessel.

Timely and reliable detection of loose parts entrained in the coolant can
avoid subsequent damage, e.g. to cladding, pump blading or fuel assemblies.
The benefits offered become more evident when one considers the fact that
loose parts are detected while still attached. These stationary acoustic
events, typically of low intensity, can be precursors of incipient or complete detachment of internal parts.

The system's diagnostic capabilities can best be demonstrated by an account of a recent incident when LPMS alarms and analysis of the information
provided led to a shutdown of the plant in order to secure a loose part [9].
During the restart phase of a PWR after refuelling, the LPMS signals sur-
passed thresholds in both surveillance channels of a steam generator at ir-
regular time intervals 2 - 3 times per second. The audio signals gave the
impression of metallic impacts. Plots of the signals showed burst structures typical for impacts of loose parts with amplitudes equivalent up to
30 g (g = acceleration due to gravity) and varying risetimes (Fig. 2).

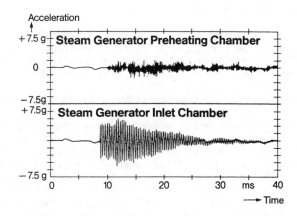

Figure 2: Impact Signals of LPMS

The events observed in the two surveillance channels were obviously corre-
lated, showing time lags varying between 0 and 1.8 ms.
The following interpretation was consistent with the information supplied by
LPMS events:
- Events with steep risetimes recorded at the monitoring channel "lower steam
  generator" and time lags of 1.8 ms over of recorded at the monitoring channel "upper steam generator" indicated impacts closer to the first sensor.
  Events with varying time lags are associated with impacts at different locations.
- A detached part was therefore suspected in the entrance chamber of the
  steam generator. Comparing the amplitudes of the signals with reference
  data, the mass of the detached part was estimated as more than 100 g.

The plant was consequently shut down in such a manner that the probability of the detached part reaching the reactor vessel was small. The LPMS was
used to monitor that the part actually did stay in the steam generator entrance chamber. After lowering the water level in the steam generator, the
part could be secured.
Inspection of the inner walls of the steam generator entrance chamber revealed that serious damage would have resulted if the part of about 200 g
mass had been allowed to remain in the chamber longer. Timely LPMS detection
of incipient damage can avoid repairs and prolonged outage times.

The above is a good example of the criteria and parameters which LPMS
evaluation and analysis are capable of providing. The salient features are:
- for the input signal of one channel
  + risetime
  + maximum amplitude
- for continuous signals of one acoustic event on various monitoring
  channels
  + time lags
  + ratios of the maximum amplitudes
- for results of acoustic events
  + response times (real time)
  + distribution of burst interval times
  + amplitude distribution
  + distribution of time lags

The KWU "Series '86" model line is capable of determining and documenting
these constants and of performing statistical functions, using software rou-
tines, high resolution graphics and simple interactive operation. Amplitude
distribution, shown in Fig. 3, is a typical example of LPMS.

Two further significant advantages offered by the new system are worthy
of mention:
- Absolutely every event which exceeds either the floating or the fixed
  threshold value is recorded, since the monitoring function is continuously accompanied by a high memory depth transient recorder. Recording
  is via fixed disk onto digital magnetic tape. At very high signal
  rates, at least the signal envelope (short time) is recorded to ensure
  that the goal of acquisition is met without any time gap.
- In addition to calibration of the instrument chain downstream of the
  charge amplifier with noise or a sinusoidal signal, a remotely controlled, permanently installed, functional test unit (impact exciter)
  is provided for automatic testing at any time during plant operation

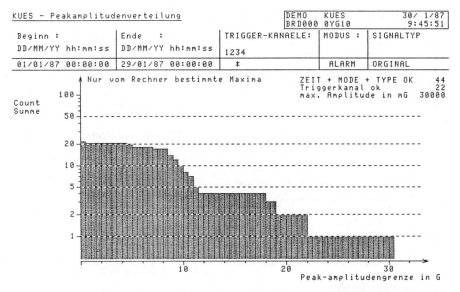

Beginn : DD/MM/YY hh:mm:ss	Ende : DD/MM/YY hh:mm:ss	TRIGGER-KANAELE: 1234	MODUS :	SIGNALTYP
01/01/87 00:00:00	29/01/87 00:00:00	*	ALARM	ORGINAL

Figure 3: Amplitude Distribution of LPMS Signals

using genuine acoustic signals. This device, designated "HIT 1" (see Fig. 4) can also replace the impacts currently performed only during major inspections. The unit is shielded against pressure, temperature and radiation and designed for years of maintenance-free operation. Calibration impacts are reproducible within narrow limits and thus allow a quantitative self-test of the individual channels. For four loop plants, two impact exciters are recommended. Backfitting involves a minimum of effort.

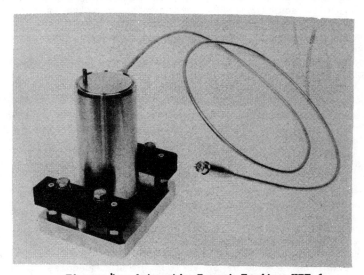

Figure 4: Automatic Impact Exciter HIT 1

3.2 Vibration Monitoring Systems (VMS) [5, 10]

Whereas vibration monitoring in active systems - rotating parts, bearings, gearboxes, motors, turbines etc. - is well known and accepted in the non-nuclear field, this system - with the exception of the reactor coolant pumps - deals with passive components of the primary system. Vibration is induced chiefly by the circulation of reactor coolant and the flexible nature of component supports provided to compensate for temperature changes.

The vibration monitoring system is intended to monitor the reactor coolant system including the reactor pressure vessel internals to ensure that changes in the mechanical integrity, particularly of the internals, are detected at an early point in time, even during operation.
VMS requirements for pressurized water reactors are given in RSK Guidelines [11] and KTA 3204 [8]. These regulations stipulate that it must be possible to perform vibration monitoring at any time, although the discontinuous mode is permitted, and monitoring must be performed at least three times per fuel cycle.

Standard VMS instrumentation encompasses over 30 measuring signals for a four loop PWR, which fall into the four following categories:
- absolute displacement
- relative displacement
- pressure fluctuations
- ex-core neutron flux noise

The task of the VMS consists chiefly of detecting changes of eigenfrequencies. Although some amplitude changes also occur, they provide less accurate information. In order to correctly interpret the information provided by the VMS, an association of the eigenfrequences with the different reactor components and internals is necessary. This correspondence is established by [12]:
- conducting measurements during the commisssioning phase ("cold" trial operation) with additional RPV instrumentation which is removed later; evaluating these measurements using correlation techniques
- correlation analyses of commissioning measurements with signals available during power operation
- theoretical and experimental modal analysis to simulate the mechanical behaviour of component structures [13].

The result of these activities is the knowledge of the vibration modes (e.g. pendular motion, vertical motion, flexural modes, shell modes, etc.), their assignment to the reactor components and distinction from fluid resonances (Fig. 5).

With this theoretical and empirical background, the spectra of the signals (mostly power density spectra (PSD)) can be analyzed and frequency shifts can be detected and correlated. The difficulty lies in determining whether the detected frequency shifts imply:
- a structural anomaly,
- a change which is normal for the prevailing reactor conditions (temperature, pressure, mass flow, power) or
- a natural tendency within design limits. This does require an exact knowledge of the dependency of various eigenfrequencies on the process variables.

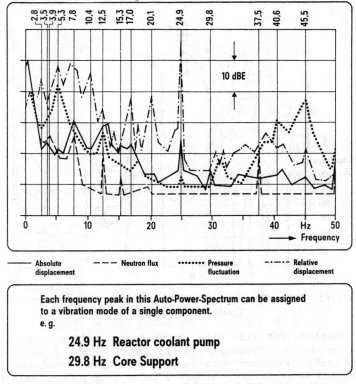

Figure 5: VMS – Frequency Peaks and Vibration Modes

In order to take anticipated frequency changes properly into account when analyzing VMS signal spectra, KWU has carefully acquired data at many different reactor conditions. For examples see Fig. 6, which shows PSD of reactor pressure vessel (RPV) displacement signals as a function of temperature [14].

In this figure, spectra peaks are seen which shift very little or not at all (particularly obvious for the peaks at 25 Hz which are due to the reactor coolant pump rotation) and others shifting quite a bit but in a gradual manner as a function of the corresponding internal state variable (e.g. peaks due to the core barrel motion around 7.5 and 10 Hz in the RPV displacement signals).

Once all these fundamentals are well understood and quantified, the VMS provides large amounts of information and often pinpoints the components and even the cause of anomalies, which can then be corrected.

Examples of early diagnosis of damage include [15]:
- contact of a reactor coolant pump casing with the DBA support
- fuel rod flexural vibration anomaly near a spacer
- integral relaxation of fuel assembly spacers
- loss of initial stress in the core barrel restraints
- loss of tension in the bolts of the core support assembly mounting.

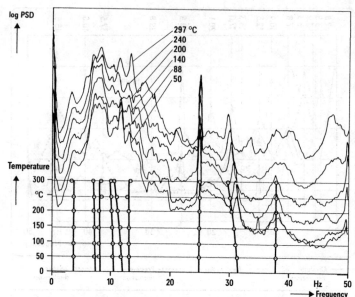

Figure 6: PSD - Spectra of RPV Displacement as a Function of Coolant Temperature

The KWU "Series '86" line also includes a vibration monitoring system, first installed in all "Convoy" plants, which offers a multitude of new possibilities and advantages with respect to signal acquisition, storage, documentation and analysis. This ensures, to an even greater extent than previously, increased plant availability and reliability and thereby lifetime extension.

3.3 Leakage Monitoring [16]

Leak detection and leakage monitoring in nuclear power plants are at present performed by a number of different systems and methods. These systems survey either whole compartments in the plant (by measurement of moisture, dew point, sump water level, temperature, air cooler condensation rate, and noble gas activity) [9] or a limited part of a component, e.g. a valve or a welding seam (moisture tapes).

The first category provides only a limited ability to pinpoint the position of the leak (identification of the component or system concerned), while in the second category the region covered by the surveillance is limited.

The KTA guideline 3201.4 [17] which is currently under revision is expected to stipulate leakage monitoring of the primary system employing either acoustic techniques with acoustic emission transducers directly coupled to the structure or the above-mentioned system based on combined acquisition of moisture, temperature, sump level, condensate activity, etc. The latter system is part of the scope of supply of newly erected KWU plants in the FRG and will be partially backfitted in certain existing plants.

The acoustic leakage monitoring system, also developed by KWU on the basis of microprocessor technology, has been tested for more than two years in a 900 MWe PWR in Germany [18]. In the preceeding years, extensive fundamental investigations were conducted [19].

This paper, however, focuses on a system which employs a new and unique method of leakage detection which is particularly well suited for slowly evolving leaks. That is, it shows high sensitivity (better than 1 kg per hour) but, compared with the acoustic system, a rather high response time (10 - 15 minutes) [20].

The main task of this system is the surveillance of long, insulated pipes or networks carrying water or steam.

The principle of operation can be described as follows (Fig. 7):
A permeable hose is mounted parallel to the pipe within the insulation. Moisture escaping from a leak diffuses through the wall of this hose. The moisture distribution in the interior of the sensor hose give a true image of the atmosphere in the insulation. The leak is detected and pinpointed by repeated flushing of the hose and measurement of the longitudinal distribution of the moisture. If the height of the leakage peak exceeds a specified level, a "leak alarm" is activated and the leak location is immediately determined from the flight time of the leakage peak and displayed.

Calibration of the measurement system is automatically carried out at preset time intervals by introducing a defined test leakage into the sensor hose and measuring it. In this way, a determination of measurement sensitivity can be made, and secondly, an exact determination of flow speed during pump operation, and hence the pinpointing of a leak is possible.

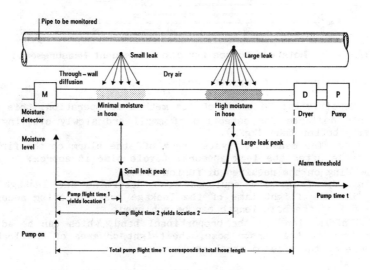

Figure 7: Monitoring of Moisture Level and Leaks Using the Sensor Hose Method

The technical design is summarized below:

- Sensor hose: The sensitivity of the measurement system is determined by the construction, wall thickness, diameter and material of the sensor hose. For medium-high temperatures (up to approx. 150 °C) with low radiation exposure, a plastic hose (e.g. PTFE) in an insulating tube made of VA is used. For higher temperatures and high radiation exposure, the hose is made completely in special steel with discrete diffusion points of sintered material. The hose is generally fitted directly on the pipe surface under the insulation.

- Moisture Detector: A central, capacitive moisture detector (modified Al_2O_3 probe) with associated measurement processing has performed very well.

- Data Acquisition and Evaluation: Fig. 8 gives an example of data output.

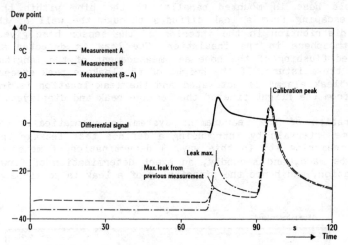

Figure 8: Moisture Curves for Two Subsequent Measurements

Thus the main features of the system are:

- Detection Sensitivity: In terms of its method of operation, this system is particularly designed for detection of small and slowly evolving leakages (sensitivity better than 1kg/h).
- Response Time: The measuring system sets off the alarm on the first interrogation cycle after the leak appears. (Cycle time is approx. 10 - 15 minutes, depending on the required diffusion time).
- Pinpointing the Leak: The equipment can determine the leakage position directly from the flight time of the leakage peak. Locating accuracies of approx. ± 5 % of the hose length can be achieved.
- Leak Rate Information: In the proportional band, which can be adjusted by the dimensions of the sensor hose, the height or area of the leakage peak is a measure of the size of the leak.

The occurrence and growth in size of a leak can be directly traced using a microprocessor to compare the periodically acquired and stored moisture profile data.

REFERENCES

[1]   Figlhuber, D., Streicher, V.: Betriebsüberwachung und wiederkehrende Prüfung des Reaktorkühlkreislaufes. 10. MPA-Seminar 1984, Band 1, Vortrag 20

[2]   Streicher, V., Jax, P., Ruthrof, K.: Unterstützung des Betreibes durch Schadensfrüherkennungssysteme, DAtF-Fachtagung "High Serre", Bonn, 1986

[3]   Jax, P., Ruthrof, K., Streicher, V.: Early Failure Monitoring Systems for LWR Operation. Proc. IAEA-Symposium "Nuclear Power Plant Availability, Maintainability and Operation", Vienna, 1985

[4]   Ruthrof, K., Streicher, V.: New Developments in the Field of Monitoring Systems. Atomkernenergie-Kerntechnik Vol.47 (1985) No.1, pp.22-26

[5]   Bauernfeind, V., Olma, B., Sunder, R., Wach, D.: Bewertung und Untersuchungen von Schadensfrüherkennungsverfahren am Primärkreis von Kernkraftwerken. GRS-Report GRS-A-1193, Munich, 1986

[6]   Dio, W.H., Geißler, K., Stölben, H.: Körperschallüberwachungssystem für DWR und SWR, Systemaufbau und Betriebserfahrung. Reaktoragung des DAtF, Düsseldorf, 1976, p.573

[7]   Olma, B.J.: Source Location and Mass Estimation in Loose Parts Monitoring of LWRs. Proc. SMORN IV, Dijon, 1984

[8]   Reaktordruckbehälter-Einbauten, KTA 3204, 10 April, 1984

[9]   Jax, P., Gast, P., Krien, K., Preußer, G.: Enhancing Reliable Operation by On-Line-Monitoring. Transactions ENC86, Geneva, 1986, Vol.2, pp.267-278

[10]   Sunder, R., Wach, D.: DWR-Schwingungsüberwachung, internationaler Status. GRS-Report GRS-A-1115, Munich, 1985

[11]   Leitlinien der Reaktorsicherheitskommission Druckwasserreaktoren 10-81 (1981)

[12]   Bauernfeind, V. et al.: Langzeituntersuchungen zum Schwingungsverhalten der RDB-Einbauten und Primärkreiskomponenten von Druckwasserreaktoren. Joint Final Report GRS/KWU GRS-A-875, September 1983

[13]   Wehling, H.J., Schüz, W., Wiemerslage, D.: Experimental Modal Analysis - An Auxiliary Means in Reactor Vibration Monitoring. Proc. CSNI Specialists Meeting on Continuous Monitoring for Assuring Coolant Circuit Integrity, London, August 12-14, 1985

[14]   Wehling, H.J., Klingler, K., Stölben, H.: The Influence of Thermohydraulic Parameters on the Dynamic Behaviour of KWU-PWRs. Proc.SMORN IV, Dijon, 1984

[15]   Sunder, R., Wach, D.: Überwachungs- und Diagnosesysteme zur Schadensfrüherkennung. GRS-Topical Meeting, 7th and 8th November 1985, Munich, 1985

[16]   Streicher, V., Jax, B., Leuker, W.: Localization and Sizing of Leaks by Special Techniques. Transactions ENC 86, Geneva, 1986, Vol.3, pp.553-559

[17]   Komponenten des Primärkreises von Leichtwasserreaktoren. Teil: Wiederhehrende Prüfung und Betriebsüberwachung. KTA 3201-4

[18]   Streicher, V., Leuker, W.: Acoustic Leakage Monitoring Systems - One Year of Experience. XII. Meeting of the European Working Group on Acoustic Emission (EWGAE), Cologne, 1983 (unpublished text is available from Kraftwerk Union, Erlangen, FRG)

[19]   Fischer, K., et al.: Leak Detection and Location by Means of Acoustic Methods. Trans. Am. Nucl. Soc. 31 (1979) 123

[20]   Issel, W., Swinger, P.: LASP - a Leakage Alarm System for Pipe Lines. Pipe Line Industry, June 1985, pp.26-31

MONITORING TECHNIQUE DEVELOPMENT FOR EQUIPMENT LIFE EVALUATION

T. Tsunoda and Y. Andoh
Nippon Atomic Industry Group Co., Ltd.,
Kawasaki (Japan)

T. Morioka and S. Ebata
Toshiba Corporation
Yokohama (Japan)

ABSTRACT

Recently, interest in plant life extension for the light water reactor has increased in Japan. To attain plant life extension, it is necessary to evaluate the life of equipment or components used in a plant. Many kinds of development to attain this purpose are now being carried out.

In this paper, the following three kinds of development concerned with plant life extension are discussed :

1. Techniques for the analysis and evaluation of problems occurring in plants.

2. Ultrasonic inspection techniques for the inner walls of pipes.

3. Techniques for monitoring control systems including pumps and valves using neutron and process instrumentation.

By analysing and evaluating any trouble occurring in a plant it is possible to understand the relationship between component reliability and operational history and it is also possible to find the fundamental data to estimate the component life. Ultrasonic techniques have been developed to evaluate pipe life by inspecting for any abnormal state on the inner wall.

The process instrumentation which is used for plant operation is useful for monitoring the abnormal condition of the control system including pumps and valves. Up to the present this technique has been used mainly as a diagnostic system in order to detect the abnormal condition at an early stage. Small vibration of the reactor core surroundings and abnormal conditions in the control system, including pumps and valves, were detected. This technique will be useful for component life evaluation.

MISE AU POINT DE TECHNIQUES DE CONTROLE EN VUE DE L'EVALUATION DE LA DUREE DE VIE DES EQUIPEMENTS

RESUME

Depuis peu, le Japon porte un intérêt croissant à la prolongation de la durée de vie des centrales nucléaires équipées de réacteurs à eau ordinaire. Pour pouvoir prolonger la durée de vie des installations, il faut évaluer celle de leurs équipements ou de leurs composants. Un grand nombre de techniques ont été mises en oeuvre à cet effet.

Ce document présente trois de nos techniques utilisées pour évaluer la prolongation de la durée de vie des installations .

1. Technique d'analyse et d'évaluation des anomalies constatées sur une installation

2. Contrôle par ultrasons de la paroi interne des tuyauteries

3. Technique de surveillance du système de regulation, y compris des pompes et de la robinetterie, au moyen de l'instrumentation neutronique et de l'instrumentation de conduite.

Grâce à l'analyse et à l'évaluation des anomalies se produisant sur une installation, il est possible, d'une part, de comprendre les relations existant entre la fiabilité des composants et les résultats d'exploitation des installations et, d'autre part, de trouver les données essentielles permettant d'apprécier la durée de vie des composants. Une technique par ultrasons a été mise au point pour évaluer la durée de vie des tuyauteries d'après l'altération de leur paroi interne.

L'instrumentation utilisée pour conduire la centrale sert à surveiller les états anormaux du système de régulation, y compris des pompes et de la robinetterie. Jusqu'à présent, cette technique est principalement utilisée comme aide au diagnostic pour déceler tout état anormal à un stade précoce. On a ainsi décelé de petites vibrations des éléments avoisinants le coeur du réacteur et un état anormal du système de régulation, y compris les pompes et la robinetterie. Cette technique sera utile pour évaluer la durée de vie des composants.

1. INTRODUCTION

Many discussions regarding plant life extension activities have been carried out. To attain plant life extension , it is necessary to evaluate the life of equipments and/or components used in a plant. The effort to attain life extension for the major components of the LWR , - reactor pressure vessel (RPV), reactor internals, containment, pipes and turbines. Of equal importance in a plant life extension program, however, is the instrumentation and control system including pumps and valves, which provides the necessary data and means to operate the plant within designed parameters. One of the key goals for life extension is the estimation of remaining equipment/component service life.

This paper discusses three kinds of developments, concerned with the plant life evaluation . At first, to evaluate and to investigate the relationship between component reliability and operating plant history, techniques to evaluate data on trouble which has occured in a plant have been developed. Data for equipment/component life evaluation and remaining equipment/ component service life will be estimated by the system. Ultrasonic inspection techniques for the inner walls of pipe are discussed for pipe life evaluation, by inspecting surfase condition (crack, erosion or corrosion) in the inner wall. The neutron and process instrumentation, which is used for plant operation, are useful for monitoring abnormal conditions in the control system, including pumps and valves. Up to the present, this technique has mainly been used as a diagnostic system, so as to detect abnormal conditions in the early stage. This technique will be great use for equipment/component life evaluation. Thermal cycles of a plant will decrease by utilizing these techniques.

2. TROUBLE DATA ANALYSIS SYSTEM

For plant life extension, it is important to analyze and to evaluate data on equipment/component trouble which has occured in a plant, because trouble data include important information concerning operating plant history and equipment/ component life. In order to meet these requirements, it is planned to develop a trouble data analysis system based on statistical analysis of equipment/component troubles[1].

The main functions of this system are as follow:
1) Management of equipment and trouble data,
2) Evaluation of equipment reliability and life span data,
3) Utilization of maintenance experience information,
4) Guide for equipment maintenance plan.

Figure 1 illustrates a conceptual scheme for the computer based trouble data analysis system. The system is composed of the following functions and data base:
1) Easy data input (keyword selection by mouse driver to pick up failure data, such as equipments, components , failure causes which are shown on a color CRT).
2) Data retrieval to obtain required information.
3) Evaluation of the failure occurance tendency, based on

statistical analysis.
4) Estimation of MTBF (Mean Time Between Failures) for equipments or components, and failure distribution based on reliability analysis.
5) Recommendation of an appropriate maintenance plan, determined as a result of a the comparison between actual trouble history and the present maintenance interval.
6) Four kinds of data base : trouble data, maintenance history data, equipment and component data, and technical specification data for replacement(components renewal cycle and equipment maintenance cycle).

Maintenance guide is provided through a series of data processings composed of above mentioned functions : data retrieval, statistical analysis, reliability analysis and judgement for appropriate maintenance plan. Items 3), 4) and 5) are especially useful for equipment/component life evaluation.

There are few data available regarding trouble in nuclear power plants, because equipment/components are usually replaced before trouble occurs. Therefore, it is very difficult to estimate MTBF for equipments/components due to the lack of data. In this system , it is possible to apply an "internal estimation" method for total time to determination without failure. Interval estimation for MTBF is based on a fixed time testing plan, that is obtained by confidence limits calculated using gamma-square distribution expressed by Eq.(1).

$$ (MTBF)_L = \frac{2T}{\chi^2(2(r+1),\alpha)} \tag{1} $$

where
$(MTBF)_L$: MTBF for one-tail(lower) confidence limit,
T : total time to determination or to failure,
χ^2 : gamma-square distribution function,
r : total number of observed failures,
α : significant level.

On the other hand,the Weibull-distribution function is given by Eq. (2).

$$ f(t) = m\,\frac{t^{m-1}}{t_o}\,\exp\left(-\frac{t^m}{t_o}\right) \tag{2} $$

Parameters m and t_o are shape parameter and scale parameter, respectively. Shape parameter shows characteristics of failure distribution as follows:
$m<1.0$ initial failure,
$m=1.0$ random failure,
$m>1.0$ wear-out failure.

The scale parameter is determined by life span. Maintenance guide is based on these parameters, as mentioned above and other information about failure cause, component failure rate during maintenance period or plant operation. If estimated MTBF is shorter than the specified maintenance cycle, it is not always neccessary to reduce the present maintenance cycle, as long as there is no wear out failure. On the other hand, even if estimated MTBF is much longer than the specified maintenance cycle, it may be necessary to consider a reduction in the maintenance cycle, in case the slightest wear-out failure is observed . In addition to the statistical trouble data analysis, the effect of supposed trouble, if such occurs , on plant operation should be taken into consideration, in order to change the maintenance cycle. As an example, Table 1 shows the results of reliability analysis on the point strip chart recorder . Failure mode is classified using the Weibull shape parameter. Maintenance guide is provided using the failure mode, MTBF, and the failure distribution. From the table, the following results are obtained:

1) Gear wheel failure and bearing failure caused by wear out (degradation) are estimated by the wear-out region of it's failure distribution. So, these components are in the end of the life time.

2) Positioner failure, caused by drift is estimated by the random region of it's failure distribution, but the occurence rate is comparatively high. Thus, reliability for this components is on the decrease.

This system is applicable to any equipment/component. The following information can be obtained:

1) A system has been developed, which has several fundamental functions, to manage equipment and trouble data, to analyze equipment reliability, to guide maintenance work and to estimate equipment life.

2) It is verified that this system is able to provide useful information for equipment maintenance and equipment life estimation.

3. ULTRASONIC INSPECTION SYSTEM FOR INNER WALL OF PIPING

Inspection for cracks, erosion or corrosion in piping is important for the plant life evaluation. To monitor the inner surface of the piping without removing the heat reserving material, an ultrasonic inspection technique has been developed. An ultrasonic transducer is installed inside the piping to be monitored. The ultrasonic pulse beam, 1 MHz , is projected through air or water to the inner wall of the piping. The reflected ultrasonic pulse at the inner wall is detected by the transducer again. If the transducer moves along a predetermined route, the reflected ultrasonic pulse is influenced according to the inner surface conditions. Figure 2 shows a blockdiagram of the system. The transducers are operated in the pulse-echo ultrasonic mode. The peak amplitude, pulse width and/or time difference between emitted and reflected pulse are used to identify the inner wall conditions. The peak amplitude and pulse width for the reflected signal are measured by the peak detector. The time difference between the emitted and reflected ultrasonic pulse is measured by the timer analyzer. The information on peak amplitude, pulse width and the time difference are applied to the micro-computer. These data are then displayed on the CRT.

Fundamental tests were performed using several test pieces which simulated cracks, erosion and corrosion . The following results were obtained:

1) Reflected ultrasonic signal peak is most sensitive to detect a small crack, erosion or corrosion,

2) Time difference is related to the depth of the crack, erosion
   or corrosion,
   Figure 3 shows a two dimensional pattern for the peak
amplitude for the simulated off normal surface condition. The
left hand side (A) shows a simulation of corrosion (about 20mmϕ
and 0.6 mm depth). Right hand side (B) shows a 1mmϕ and 1.5mm
depth hole. From the figure, it is found that the small off
normal surface condition is easily detectable. The simulated test
was also carried out, using the piping. It was found that the
system can be used to accurately inspect the inner wall.

4. NOISE ANALYSIS SYSTEM FOR MONITORING REACTOR CORE SURROUNDING
AND CONTROL SYSTEM
   An on-line diagnostic system, using neutron and process
instrumentation, has been used to maintain reliable operation for
a nuclear power plant[2],[3]. Main purposes of the system are to
aquire base line data and analyze the characteristics of the
plant and to detect abnormal conditions in the early stage. By
assisting in finding countermeasures for the trouble, the system
contributed to the plant availability and components life
extension. Especially, noise analysis is considered to be a
highly efficient tool for detecting abnormal conditionins in the
early stage. Noise (fluctuating) components in neutron or
process signals contain much information concerning process
dynamic characteristics. These components show the same
statistical characteristics, if core surroundings or process
conditions do not change very much.
   Therefore, in addition to the presently available monitoring
for process signals (DC components) , information contained in
noise component can be utilized effectively. If the noise
characteristics for process signals under normal operating
conditions are known, any significant change in these
characteristics suggests a change in core surroundings condition
or process dynamics (Fig.4). This leads to early detection of an
anomaly, because the change in core surroundings or process
characteristics may suggest an incipient failure of a component,
which is too small a change to be detected by a conventional
instrumentation system.
   Figure 5 shows a conceptional diagram of this system. The
system has five main functions, signal monitoring, data
recording, data analysis, data output and system control. Main
features of each function are described below.
1) Signal Montoring: Neutron signals and main process signals
   are monitored constantly. If the signal level or the signal
   noise level exceeds predetermined levels, the automatic
   data recording and data output functions are invoked. The
   system also monitors ON/OFF signals for plant scram and
   turbine trip and invokes the same action as needed.
2) Data Recording: Main process signal data for a maximum of
   256 signals are recorded by the trigger signal or manual
   demand. By the constant sampling and cyclic usage of memory
   area, data from 1 minute before to 4.5 minutes after the
   trigger can be recorded.
3) Data Analysis: The auto-power spectral density (APSD) for
   input signals and coherence or cross-power spectral density

(CPSD) for any two signals can be analyzed.
4) Data Output: Raw data or analysis results are output, using a plotting device. The data can be output automatically by trigger from signal monitoring or manual demand.
5) System Control: Sets up or changes system control parameters and also help editing the recorded data files.

Normally, the system is operated in automatic mode and no manual operation is necessary. With this system, plant signals are monitored constantly. If any change in the process signal is detected, the system automatically records the data, before and after the transient, and also outputs the recorded data to the operator. When the plant is stable, the system reports statistic information on monitoring signals and also acquires steady data to create a plant history database periodically.

Figure 6 shows a simplified blockdiagram for a BWR core and control systems. The reactor core is monitored, using many LPRM's, which are selected for each axial direction (B,C level). A total of 62 LPRM's are used for core surroundings diagnosis. With regard to control systems, components in control systems, including pump and valve, are divided into several components and are monitored so as to determined from which component an anomaly occurs, using input/output signals for each component.

Here, some examples related to the equipment or component life evaluation are discussed.

4.1 Core Surrounding Monitoring

It is very important to evaluate the behavior of the reactor core surrounding or RPV . Especially, thermal cycle or mechanical/neutronic vibration of the reactor core surroundings or the RPV have an important effect on plant life evaluation. Thermal cycle for the RPV or reactor core surroundings is monitored by measuring the temperature to be monitored. On the other hand, mechanical or neutronic vibration in the reactor core surrounding is monitored by noise analysis. One of the examples concerned with core surrounding vibration is LPRM cover tube vibration, which occurred about 7 years ago on BWR-4 plants[4]. The feature of this phenomenon is that out-channel leakage flow induces cover tube vibration and cover tubes hit channnel boxes. LPRM's in cover tubes vibrate at the same frequency as cover tube resonance frequency of about 3 Hz. Figure 7 shows an example of APSD pattern for an LPRM signal. The peak APSD about 3 Hz is caused by LPRM vibration. The vibration is able to detected by monitoring APSD around 3Hz. After repair, the LPRM tube cover stopped vibration and the peak APSD disappeared at once.

The RPV/core barrel vibration and fuel assembly vibration in PWR's were also monitored, using ex-core and in-core nuetron detectors[5]. In PWR's the core is contained in a cylindrical core barrel with its top rim supported at the vessel flange, as shown in FIG. 8. The time domain ex-core nuetron data shown in the same figure were capable of showing abrupt directional reversals, in which the mechanical shock was transmitted an accelerometer. Lack of proper barrel clamping at the vessel flange led to excessive motion and influenced the neutron signal and accelerometer. Abnormal vibration monitoring for fuel assembly associated with baffle-jetting was also made, using in-core and ex-core neutron detectors [6].

4.2 Control System Monitoring

The process instrumentation, which is used for plant operation, is useful for monitoring abnormal conditions for the control system. Usually, the control system is composed of sensor, electronic circuit and control devices, such as valves or pumps. Several abnormal conditions, monitored by the system, have been reported [7].

Figure 9 shows incipient trouble which occurred in the recirculation flow control system. The NRMS (normalized root mean square) of the speed controller (A) was increased by the noise level increase in the controller. After the speed controller was replaced, the NRMS value decreased to the normal level. Figure 10 shows the NRMS value change for a jet pump differential pressure. The normal jet pump differential pressure is also shown. The NRMS increase was caused by the amplifier, which is used as differential pressure to electric signal converter. After the amplifier was replaced, the NRMS value decreased to the normal value.

An incipient trouble occured in the feed water control system. The NAPSD (normalized auto power spectral density) of the feed water flow noise was decreased in the middle of the operating cycle (FIG.11). This phenomenon was caused by the decrease in the gain for the feedwater controller. Plant operation was continued after it was confirmed that the trouble did not directry affect the plant operation. During the next maintenance period, the feedwater controller was repaired. After repair, the NAPSD for the feedwater flow noise increased to the normal level.

5. CONCLUSION

Attaining plant life extension equipment or component life evaluation is very important. Here, three kinds of developments, concerned with the plant life extension, are discussed.

Although these techniques are very useful , it is necessary to develop many other techniques for plant life extension. Especially, inspection and monitoring RPV and core internals is most important for plant life extension, because these components are very dificcult to replace.

Inspection or monitoring techniques should be developed for key components. Also, a synthetic monitoring system for plant life extension should be developed.

REFERENCES
(1) S.SHIMIZU, et al.; "Equipment Maintenance Guide System Based on Statistical Trouble Data Analysis", NAIG Annual Review, (1986)
(2) Y.ANDOH, et al.; "Development of BWR Plant Diagnosis System Using Noise Analysis",J.Nucl. Sci. Tech., vol.20,769-780, (1983)
(3) A.KISHI, et al.; "Experience and Development of On-line BWR Surveillance System",2nd International Topical Meeting on

Nuclear Plant Thermal Hydraulic and Operation, (APRIL 1986), 8.30-8.35

(4) K.BERINGER,et al.; "Observation of In-core Instrument Tube Vibration in a BWR by Evaluating Reactor Noise Data",Prog. Nucl. Energy, vol.1, 183-185,(1977)
(5) J.A.THIE; "Theoretical considerations and their Application to Experimental Data in the Determination of Reactor Internals' Motion from Stochastic Signals", Prog. Nucl. Energy ,vol.2, 253-259, (1975)
(6) P.BERNARD, et al.; "PWR Core Monitoring by In-core Noise Analysis", Prog. Nucl. Energy, vol.9, 541-556, (1982)
(7) A.TANABE, et al. ; "On-line Operation of a BWR Plant Surveillance System for Practical Use",The Thermal and Nuclear Power(in Japanese),vol.37,54-63,(1986)

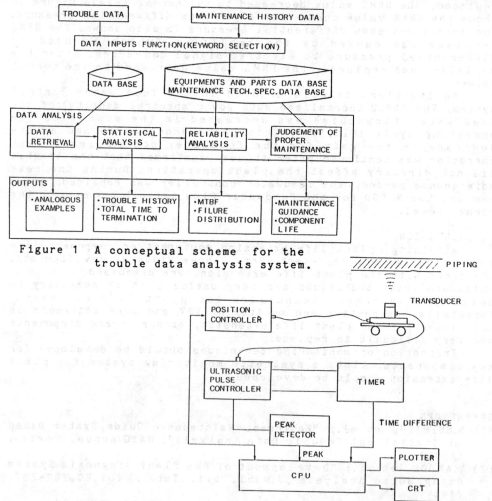

Figure 1 A conceptual scheme for the trouble data analysis system.

Figure 2 Blockdiagram of the ultrasonic inspection system.

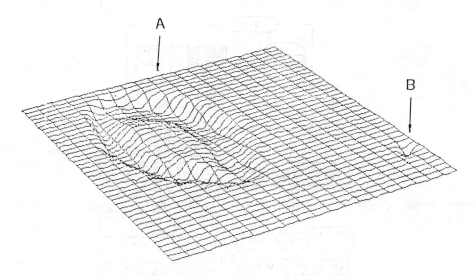

Figure 3　Reflected ultrasonic pulse peak pattern.

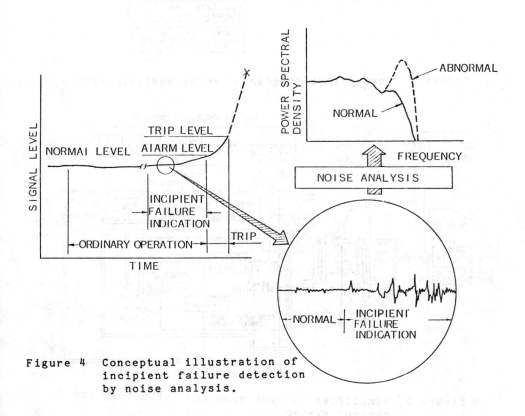

Figure 4　Conceptual illustration of incipient failure detection by noise analysis.

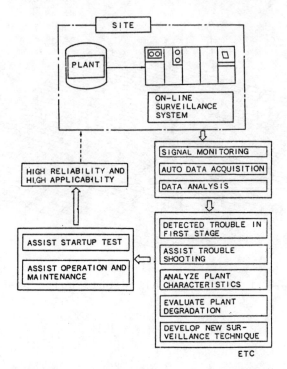

Figure 5 Conceptinal diagram of noise analysis system.

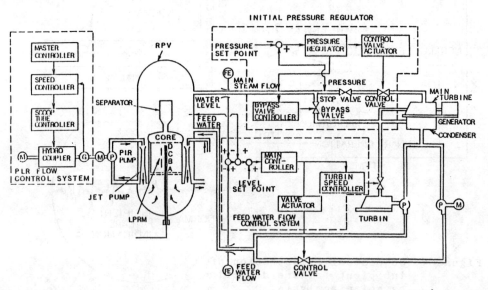

Figure 6 Simplified blockdiagram for a BWR core and control system.

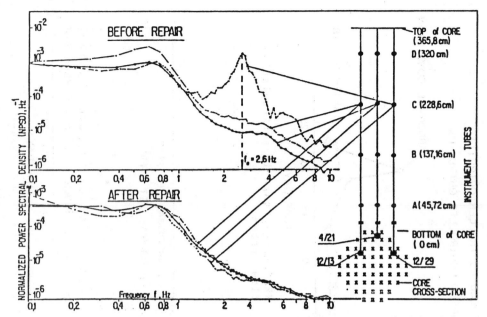

Figure 7   NPSD of three in-core chamber output signals
at the same core height (C- position).

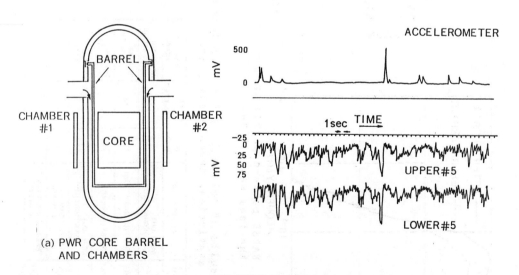

(a) PWR CORE BARREL
AND CHAMBERS

(b) OUTPUT SIGNALS OF VESSEL
ACCELEROMETER AND ION CHAMBER
BEFORE REPAIRING

Figure 8   PWR core barrel and output signals for accelerometer
and ion chambers before repairing.

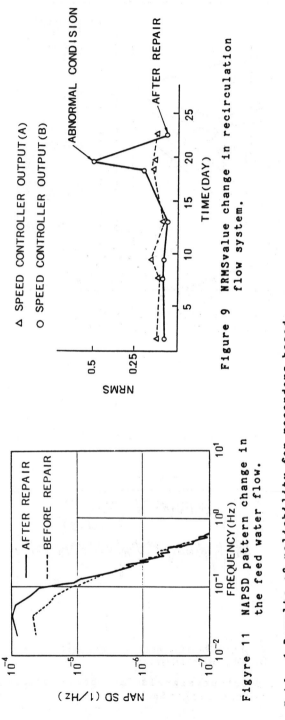

Figure 9 NRMS value change in recirculation flow system.

Figure 11 NAPSD pattern change in the feed water flow.

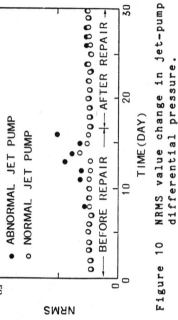

Figure 10 NRMS value change in jet-pump differential pressure.

Table 1 Results of reliability for recorders based on statistical trouble analysis.

NO	COMPONENT	FAILURE CAUSE	MTBF (year)	WEIBULL SHAPE PARAMETER	FAILURE MODE
1	GEAR WHEEL	WEAR OUT (DEGRADATION)	19.4	1.78	WEAR-OUT FAILURE
2	POSITIONER	DRIFT (DEGRADATION)	20.7	0.86	RANDOM FAILURE
3	PEN HOLDER	INJURY (RANDOM)	25.9	0.76	INITIAL FAILURE
4	BEARING	WEAR OUT (DEGRADATION)	32.3	2.10	WEAR-OUT FAILURE
5	POSITIONER	MIS-ADJUSTMENT (INITIAL)	–	–	–
6	ELECTRIC COMPONENTS	INFERIOR QUALITY (INITIAL)	–	–	–

DISCUSSION

H. ALDER, Switzerland

The replacement of the recirculation pipes at Muehleberg was not done because of past transient analysis, residual life consideration, lab samples, etc., but ultrasonic inspection showed that cracks went 3/4 through the wall. Only then did the utility and the authorities decide to act. The lesson is that close and good monitoring is the strongest argument for action. Here a major effort is justified.

G. ECKERT, Federal Republic of Germany

I agree with you. There was urgent need to repair or replace.

US utilities who face the same problems prefer the local and continuous repairs and inspections (IHSI, overlay cladding) which I think are short-term and also short lasting measures.

L. DI PALO, Italy

Has the NPP at Santa Maria de Garona ever had induction heating technique applied, in order to avoid intergranular stress corrosion cracking?

J. OLASO, Spain

No. After replacing the pipe we have injected hydrogen to control chemistry in the loop. Laboratory results give us confidence that this will avoid corrosion cracking, but we have never applied induction heating treatment to the welds.

G. SCHÜCKTANZ, Federal Republic of Germany

In late 1984 you performed overlay cladding of the recirculation piping. What was the reason for replacing this piping in 1985 ?

J. OLASO, Spain

Because the Spanish Regulatory Agency refused to give us credit for this type of repair. They did not consider this repair valid for more than one cycle.

P.R. PARKMAN, United Kingdom

Could Herr Streicher clarify how the sensitivity of the leak detection system is improved by being cumulative, as I understood the system to display differences ?

V.J. STREICHER, Federal Republic of Germany

The system measures and displays the moisture distribution along the measuring (sensor) hose. Thus it measures the moisture _accumulated_ during a preset diffusion time (e.g. 1/2 h). The display can also inform on _differences_ between two or more sequential measurements as well as the result of only one cycle.

A. BUONO, Italy

With reference to loose part monitoring system, if I understood correctly, you have sensors only on the primary side of Nuclear Steam Supply System. Can your Loose Parts Monitoring System detect loose parts in the secondary side of steam generator ? Do you have any experience on that ?

V.J. STREICHER, Federal Republic of Germany

On each Steam Generator (SG) as well as transducer in the primary chamber we have one mounted near the inlet of the feedwater line. It is mainly devoted to excluding extraneous noise and thus avoid false alarms. Of course it is also used for detecting transient signals in the secondary SG-part. Evaluation and identification of these signals are more difficult due to complex wave paths.

Experience, however, is available based on some actual events which occurred recently.

A. REMOND, France

Is your equipment for acoustic leakage monitoring able to detect and localise a SG leaking tube ?

V.J. STREICHER, Federal Republic of Germany

Although acoustic leakage monitoring is basically able to detect tube leaks in heat exchangers and is performed in fossil fuelled plants, monitoring of radioactivity is far more sensitive for detecting leakages.

Is the reactor diagnosis system, developed by Mr. Tsunoda's group, already installed as a whole or is it a conceptual study ?

T. TSUNODA, Japan

Several parts of the system have already been used in support of reactor operation. Some small abnormal conditions during operation were detected by sub-systems and appropriate countermeasure were carried out. But the whole system has not yet been installed in an actual plant.

V.J. STREICHER, Federal Republic of Germany

What is the origin of the reactor noise data you presented ?

T. TSUNODA, Japan

These data were obtained at a BWR plant.

G. ECKERT, Federal Republic of Germany

Can anyone quote a study initiated or completed that gives economic comparison of major replacement with repeated repairs ?

A. BUONO, Italy

The economic evaluation for repair or the replacement of a piece of equipment is always performed by the utility on the basis of many parameters : manrems, cost of repair or replacement, shut-down duration, time schedule, cost of replacing energy, etc. It is not easy nor always effective to transfer all these parameters to the manufacturers. Manufacturers should be able to give utilities "cost" data in order that they may evaluate "benefit" for different solutions.

G. SCHÜCKTANZ, Federal Republic of Germany

I am interested in utilities' opinion on the use of monitoring systems which are now available on the market.

P.R. PARKMAN, United Kingdom

Perhaps I can provide a reply from one of the utilities. CEGB uses surveillance systems to monitor those plant areas where experience has shown that problems may arise or from which designers require information. These have been successful in giving early indication of a deteriorating condition which enables remedial work to be planned. However, I would like to know from the speakers how these systems can be used for making life extension decisions as opposed to avoiding sudden plant failure.

V.J. STREICHER, Federal Republic of Germany

Monitoring systems, especially those which acquire continuously acoustic or vibrational waves in all frequency ranges can provide much more information than can be derived from simple "threshold crossing" methods. Problems up to now are evaluation criteria and methods. But with longer operational experience the data base is increasing and more sophisticated analysis methods can be expected.

C.J. MARCHESE, United Kingdom

Plant life extension decisions will depend on the economics of the main components in the nuclear steam supply system. Such components are subject to many types of problem such as IGSCC and are not amenable to the types of monitoring discussed. Therefore while component monitoring will be useful in optimising the maintenance of normally replaceable items, its use for justification of plant life extension alone could be limited.

SESSION V

ECONOMIC ANALYSES ON PLANT LIFE EXTENSION

SEANCE V

ANALYSE ECONOMIQUE DE LA PROLONGATION DE LA DUREE DE VIE DES CENTRALES

Chairman – Président

T.T. FLETCHER

(United States)

ELECTRICITY-COST SAVINGS OBTAINED BY MEANS OF NUCLEAR PLANT LIFE EXTENSION

L. Forest and T. Fletcher
Data Resources, Inc.
Washington, D.C., USA

A. DuCharme
Sandia National Laboratories
Albuquerque, N.M., USA

D. L. Harrison
U.S. Department of Energy
Washington, D.C., USA

ABSTRACT

This study examines savings caused by nuclear-plant life extension (NUPLEX) and describes the effects of changes in assumptions on costs and technology using an approach simpler than the large economic-model simulations used in other reports. Under the simplified approach, we estimate savings at the broad national level by comparing projected costs/kWh for the typical NUPLEX plant with those for new coal-fired (NEWCOAL) plants, which seem the most likely alternative in most regions. While ignoring some complications handled by the large, regionally disaggregated econometric models, the approach used in this study has advantages in sensitivity analyses. It reveals relationships between savings and basic assumptions on costs and technology in a more transparent way than in large-model simulations.

We find that, absent major technological breakthroughs for present generating options, NUPLEX saves consumers money on their electric bills under most plausible economic scenarios. Using mid-range assumptions, we find that NUPLEX saves consumers a total of about $180 billion spread over the period 2010-50. Under optimistic assumptions, the savings swell to over $900 billion. Under extremely pessimistic assumptions, the savings actually turn negative.

This wide range of estimates largely reflects the uncertainty in cost projections. Within plausible limits, higher- or lower-than-expected load growth does not affect the savings estimates. The NUPLEX construction costs stand out as the most critical unknown. If they turn out to be 50 percent ($500 billion) above the baseline estimate (with all other assumptions constant), savings would fall by almost 60 percent ($105 billion). A 50 percent rise in nuclear fuel costs would drop baseline savings by almost 22 percent. A 50 percent increase in nuclear-plant operations-and-maintenance (O&M) costs, would cut baseline savings by about 36 percent. These sensitivities highlight the need for continued monitoring of economic developments.

REDUCTION DU COUT DE L'ENERGIE ELECTRIQUE AUX ETATS-UNIS D'AMERIQUE GRACE A LA PROLONGATION DE LA DUREE DE VIE DES CENTRALES NUCLEAIRES

RESUME

Cette étude, qui fait appel à une méthode plus simple que les grandes simulations de modèles économiques utilisées dans d'autres rapports, examine les économies découlant de la prolongation de la durée de vie des centrales nucléaires (NUPLEX) et décrit l'incidence de la variation des hypothèses visant les coûts et la technologie. Cette méthode simplifiée nous permet d'estimer les économies au niveau national en comparant le coût prévu du kWh pour une centrale NUPLEX typique avec celui des nouvelles unités au charbon (NEWCOAL) qui semblent représenter la variante la plus vraisemblable dans la plupart des régions. Tout en évitant certaines complications traitées par les grands modèles économétriques à ventilation régionale, la méthode utilisée dans cette étude présente des avantages pour les analyses de sensibilité. En effet, les relations entre les économies réalisables et les hypothèses de base retenues pour les coûts et la technologie sont mises en évidence de façon plus transparente que dans les simulations des grands modèles.

Il apparaît qu'en l'absence de progrès technologiques majeurs dans les techniques de production actuelles, NUPLEX réduit la facture d'électricité des consommateurs dans les scénarios économiques les plus vraisemblables. Sur la base d'hypothèses moyennes, nous avons calculé que NUPLEX permet aux consommateurs d'économiser globalement quelque 180 milliards de dollars étalés entre 2010 et 2050. Sur la base d'hypothèses optimistes, les économies passent à plus de 900 milliards de dollars. Sur la base d'hypothèses extrêmement pessimistes, NUPLEX se traduit par une augmentation des coûts.

Cette large fourchette d'estimations reflète bien l'incertitude des prévisions de coûts. A l'intérieur de limites plausibles, une croissance de la consommation supérieure ou inférieure aux prévisions n'a aucune incidence sur les estimations d'économies. Les coûts de construction des centrales NUPLEX représentent la grande inconnue. Si ces coûts se révélaient supérieurs de 50 pour cent (500 milliards de dollars) à l'estimation de base (toutes hypothèses étant égales par ailleurs), les économies diminueraient de près de 60 pour cent (105 milliards de dollars). Une augmentation de 50 pour cent du coût du combustible nucléaire entraînerait une réduction de près de 22 pour cent des économies estimées dans l'hypothèse de base. Une augmentation de 50 pour cent du coût d'exploitation et d'entretien des centrales nucléaires réduirait ces mêmes économies d'environ 36 pour cent. Cette sensibilité des résultats souligne le besoin de continuer à contrôler l'évolution économique.

This study compares the relative cost and efficiencies of nuclear plants with new coal-fired plants, which are viewed on average as the most likely new generating capacity alternative. This paper is divided into two sections. We begin by reiterating briefly the point made in an earlier U.S. paper that the United States will need either to extend the operating lives of its nuclear plants or to replace them with alternative generating capacity. We make the point here by showing that, even under extremely pessimistic projections of economic growth and optimistic assumptions on energy conservation that together lead to slow load growth, the United States will need the domestic generating capacity that could be provided by NUPLEX. The rest of the section derives the NUPLEX savings estimates and measures their sensitivity to changing economic assumptions.

U.S. NUCLEAR CAPACITY NEEDS TO BE EXTENDED OR REPLACED

Despite uncertainty over the outlook for electricity demand, the aging and normal retirement of U.S. electricity-generating facilities over the next 20-50 years will so decimate existing capacity that the United States will have no choice but either to extend the service lives of nuclear plants or to replace them with alternative generating plants. As Figure 1 shows, if we assume no nuclear-plant extension, service-life extension for most larger fossil plants, and no new capacity other than that currently planned, normal retirement would cause the United State's ability to satisfy electricity demand to fall by two-thirds during 2010-2030. Further, as Table I shows, even under extremely pessimistic projections of load growth, the share of existing and currently planned capacity that would survive to 2030 would be woefully inadequate. Clearly, cogeneration, importation of power, and energy-conservation incentives such as seasonal or time-of-day rates could do little to ameliorate this large shortfall. Thus, concerns over the level of demand in 2010-30 have little to do with the question whether NUPLEX makes sense. Costs of fuel, capital, and operations and maintenance will determine whether NUPLEX saves money compared with competing options. We turn to this issue next.

NUPLEX SAVES MONEY IN COMPARISON WITH NEWCOAL

Under most plausible assumptions on fuel and plant-construction costs, NUPLEX saves money in comparison with NEWCOAL. We estimate the electricity-cost savings by comparing projections of bus-bar costs/kWh (that is, costs/kWh at the generating plant) for NUPLEX and NEWCOAL plants. These savings estimates mainly reflect assumptions on the costs (of fuel, capital, and O&M) and the efficiencies (heat rates and availabilities) of NUPLEX and NEWCOAL facilities. By assuming similar capacity factors for both types of plants, the estimates exclude the savings that might arise from preferential use of NUPLEX plants, allowing the displacement of higher-cost fuel (coal). On the other hand, they ignore the costs of having capacity unavailable during plant overhaul, which is a drawback of NUPLEX but not of NEWCOAL. We express all savings estimates in 1986 dollars to make interpretation of the results easier.

KEY ASSUMPTIONS ON COSTS AND PLANT EFFICIENCIES(1)

Table II lists the important assumptions on costs and plant efficiencies. These assumptions specify values for uncertain variables over the distant future, so we present a range of possible outcomes. The base assumptions represent the midpoints of the ranges projected for all of the key variables. The pessim assumptions combine extreme (either high or low) values that are most unfavorable to NUPLEX, whereas the optim assumptions combine extreme values that are favorable to NUPLEX. Note that we emphasize movements in costs affecting NUPLEX and NEWCOAL relative to each other, since, so long as these are the competing generating options, relative rather than absolute costs will determine whether NUPLEX saves money. We express costs in terms of real (that is, constant 1986) dollars. This choice of measurement

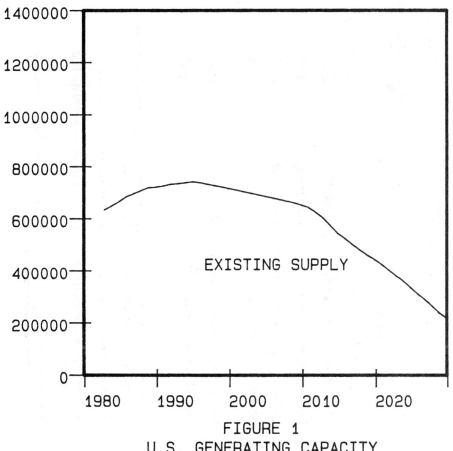

FIGURE 1
U.S. GENERATING CAPACITY
(MEGAWATTS)

Table I

ASSUMPTIONS GIVING RISE TO LOW-GROWTH PEAK LOAD

	Average Annual Growth 1986 - 2030
Pessim GNP a/	1.7
PLUS: Low-growth in ratio (energy/GNP) b/	(2.0)
PLUS: Low-growth in ratio (electricity/energy) c/	(0.0)
PLUS: Low-growth in ratio (peak load/annual)	(.5)
EQUALS: PEAK LOAD	(.8)
Memo: No-extension/expansion supply	(2.6)
Year of supply inadequacy d/	2010

a/ Labor-force growth implied by census low-range population forecast plus 1970–80 growth in real GNP per worker.

b/ 1974–85 growth rate in BTUS consumed per dollar of real GNP.

c/ No growth in electricity share falls short of all recent historical experience.

d/ Year in which projected peak demand moves within 15 percent of no-extension/no-expansion supply.

Table II
ASSUMPTIONS FOR EACH OF THREE SCENARIOS

Item	Base	Scenario Pessim	Optim
Fuel Costs	Real coal prices grow 1 percent annually from $1.60/MBtus in 1986; No change from $.60/MBtus in real price of nuclear fuel; Midrange estimate of $.06/MBtus for nuclear fuel reprocessing/disposal.	No real growth in coal prices. Delivered costs of nuclear fuel same as in base; High range estimate of $.15/MBtus for nuclear fuel reprocessing/disposal.	Real coal prices grow 3 percent annually. Delivered cost of nuclear base; Low range estimate of $.03/MBtus for nuclear fuel reprocessing/disposal.
Capital Costs	$1000/kw overnight construction costs for NUPLEX in 1986 plus 1 percent annual real rise;$1300/kw overnight construction costs for NEWCOAL in 1986 plus 1 percent annual real rise; 3 percent annual real after-tax cost of capital.	$1700/kw overnight construction costs for NUPLEX in 1986 plus no real growth;$1300/kw overnight construction costs for NEWCOAL in 1986 plus no real growth; 3 percent annual real after-tax cost of capital.	$300/kw overnight construction costs for NUPLEX in 1986 plus 2 percent annual real rise;$1300/kw overnight construction costs for NEWCOAL in 1986 plus 2 percent annual real rise; 3 percent annual real after-tax cost of capital.
O & M Costs	NUPLEX: $40/kw-yr fixed plus $.0003/kWh variable in 1986; NEWCOAL:$28/kw-yr fixed plus $.0014/kWh variable in 1986; 1 percent annual real growth.	NUPLEX: same as base in 1986; NEWCOAL:$22.50/kw-yr fixed plus $.0011/kWh variable in 1986; 1 percent annual real growth.	NUPLEX: sames as base in 1986; NEWCOAL:$34/kw-yr fixed plus $.0017/kWh variable in 1986; no real growth.
Capacity Factor	NUPLEX: 65% NEWCOAL: 65%	NUPLEX: 62% NEWCOAL: 65%	NUPLEX: 65% NEWCOAL: 62%
Heat Rates	NUPLEX: 10,700 MBtus/kWh NEWCOAL: 10,000 MBtus/kWh	NUPLEX: 10,700 MBtus/kWh NEWCOAL: 9,500 MBtus/kWh	NUPLEX: 10,700 MBtus/kWh NEWCOAL: 10,700 MBtus/kWh

units does not affect the basic analysis, but it leads to savings estimates expressed in the 1986 dollars that are most familiar to us.

Fuel Costs: The different scenarios specify a range of forecasts for delivered prices (including transportation and other distribution charges on the way to the generating station) of coal and nuclear fuel. We also give a range of values for the costs of reprocessing or disposing of spent nuclear fuel.

The baseline assumes that delivered prices for coal rise 1 percent per year faster than for nuclear fuel, reflecting the view that supplies of low-cost coal are more limited relative to demand than supplies of nuclear fuel. For this scenario, we assume that reprocessing or disposal of nuclear fuel costs $.06/MBtu (1986 $'s), near the midpoint of a range of estimates reported in a recent DOE study. The pessim assumes no growth in coal prices relative to nuclear fuel and a $.15/MBtu high-range estimate for nuclear reprocessing/disposal costs. The optim assumes that coal prices rise 3 percent per year faster than nuclear-fuel prices and that reprocessing/disposing of used nuclear fuel costs only $.03/MBtu.

Capital Costs: Capital costs may be measured by the annual average (real) payment required over the life of an investment so as to pay back the outstanding principal with interest and a competitive return on equity. Although utilities may well choose to time the recovery of capital costs in rates in ways different than implied by a constant real charge, whatever timing they choose must yield an annual average cost equalling the one being computed here.(2) Such annualized capital costs depend on 4 things: (1) costs of initial plant construction (or overhaul) plus the present (discounted) value of any interim investments required over the life of the plant as well as decommissioning costs less scrap value; (2) the service life of the plant, determining how quickly the investment cost needs to be charged to depreciation; (3) the utility's cost of capital, measuring the percentage return on total capital that must be earned so as to pay interest on debt and a competitive yield on equity; and (4) the net costs (or benefits) of taxation, counting as costs all related income- and property-tax liabilities and as benefits the tax savings due to depreciation deductions and the like. We hold tax effects constant across the 3 scenarios. Each scenario assumes taxation will remain as projected by DRI in its July 1986 long-run forecast. This forecast assumed passage of a tax-reform package resembling the Senate bill. We also hold fixed the assumptions on service lives: 20 years for NUPLEX and 50 years (30 years plus 20 years PLEX) for NEWCOAL. The other assumptions can vary widely across the scenarios, reflecting the enormous uncertainty in projected values for utilities' costs of capital and for the costs of NUPLEX and NEWCOAL construction.

The baseline assumes that, in 1986, overnight construction costs $1000/kw for NUPLEX and $1300/kw for NEWCOAL (including pollution-abatement facilities and interim and PLEX investments). The baseline assumes that both of these costs will grow 1 percent annually in real terms (1986 dollars) and that utilities' real after-tax cost of capital averages 3 percent per annum. The pessim assumes that 1986 overnight construction costs $1700/kw for NUPLEX and again $1300/kw for NEWCOAL. This scenario assumes that these construction costs stay fixed in real terms. The pessim assumes that utilities' real after-tax cost of capital averages 3 percent per annum. The optim assumes that, in 1986, overnight construction of NUPLEX costs only $300/kw, compared with the $1300/kw value for NEWCOAL. This scenario assumes that costs of both types of construction rise at a 2 percent annual real rate. As in the baseline, we assume that utilities face a 3 percent annual after-tax real cost of capital. Later, we show how these varying assumptions lead to different annual real costs of owning NUPLEX and NEWCOAL plants. These annual ownership costs spread over kwh-generation affect average costs per kwh.

O&M Costs: These costs consist of all production expenses except fuel costs. They include compensation of operators, maintenance workers, security guards, and supervisors, as well as costs of spare parts, insurance, and materials used in maintenance or operations. For the most part, these costs are fixed with regard to kwh generation. However, some materials such as lubricants in nuclear plants and water and chemicals used in pollution-abatement facilities at coal plants will vary with generation.

The baseline assumes that, as of 1986, fixed O&M costs $40/kw-yr at NUPLEX and $28/kw-yr at NEWCOAL plants, and variable O&M costs $.0003/kWh at NUPLEX and $.0014/kWh at NEWCOAL plants. The larger variable costs at NEWCOAL plants stems from the chemicals used for pollution abatement. The baseline assumes 1 percent real growth for each of these categories of O&M costs.(3) The pessim and optim use the baseline assumptions for 1986 O&M costs at NUPLEX plants but vary the other assumptions. The pessim scenario assumes that, in 1986, NEWCOAL fixed O&M costs $22.50/kw-yr and variable O & M costs $.0011/kWh. The pessim assumes 1 percent real growth in NUPLEX and NEWCOAL fixed and variable O&M. The optim assumes that, in 1986, NEWCOAL fixed O&M costs $34/kw-yr and variable O&M costs $.0017/kWh and that all categories of O&M costs stay fixed in real terms.

Capacity Factors: Availability rather than the capacity factor represents the key variable underlying comparisons between NUPLEX and NEWCOAL, reflecting our focus on supply conditions. However, we need the capacity factors for the bus-bar calculations and we vary the factors to mirror different assumptions on availability.

The baseline assumes a 65 percent capacity factor both for NUPLEX and NEWCOAL. Although the baseline 65 percent capacity factor may appear to be too high, we take the position that 65 percent will be possible in the future. The pessim assumes greater availability for NEWCOAL as indicated by a capacity factor of 65 percent compared with 62 percent for NUPLEX. The optim reverses this assumption, specifying a capacity factor of 65 percent for NUPLEX and 62 percent for NEWCOAL.

Heat Rates: Under current technology, coal plants operate at higher temperatures and thermal efficiencies than nuclear plants. However, pollution-abatement facilities will rob coal-fired plants of some of this advantage and the efficiencies of nuclear plants could rise over the next 30-40 years. Thus, we use a range of assumptions on heat rates.

The baseline assumes 10,700 MBtu/kWh for NUPLEX and 10,000 MBtu/kWh for NEWCOAL. The pessim assumes somewhat higher than baseline efficiency for NEWCOAL (9,500 MBtu/kWh) and the optim assumes that NUPLEX efficiency reaches parity with NEWCOAL (10,700 MBtu/kWh).

CALCULATING BUS-BAR COSTS/KWH

The assumptions just discussed allow us to calculate, for each of the 3 economic scenarios, costs/kwh at the generating plant for NUPLEX and NEWCOAL facilities. Tables III through V show the derivation of these values for costs/kWh.

Table III shows the calculation of annual capital costs. Overnight capital costs appear on line (1). (Note that these costs include the discounted value of future interim investments plus decommissioning costs less plant scrap value.) These costs combined with assumptions on the speed of construction and the cost of capital determine AFUDC listed on line (2). The sum of overnight construction costs and AFUDC gives the investment value on line (3) that must be paid off with interest over the life of the plant. Some of this investment get paid for through tax benefits. For example, the investment entitles the utility to depreciation deductions reducing taxable income and thereby tax liabilities over several years. This stream of tax savings may be viewed as paying for a part of the investment. Capitalizing these tax savings, -- on line (4) -- we get the investment value paid off in this way. Deducting line (4) from (3), we get -- on line (5) -- the value of capital that must be paid for through

	SCENARIO					
	BASE		PESSIM		OPTIM	
	NUPLEX	NEWCOAL	NUPLEX	NEWCOAL	NUPLEX	NEWCOAL
1) Overnight Construction Cost($/kw)	$1403	$1823	$1700	$1300	$588	$2549
2) PLUS: AFUDC[a/] ($/kw)	53.95	113.89	65.37	81.22	22.61	159.25
3) EQUALS: Invested Capital ($/kw)	1456.95	1396.89	1765.37	1381.22	610.61	2708.25
4) LESS: Present Value of Tax ($/kw) Benefits[b/]	351.89	437.52	408.00	312.00	141.12	611.76
5) EQUALS: Capital at Risk ($/kw)	1105.06	1499.37	1357.37	1069.22	469.49	2096.49
6) Annualized After-Tax Real ($/kw-yr) Cost of Capital[c/]	73.48	57.90	90.25	41.29	31.22	81.00
7) DIVIDED BY: (1-Marginal Tax Rate)	.6	.6	.6	.6	.6	.6
8) EQUALS: Annualized Before- ($/kw-yr) Tax Real Cost of Capital	122.47	96.50	150.42	68.82	52.03	134.93
9) PLUS: Annual Average Real ($/kw-yr) Property Taxes[d/]	56.12	72.92	68.00	52.00	23.52	101.96
10) EQUALS: Annualized Before-Tax Real Cost of Capital Including Property Taxes ($/kw-yr)	178.59	169.42	218.42	120.82	75.55	236.89

[a/] Assume that cumulative construction costs, c, occur at a uniform rate $c = C/P$ over the construction period, P, we compute (after-tax) AFUDC by

$$AFUDC = \int_0^P r \int_0^t c\, e^{r(t-z)}\, dz\, dt = c(((e^{rP}-1)/r)-P)$$

where r = real after-tax cost of capital. We assume $P = 2\frac{1}{2}$ for NUPLEX and $P = 4$ for NEWCOAL.

[b/] Taken from the DRI July 1986 long-run trend forecast.

[c/] We get the annualized after-tax real cost of capital, C_k, by solving the integral equation

$$CAPITAL\ AT\ RISK\ (86\ \$'s) = \int_0^L C_k\, e^{-rt}\, dt$$

where L = service life of plant, and r = after-tax real cost of capital. Solving, we get

$$C_k = r\,(CAPITAL\ AT\ RISK)/(1-e^{-rL}).$$

[d/] We assume a 4 percent property-tax rate applied to the real value of the initial investment on line (1).

Table IV

ASSUMPTIONS DETERMINING COSTS/KWH OF NUPLEX AND NEWCOAL PLANTS
(As of 2030, 1986 $'s where applicable)

	BASE	PESSIM	OPTIM
(1) Fuel Costs ($/MBtu)			
Nuclear (inc. reprocessing/disposal)	.66	.75	.63
Coal	2.48	1.60	5.87
(2) Annual Capital Costs ($/kw–yr)			
NUPLEX	178.59	218.42	75.55
NEWCOAL	169.42	120.82	236.89
(3) Fixed O & M ($/kw–yr)			
NUPLEX	61.97	61.97	40.00
NEWCOAL	43.38	34.86	28.00
(4) Variable O & M ($/kwh)			
NUPLEX	.0005	.0005	.0003
NEWCOAL	.0022	.0017	.0017
(5) Capacity Factor (%)			
NUPLEX	65	62	65
NEWCOAL	65	65	62
(6) Heat Rate (Btu/kwh)			
NUPLEX	10,700	10,700	10,700
NEWCOAL	10,000	9,500	10,700

Table V
BUS-BAR COSTS/KWH OF NUPLEX AND NEWCOAL PLANTS
(As of 2030, in 1986 $'s)

| | CAPITAL a/ | | OPERATING b/ | | TOTAL c/ | | PLEX SAVINGS |
	NUPLEX	NEWCOAL	NUPLEX	NEWCOAL	NUPLEX	NEWCOAL	
Base	.031	.030	.018	.035	.049	.065	.016
Pessim	.040	.021	.020	.023	.060	.044	(.016)
Otim	.013	.044	.014	.070	.027	.110	.083

Refer to Table IV:

a/ (2) / (8766 x ((5)/100))

b/ ((1) * ((6)/1000000)) + (3) / (8766 x ((5)/100)) + 4

c/ CAPITAL + OPERATING

d/ TOTAL NEWCOAL - TOTAL NUPLEX

after-tax interest, depreciation, and after-tax earnings. We show the annual average real payment covering this value of capital on line (6). This payment must be made after tax. Dividing this value by one minus the utility's marginal tax rate -- line (7) -- we get -- on line (8) -- the annual (before-tax) real payment that must come from revenues so as to pay back investors. Adding property taxes -- line (9) -- we get the final figure for annual real capital cost -- line (10) -- also shown on line (2) in Table IV.

This next Table summarizes all the key assumptions on costs and plant efficiencies for each scenario. We show the parameter values for the year 2030, since this stands near the midpoint of the potential extensions in operating lives of all nuclear facilities.

Table V shows bus-bar costs/kWh (1986 $'s) for NUPLEX and NEWCOAL plants in 2030 under each set of assumptions. We see that, given the baseline assumptions, NUPLEX saves about 1.6± per kWh. Since this savings per kw applies to about 100,000 megawatts of generating capacity operating at an assumed capacity factor of 65 percent for 20 years, we get an overall savings of about $180 billion (1986 $'s).(4)

SENSITIVITY OF SAVINGS ESTIMATES

The range of numbers in Table V helps one gauge the uncertainty in the savings estimates arising from the simultaneous uncertainty in projections of all the key variables. This section focuses on sensitivity of the savings estimates to isolated changes in each of the basic cost assumptions.

Table VI shows how the estimated savings varies as each of the key cost variables changes from its assumed baseline value. Construction costs appear most important. A $100/kw (10 percent) fall in NUPLEX 1986-overnight construction costs would cause baseline savings to rise about $21 billion (11.5 percent). Thus, the elasticity of baseline savings with respect to NUPLEX construction costs is about 1.2 A $.10/MBtu (15 percent) rise in year 2030 costs of nuclear fuel would cause savings to drop by about $12 billion (6.6 percent), indicating an elasticity of about 0.4. The elasticity of baseline savings with respect to changes in NUPLEX fixed O&M costs is almost twice that (0.73).

CONCLUSION

Absent major technological breakthroughs making present generating options obsolete, NUPLEX saves consumers money on their electric bills under most plausible economic scenarios. Using midrange assumptions, we find that NUPLEX saves consumers a total of about $180 billion spread over the period 2010-50.(5) Under optimistic assumptions, the savings swell to over $900 billion. Under extremely pessimistic assumptions, the savings could actually turn negative.

This wide range of estimates largely reflects the uncertainty in cost projections. The NUPLEX construction costs stand out as the most critical unknown. If they turn out to be 50 percent ($500 billion) above the baseline estimate (with all other assumptions constant), savings would fall by almost 60 percent ($105 billion). However, a 50 percent decrease in nuclear fuel costs would increase baseline savings by almost 22 percent. Similarly, a 50 percent drop in nuclear-plant O&M costs, would raise baseline savings by about 36 percent. These sensitivities highlight the need for continued monitoring of economic developments.

Table VI

SENSITIVITY OF SAVINGS ESTIMATES

Variable	Change From Baseline In Assumed Value (...1986 $s, where applicable)	Calculated Increase in 2010-2050 Savings	Point Elasticity of Baseline Savings With Respect to Change in NUPLEX Cost
1986 NUPLEX (NEWCOAL) Overnight Construction Costs	$100/kw drop(rise)	21 billion	1.15
2030 Nuclear-fuel (coal) delivered cost	$.10/MBtu drop(rise)	12 billion	.43
2030 NUPLEX (NEWCOAL) fixed O&M	$5/kw-yr drop(rise)	10 billion	.68
2030 NUPLEX (NEWCOAL) variable O&M	$.0001/kwh drop(rise)	1 billion	.03

Source: Authors calculation in accord with Tables II-V.

REFERENCES

1. The assumptions on 1986 costs and plant efficiencies come, for the most part, from the August 1982 DOE publication, Projected Costs of Electricity From Nuclear and Coal-Fired Power Plants, (DOE/EIA-0356/1 and 2). The capital cost estimates for coal-fired plants have been updated (without major change) in two more recent studies. See Determinants of Capital Costs for Coal-Fired Power Plants, (DOE/EIA-0479, October 1985), and New Electric Power Technologies, Office of Technology Assessment (OTA-E246, July, 1985). The estimates of NUPLEX costs reflect industry estimates based on scanty data.

2. Suppose K denotes the initial real investment, $c(t)$, a function determining real capital charges at time t and r the real cost of capital. The function $c(t)$ must obey the relation:

$$K = \int_0^L e \quad c(t)\, dt$$

where L denotes the life of the investment. Weighting by the discount factors e $-rt$, we compute a weighted average charge, c -, as follows:

$$c = \int_0^L e^{-rt} c(t) \Big/ \int_0^L e^{-rt}$$
$$= rK/(1-e^{rt})$$

But this is the formula we use for annual average real capital costs. QED.

3. Recently, due to unanticipated safety concerns and regulatory pressures, nuclear O&M costs have risen faster than fossil-fuel O&M costs. This study assumes that this above-average growth will not persist. However, if it does, the savings from NUPLEX will fall.

4. We compute this as follows:

Savings = ($.015/kwh) x 100 x 10^6 kw x 8766 hrs/yr x .65 x 20 yrs.

If we discount savings from 2020-2040 back to 1986 we obtain

Savings discounted to 1986 = $e^{-.03(2020-1980)}$ *(Savings/20)(($1-e^{20(.03)}$)/.03)
= $49.62 billion.

5. Since the operating licenses expire in 2005-2030 and 20-year life extensions would prolong service at some plants to 2050, the savings accrue over 2010-2050.

FACTORS CONTRIBUTING TO THE ECONOMIC WORTH OF CEGB
MAGNOX PLANT

Dr. C.J. Marchese
Nuclear Co-ordination Group
Central Electricity Generating Board
United Kingdom

ABSTRACT

The lives of CEGB Magnox stations were considered to have two
components when they were first built. The engineering of the structures was
conceived to provide substantial margins within the plant for the proposed duty.
These structures were believed to be capable of at least 20 years continuous
operation and good chances of even 40 years for certain parts of the structures.
For financial planning purposes, the initial authorisation of the costs of
building and operation were to be spread over 20 years.

After 10 years of operation a planned lifetime of 25 years, for each
Magnox plant with a steel pressure vessel, was declared by the CEGB. More
recently a review in 1984 led to extending their lives further. The paper to be
presented reviews the factors used by the CEGB to derive the economic worth of
these stations in terms of the marginal savings that could arise from extending
the operation of the plants. These factors and the model incorporating them
form the basis of the decisions taken by management on lifetime issues.

FACTEURS CONCOURANT A L'INTERET ECONOMIQUE DES CENTRALES MAGNOX DU CEGB

RESUME

Lors de la construction des centrales nucléaires Magnox du CEGB, on a examiné leur durée de vie sous deux aspects. D'une part, les structures ont été conçues techniquement de façon à disposer d'importantes marges de sécurité compte tenu des conditions d'exploitation prévues. On pensait en effet que ces structures étaient capables de supporter un fonctionnement continu pendant au moins 20 ans et que certains éléments de ces structures avaient même de bonnes chances de durer quarante ans. D'autre part, dans le cadre de la planification des investissements, on a prévu d'amortir les coûts de construction et d'exploitation sur une durée de vingt ans.

Après 10 ans d'exploitation, le CEGB déclara qu'il prévoyait une durée de vie de 25 ans pour chaque centrale Magnox dotée d'une cuve en acier. Plus récemment, un bilan effectué en 1984 conduisit à prolonger une nouvelle fois leur durée de vie. La présente communication passe en revue les facteurs utilisés par le CEGB pour déterminer l'intérêt économique de ses centrales en termes d'économies marginales susceptibles de résulter de la prolongation de leur exploitation. Ces facteurs et le modèle qui les prend en compte sont à la base des décisions prises par les dirigeants du CEGB au sujet de la durée de vie des centrales.

INTRODUCTION

The essential feature which determines whether a utility operates a particular plant which has already been constructed and commissioned is that it should continue to be good value for money including the cost of engineered safety. This is to say that the plant or group of plants maintains a profit and is therefore described as being economic. In principle a plant will be retained in service until it becomes more economic to replace it with new capacity. Two issues arise from this principle; firstly, the future economic status of the plant must be forecast to set planning assumptions and secondly, that the economic status should be monitored to assess whether the forecasts need amending. Within the CEGB this first issue gives rise to a planning assumption of the operating life of the plant and the second to a review, annually, of the capacity needed to provide an economic supply of electricity to the consumer.

Various factors contribute to the operating life of a plant. These can be divided into:

(i)   Licensing
(ii)   Operability
(iii)   Costs
(iv)   System Operation and Capacity
(v)   Forecasts of Electrical Production

Each of these factors have a bearing on the economics of the plant. Because this Symposium is not intended to review safety and regulatory criteria, these factors affecting the licensing of the plants will not be discussed but are reviewed elsewhere (Clarke). The operation of a system and the capacity required by the system is subject to the unique requirements for electrical supply within each country and are also excluded from this paper.

The remaining items, operability, forecast of electrical production and the costs of operation are now discussed in connection with CEGB Magnox plant. They lead to inputs to an economic model which is used to test scenarios of operation over different planned lives. The paper highlights some of the methods used by the CEGB to aid decision making but will not give itemised data.

BACKGROUND

The Magnox stations representing approximately 3500 MW of capacity today, Table I, were originally given operating lives of 20 years. This was chosen as a conservative figure with the expectation that individual plant items would continue to fulfil their design function safely for much longer periods and that, in practice, there would be an economic incentive to operate the stations for as long as a satisfactory safety case could be demonstrated. It should be noted that the demonstration to continue safe operation did not at this time require assessments about station lifetimes to be made. This was because the safety case relied upon a soundly based design linked to a continuous process of safety review throughout the life of the station. In particular, each station's operating condition is reviewed by the UK Nuclear Installations Inspectorate at the end of each reactor's statutory biennial overhaul. This is currently required after each 2 year period of operation since the previous consent to return to power operation.

In about 1978 there was a need to consider what lifetimes should be assumed for longer term future planning purposes. The assessments of potentially life limiting features were carried out in the light of 15 years operation at the oldest of the Board's nuclear stations. It was concluded for every station, except Wylfa, that a lifetime of 25 years was a reasonable basis upon which to plan. The main technical considerations related to the inspection of in-reactor mild steel components (Broom), which was thought to be the most important factor at stations other than Oldbury and Wylfa, and to the radiolytic corrosion of the graphite moderator (Best). There was also a recognition of the inherent uncertainties involved in trying to foresee problems that might arise 10 years or more ahead. In the case of Wylfa, pessimistic assumptions about the effects of radiolytic corrosion of the graphite moderator indicated that a 25 year life might not be achievable (Hart). In addition, the station had experienced a substantial number of boiler tube failures during the early life which were attributed to gas flow induced vibration effects. Whilst it was conceivable at that time, that total or partial boiler replacement was economically possible, this additional uncertainty about boiler performance led to the adoption of a 20 year life for planning proposes for Wylfa.

During the next few years, the position had been kept under review. The operational data obtained had generally indicated that the extent of ageing of in-core components was less likely to become life limiting than was previously thought, and, on this basis alone it would have been possible to have recommended increased lifetime estimates for most stations. However, another factor emerged in 1979 (Clarke, Giblin), which could have substantially altered lifetime estimates when welding defects in attachments to the pressure circuits were discovered during routine inspections on some stations e.g. Dungeness 'A'. It is now well known that comprehensive programmes of inspection and assessment were subsequently undertaken at each station in order to confirm the integrity of the pressure circuits. In particular, it was established that the defects discovered in 1979, and subsequently, were formed during original manufacture and that there is no evidence that any have grown in service. The defects were discovered because new inspection techniques were employed which were not available at the time of construction. Practical tests have been carried out to demonstrate that apparently defective units have very large reserve strength factors.

Following the successful completion during 1982 of the major part of the work aimed at demonstrating the continuing integrity of pressure circuits, a further review of the lifetimes to be assumed for planning purposes was made against the background that the oldest of the Board's nuclear stations were 20 years old. The question put in 1984 was, can we safely extend operating life to 30 years and would it be economic?

OPERABILITY

The major technical factors affecting the operability of Magnox plant can be summarised as follows:

(i)   Mild Steel Oxidation

Following the discovery in 1968 that breakaway mild steel oxidation in
the high temperature region within the reactor pressure vessel was
causing excessive strain in mild steel bolts, comprehensive inspection
monitoring programmes exist for each station. Each year a prediction
is made of the consequences of oxidation following a further two years
of operation. Since the reduction in operating temperatures in the
early 1970's the rate of oxidation is now lower.

Based on current experience, many repairs can be carried out remotely
and therefore the direct effect of mild steel oxidation is the cost
of carrying out repairs. These costs include the reactor outages and
the cost generation.

(ii)   Graphite Integrity

The principal duties of the graphite core are to provide neutron
moderation and to maintain the structural integrity required to permit
the free movement of fuel and shutdown devices in and out of the core.
The dominant feature here is radiolytic corrosion of the graphite
bricks and this was known to be more important for the higher pressure
reactors at Oldbury and Wylfa. Several features improved the
perception of earlier views of this topic. Much work on the mechanism
and the structural effects (Carpenter) combined with dose reduction
measures using flux flattening endcaps on Wylfa fuel led to significant
increases in possible operating lives.

(iii)   Pressure Circuit

The steel vesseled Magnox stations have both a steel pressure vessel
and steel primary coolant ducting to and from their associated boilers
used for steam raising. Modern inspection techniques have shown that
the main welds placed at the time of construction are free from
significant defects. Allied to the previous programmes of replacement
of those items found to be defective (Clarke, Giblin), such as duct
bellows, and the pre-service proof tests, fracture mechanics
assessments and materials test programmes, there was confidence in
continued operation.

For the concrete pressure vessel stations Oldbury and Wylfa, sample
prestressing tendons are examined every two years. Penetrations are
largely inspectable and have lives in excess of those considered here.

(iv)   Boilers

While isolated boiler tube failures have occurred during operation and
have, on rare occasions, led to significant lost output, they have been
repairable. They have not indicated any acceleration of wear out and
therefore are not a life limiting feature. This conclusion was of
particular importance to the Wylfa Power Station where it had been a
critical feature in maintaining a 20 year life.

(v)   General Plant and Turbine Generators

The experience of the other general plant off the reactors shows that
there are no technological limitations to their continued operation
other than the cost of repair and maintenance. This is also true for
all the large rotating machinery both gas circulators, feed pumps and
turbine-generators. It has been possible to assess upgrading of
condenser tubing to Titanium within an economic framework. Therefore
within the timespan considered, 30 years, there is no life-limiting
feature other than their cost.

In summary it was possible to show that for each reactor the technical
factors that could affect their operability, were not limiting in terms of an
operating life up to 30 years. Along with the important conclusions obtained
for Wylfa on graphite and boiler life it was then possible to conclude that
provided that these plants were economically viable over this period then all
the plants were certainly operable for 30 years. In coming to such a conclusion
on operability, it was recognised that the technical factors referred to above
would have to be continually monitored. Also this conclusion did not negate the
separate and independent processes used to assess the safety of the plants.
However, the requirements to maintain high levels of safety was the single most
important feature of the review of operability.

FORECASTS OF ELECTRICAL PRODUCTION

The forecasting of electrical production by the CEGB from a particular
nuclear plant uses the following data to derive a central estimate for each
year.

(i)   A central estimate of the unit electrical rating over the period of
        discussion.

(ii)   A central estimate for the total overhaul programme including an
        estimate of the most likely over-run which will depend on the nature
        of the tasks defined.

(iii)   A central estimate of the operating availability factor (a
        percentage in net energy terms) while the unit is operating between
        planned outages.

If item (i) is not constant through the year, for example due to
planned periods of derating of the whole unit or through limited operation of
coolant circuits and boilers, then item (iii) may require adjustments during
these periods. Data for item (iii) is derived from historical performance data
which is collected from each station on a monthly basis.

The total overhaul programme includes contributions from the biennial
outages for statutory inspection of the reactors as well as general overhaul
work necessary with a shutdown reactor. Other outages causing a restriction in

output may be necessary when some of the turbines of a multiple turbine Magnox station are overhauled.

At this point it is worth reflecting on the variability of the data used in deriving the central estimates. Historical data on the operating availability factors of Magnox plant are random and normally distributed for each plant and have a standard deviation of not greater than 5%.

However, the experience in over 20 years of operation shows that long term unplanned technical factors, either limiting the assigned plant rating, or requiring an extensive outage for either a modification or remedial work need to be taken into account. Two such events have affected CEGB Magnox plant; these were the derating in the 1970's and remedial work and inspection of ducts around 1980. Furthermore, any of the three factors above, rating, overhaul and availability, are strongly interdependent and can be significantly and systematically affected by the unplanned technical factors to a greater degree than the random factors.

In recognition of these issues the approach adopted is to develop self consistent scenarios and to test these using economic indicators. As a guide the scenarios would include allowances for further long outages every 5 years and other items affecting further capital expenditure discussed later. In each case central estimate data would be used but the course of events imposed in each scenario would be consistent.

COSTS

The costs of electrical production from nuclear plant can be separated into unavoidable and avoidable costs. Those that are important in an assessment of lifetime extension are those that could be avoided in the future. This is dealt with in detail later in the paper. At this point in the paper of those costs which can be avoided, the main subdivisions are:

(i)   the cost of the manpower resource
(ii)   the costs of day to day operation
(iii)   the costs of repair and maintenance
(iv)   the avoidable costs of the fuel cycle

The costs of the first three items ((i) to (iii)) have shown considerable stability in real terms over the historical operation of Magnox plant. Included in these items, there will have been the costs of capital projects to improve the plant and to carry out remedial work e.g. duct bellows replacement, but generally these are a small proportion of the total costs. Therefore our approach has been to assume that, given that future operation will show the same pattern as the past, the general level of such costs will continue to remain in real terms at their current level. This is a fairly robust assumption as our normal expectation would be that the efficiencies of operation will improve with operating life and costs decrease until the wearout of major plant items force the consideration of large scale replacement. Therefore in 5 year blocks, this is anticipated by extra contingency capital spending assumed,

in real terms, to amount to the levels spent in the last 10 years. These
assumptions will find application to many utilities faced with lifetime
extension decisions. Fuel cycle costs, however, show great variety between
utilities. As far as CEGB Magnox plant is concerned the elements of the costs
involved are derived from:

(i)   uranium costs
(ii)   fabrication and delivery costs to the plant
(iii)   storage of spent fuel on site
(iv)   transport of spent fuel from site
(v)   final reprocessing and storage of waste arisings and other spent
        fuel management costs.

Much of the total of such costs will arise on a continual basis as fuel
is used to generate electricity with the Magnox plant operational. However, we
must also allow for the reprocessing of final charges of fuel from each reactor
once they are, in turn, finally shutdown. Contractural arrangements must
therefore be made for reprocessing and spent fuel management services after the
closure of the Magnox tranche. As discussed earlier it will be the avoidable
cost that will be incorporated into the economic model. The costs of
reprocessing the final charge are largely unavoidable because they would arise
for all scenarios considered. However, there may be avoidable costs associated
with the timing of the final shutdown of reactors.

ECONOMIC WORTH

In principle, a plant is retained in service until it becomes more
economic to replace it with new capacity. The CEGB evaluates certain economic
indicators for existing stations and for the potential new stations that might
be built. The CEGB calculates the net effect which the construction and
operation of a new station is expected to have on overall system costs during
its lifetime by comparing the resulting operating cost saving with the capital
cost of the proposed investment. The result is expressed as an average annual
cost in units of £/kW p.a. called the Net Effective Cost (NEC). Similarly,
when construction of a new power station enables less efficient plant to be
decommissioned the cost associated with maintaining the latter in an operable
condition can be avoided. This cost, referred to as the Net Avoidable Cost
(NAC) is also expressed in units of £/kW p.a. For lifetime extension it is the
NAC that is the economic indicator that is used to formulate decisions.
Generally a substantially negative NAC is indicative that the plant under
assessment provides sufficient economic return to justify further operation.
The exact criterion for closure will be judged on other factors besides the
direct one, which is a positive NAC, such as capacity reserve margin.

Much of this process has been described at the Sizewell B Inquiry and
even earlier as regards the use of NEC (Masters). Here I concentrate on the
particular application of NACs to Magnox planning assumptions.

NACs are calculated against a particular background assumption of the
generating plant mix, including new capacity and the remaining lifetime, of

existing and committed plant. Given this particular background assumption, then the NAC of the Magnox plant can be calculated, as a marginal assessment against the background. At this point assumptions on System Operation and capacity have been input.

In practice, the general character of the background will be fairly well understood from earlier studies, which involve assumptions on new plant to be constructed, and it will not be difficult, by iteration where necessary, to ensure a common background assumption consistent with each marginal calculation. Nominal lifetime assumptions in each scenario set the limit beyond which it is not considered appropriate to assume continued output from the plant, but do not exclude the possibility that it may be economic to replace existing capacity by more economic capacity of a different type before its nominal life is reached.

The inputs to an NAC calculation are the direct costs or savings of production. That is to say, the avoidable costs of operating and maintaining the station, the fuel cost savings made against any lower merit plant if the station is retained in service, the saving from not having to advance transmission/distribution reinforcement if the station is retained in service, and the net costs or savings due to changes in the differences in the time of decommissioning.

Based on the net present value method the NAC is the discounted sum of these items annuitised over the period of the remaining life of the plant. Having calculated NACs the scenario economic worth is the summated net present value for all years and stations in the scenario. The rate applied to discounting and to calculating the annuity is 5% in real terms as recommended by the UK Government for use when assessing public sector capital expenditure (White paper Cmnd 7131 "The Nationalised Industries", March 1978). The process is complex because the various inputs and assumptions underlying the calculations – costs, performance and fuel prices over the life of the plants – are themselves subject to considerable uncertainty, so that a range of outcomes must be possible.

Chief among these uncertainties is not the costs of direct operation of the Magnox plant but of the costs of the background fossil fuel prices. A lifetime extension from 25 years (20 for Wylfa) to 30 years for all plant involved an assessment of fossil fuel prices over the period 1987 to 2001. Given the length of this period the current results have not been sensitive to the assumption of these prices remaining broadly constant in real terms.

What were the results? A typical NAC for a Magnox station at 1984 price levels was –£50/kW p.a, when operated to 30 years and can be compared to that of a station that might be considered for closure in the early 1980's of £16/kW. The scenario economic worth therefore appeared to be several billion pounds sterling from 1984 if operation was extended to 30 years. Indeed the value of the extension itself, that, is from the then current plans of 25 years/(20 for Wylfa) to 30 years, was in excess of one billion pounds.

CONCLUSION

An assessment carried out in 1984 showed that the eight Magnox plants operated by the CEGB could be safely operated to 30 years, which was a life extension of 5 years for all except Wylfa for which the extension was 10 years. The net economic worth of the extension amounting to a total of over 140TWh of Production was about one billion pounds sterling and the worth of the tranche operating from 1984 was worth in excess of several billion pounds sterling.

On this basis the CEGB announced in 1984 that it would extend the planned operating lives of these stations to 30 years. Since this time the position has been regularly reviewed and the 30 year operating lives have been confirmed as continuing to be economic to the same degree.

The methods described in this paper have been based on an assessment of net avoidable cost in the future. As a final comparison, data was published by the CEGB for generation costs over whole plant lives (Analysis of Generation Costs 1983/4 Update) for a variety of similar aged plant using the same data. The values obtained at March 1984 prices in p/kWh were as follows. For a 2% discount rate, Magnox was 2.23 and Coal-Fired 2.53 and at 5% discount rate. Magnox was 2.65 and Coal-Fired 2.63. These values will of course change with the time but, combined with the NAC results, they illustrate that the Magnox plants are economic to continue to operate to a 30 year life both on total costs and on net avoidable costs in the future

ACKNOWLEDGEMENTS

The work discussed has been carried out on behalf of several Departments within the Central Electricity Generating Board whose permission to publish this paper is gratefully acknowledged.

References:

Analysis of Generation Costs Update 1983/4, (April 1985) CEGB.

Best, J.V., Wickham, A.J. and Wood, C.J., J. Br.Nucl.Energy Soc. 1976, 15, No 4, 319-324.

Broom, T and Gow, R.S., Phil.Trans.Roy.Soc.Lond. A 276, 1974, 571-586.

Clarke, A.W., and Matthews, R.R., Nuclear Energy, 1986, 25. No 3, 169-175.

Carpenter, E.W., and Norfolf, D.J., Nuclear Energy, 1984, 23, No 2, 83-96.

Hart, J.D., Graphite Structures for Nuclear Reactors, I.Mech.E, London 1972, 1-15.

Masters, R. Nucl.Eng.Int., September 1980, 23-26.

Table I

CEGB MAGNOX STATIONS OPERATING DATA

Station (3)	Construction	(1) Commissioned	Net Rating, MW Design	DNC (2)	Age in 1987 (yrs)
Bradwell	1/57	9/62	300	245	25
Berkeley	1/57	8/62	276	276	25
Dungeness A	7/60	11/65	550	424	22
Hinkley Pt A	11/57	4/65	500	430	22
Oldbury	5/62	4/68	600	434	19
Sizewell	4/61	6/66	580	420	21
Trawsfynydd	7/59	3/65	500	390	22
Wylfa	9/63	12/71	1180	840	16

Note

(1) Mean date for commissioning of all turbine generator sets on site except Wylfa which is the date for the first 3 out of the total of 4 sets.

(2) DNC at Feb 1987.

(3) Each station consists of 2 reactors.

UN EXEMPLE DE CHOIX ECONOMIQUES LIES A LA PROLONGATION

DE LA DUREE DE VIE : LE CAS DE BUGEY 1

A. BRETON - A. MARTEL

ELECTRICITE DE FRANCE - SERVICE DE LA PRODUCTION THERMIQUE

PARIS (FRANCE)

RESUME

Un exemple d'étude économique liée à la prolongation de la durée de vie d'une centrale nucléaire peut être abordé à partir du cas de BUGEY 1, la dernière tranche de la filière UNGG .

Cette tranche, mise en service en 1972, était prévue pour fonctionner 25 ans. Après 15 années d'expérience d'exploitation de celle-ci, on peut raisonnablement penser qu'elle est exploitable, sans augmentation notable des coûts de maintenance, pendant 30 années au total.

Néanmoins, l'empilement de graphite constituant le modérateur du réacteur, subit une corrosion radiolytique dont la cinétique dépend essentiellement de l'intensité du flux neutronique. Or, le taux de corrosion ne doit pas dépasser une valeur limite afin de respecter les différents critères de la tenue de l'empilement de graphite.

Le stock résiduel de graphite ne permet pas d'atteindre les 30 années envisagées pour cette tranche au rythme de production actuel.

De plus, l'empilement de graphite est un composant qu'il n'est pas envisageable de remplacer lorsque le taux de corrosion maximal est atteint.

L'évolution du stock résiduel de graphite dépend, à la fois de l'énergie fournie par la tranche et de la puissance à laquelle est produite cette énergie. La durée de vie résiduelle de la tranche dépend donc très fortement de son utilisation.

La prolongation envisagée de la durée de vie de BUGEY 1, qui est une illustration des problèmes de vieillissement de gros composants auxquels les exploitants de centrales nucléaires auront à faire face, montre la nécessité, dans ce cas, d'optimiser, à date de déclassement fixée, l'utilisation de la tranche.

AN EXAMPLE OF ECONOMIC OPTIONS RELATED TO PLANT LIFE EXTENSION :
THE CASE OF BUGEY 1

ABSTRACT

The case of Bugey 1, the last unit of the GCR type can be discussed as an example of an economic study related to nuclear plant life extension.

This unit, commissioned in 1972, was designed for 25 years' operation. After 15 years of operating experience it can reasonably be considered as operable for a total of 30 years without any notable increase of maintenance costs.

However, the pile of graphite blocks, used as moderator for the reactor, undergoes radiolytical corrosion dynamically proportional to neutron flux intensity. Now, corrosions rate should not exceed a limit, so as to meet the various criteria of graphite stacking quality.

The residual graphite inventory does not ensure that the 30 years envisioned for the unit can be achieved at the current generation rate.

What is more the graphite core is a component which cannot possibly be replaced when maximum corrosion rate has been reached.

The graphite residual stockpile varies as a function of both the plant-generated energy and the power at which such an energy has been generated. Therefore the residual service life of the unit will depend very highly on its utilization.

The planned life extension of Bugey 1, which exemplifies the major components' aging problems that nuclear plant operators will have to face, demonstrates in this case the need for an optimum use of the unit, based on the timing of the decommissioning.

I - INTRODUCTION

La tranche nucléaire BUGEY 1 est la dernière réalisation de la filière UNGG (Uranium naturel, gaz, graphite). Elle a été mise en service en 1972 pour une puissance électrique nette de 540 MW.

Après 15 années d'expérience d'exploitation, on peut raisonnablement penser que cette tranche est exploitable, sans augmentation notable des coûts de maintenance, pendant 30 années au total.

Toutefois, l'usure de l'empilement de graphite, composant qui n'est ni réparable ni remplaçable, limite l'énergie que la tranche peut encore produire.

Cette contrainte ne permet pas d'atteindre les 30 ans envisagés si la production est maintenue au rythme observé dans le passé. Il est donc nécessaire de réduire la puissance fournie par l'installation pour diminuer l'usure de l'empilement. On peut ainsi envisager plusieurs niveaux de puissance qui correspondent tous à des vitesses différentes d'usure du graphite.

Le problème à traiter est de nature économique car il faut définir le mode d'exploitation de la tranche qui valorise au mieux son potentiel énergétique résiduel. L'approche développée pour résoudre ce problème est la suivante :

Pour une date de déclassement donnée, les durées de fonctionnement à différents niveaux de puissance sont choisies de manière à maximiser la valeur de l'énergie produite par la tranche.

Cette valeur représente le gain réalisé en substituant la production de la tranche à celle de centrales de coût proportionnel plus élevé, ou en diminuant les risques de défaillance du système électrique. Elle est calculée à partir des coûts marginaux de satisfaction de la demande d'électricité issus d'une optimisation globale, en avenir aléatoire, du système électrique. Il s'agit donc d'une évaluation à la marge de la gestion d'ensemble de ce système.

Le critère économique utilisé est la somme actualisée des valeurs instantanées de l'énergie produite.

Même si la durée de vie projetée de la tranche est de 30 ans, il ne peut pas être exclu qu'elle soit arrêtée avant pour des raisons techniques. C'est pourquoi l'analyse économique du problème tient compte d'une incertitude portant sur la durée de vie de la tranche.

De plus, l'environnement économique des prochaines années étant caractérisé par une incertitude sur le niveau de la demande d'électricité ainsi que sur le prix des combustibles fossiles, il est nécessaire d'étudier plusieurs scénarios.

La modélisation retenue conduit à un problème d'optimisation dynamique en avenir aléatoire, résolu numériquement par une méthode de programmation dynamique stochastique.

La résolution du problème de l'optimisation de la fin de vie de BUGEY 1 permet de définir la meilleure stratégie d'utilisation de la tranche dans les prochaines années et de fournir les indicateurs économiques nécessaires au choix de sa place dans l'ordre d'appel des moyens de production.

II - ASPECTS TECHNIQUES CONDITIONNANT LA DUREE DE VIE DE BUGEY 1

Parmi les causes de vieillissement de la tranche, les deux principales concernent la corrosion des aciers par le gaz carbonique et la corrosion radiolytique du graphite.

1/ Corrosion des aciers par le gaz carbonique

BUGEY 1, comme l'ensemble des tranches UNGG, subit une corrosion des aciers. Pour la limiter, la température du gaz carbonique a été diminuée, entraînant une baisse de puissance du réacteur. Ainsi, la tranche est exploitée à une puissance habituelle de 470 MW. Le fonctionnement à la puissance nominale reste néanmoins possible pendant de courtes périodes.

2/ Corrosion radiolytique du graphite

L'empilement du graphite est soumis à une corrosion radiolytique par le gaz carbonique qui dépend du flux neutronique et de la pression du gaz. Afin de respecter les critères de tenue mécanique de l'empilement, le taux de corrosion du graphite ne doit pas dépasser un seuil donné.

Pour réduire les effets de cette corrosion et, en particulier, pour diminuer la vitesse de celle-ci, différentes dispositions techniques ont été prises, parmi lesquelles figurent des injections de méthane agissant comme inhibiteur de corrosion. Cependant, cette protection ne peut être totale car la présence de méthane conduit à des dépôts dans le graphite qui provoquent une baisse de réactivité.

Compte tenu de ces diverses dispositions, la corrosion du graphite est vraisemblablement, parmi les différentes causes de vieillissement, celle qui fixe la durée de vie restante de la tranche. Il est, en effet, exclu de remplacer l'ensemble ou même une partie de l'empilement de graphite.

Il faut remarquer que la vitesse de corrosion du graphite est fortement liée au flux neutronique donc à la puissance thermique fournie par le réacteur et, par conséquent, à la puissance électrique délivrée par la tranche.

III - COMMENT OPTIMISER L'UTILISATION DE LA TRANCHE ?

BUGEY 1 peut être exploitée, sans augmentation notable des coûts de maintenance, pendant encore 15 ans. Cependant, la corrosion du graphite limiterait à environ 7 ans la durée de vie restante si la tranche continuait à être utilisée à la puissance électrique actuelle (470 MW).

Or, la quantité de graphite présente dans le réacteur constitue un stock dont l'évolution est fonction d'une part, de l'énergie produite par la tranche et, d'autre part, de la puissance à laquelle est fournie cette énergie.

Le problème consiste donc, pour une durée de vie restante de 15 ans, à répartir entre les années futures le potentiel énergétique résiduel de la tranche en définissant le niveau de puissance , variable au cours du temps, auquel la tranche doit être exploitée.

Pour cela, il faut :

- définir la stratégie de gestion optimale de la tranche dans les années futures ;

- donner les indicateurs économiques permettant d'atteindre l'optimum dans le cadre du système de gestion du système électrique.

IV - POSSIBILITES DE FONCTIONNEMENT DE LA TRANCHE

1/ Puissances de fonctionnement

BUGEY 1 a été exploitée jusqu'en 1985 à la puissance constante de 470 MW pendant les périodes de disponibilité de la tranche. Depuis, des règles décrivant les variations possibles de puissance ont été élaborées. Celles-ci font apparaître 4 paliers principaux de fonctionnement auxquels la tranche peut être exploitée durablement (200 MW - 400 MW - 470 MW - 540 MW). Le fonctionnement à puissance maximale ne doit être qu'exceptionnel compte tenu des conséquences tant sur le graphite que sur la corrosion des aciers.

Par ailleurs, l'utilisation de BUGEY 1 à des paliers bas de puissance conduit à augmenter les cadences de renouvellement du combustible pour respecter une contrainte de temps maximal de séjour des éléments combustibles dans le réacteur. Le surcoût qui en résulte est néanmoins négligeable lorsque la puissance reste supérieure à 200 MW, ce qui a conduit à retenir cette valeur comme palier minimal d'exploitation plutôt que le minimum technique théorique de la tranche.

2/ Contraintes dynamiques

Les principales contraintes affectant le fonctionnement de la tranche sont compatibles avec une gestion économique de celle-ci :

- la conception de l'élément combustible impose un nombre maximal de 100 variations de puissance par an et de 2 variations par jour ;

- les arrêts doivent durer au moins 2 jours compte tenu des contraintes d'exploitation relatives aux séquences d'arrêt et de démarrage de la tranche ;

- le nombre des arrêts, incluant les arrêts fortuits, est limité à une centaine d'ici la fin de vie de la tranche (nombre maximal de cyclages thermiques de l'acier de la sole de la tranche).

La possibilité d'exploiter BUGEY 1 à différents niveaux de puissance introduit une variable de commande qui permet d'agir sur la vitesse de corrosion du graphite et, par conséquent, sur la durée de vie de la tranche.

V - MODELISATION DE LA GESTION DE BUGEY 1

Les deux problèmes économiques consistant à définir la stratégie de gestion optimale de la tranche et à fournir les indicateurs économiques nécessaires au gestionnaire du système électrique ne peuvent être résolus que conjointement. En effet, les indicateurs économiques caractéristiques de BUGEY 1 proviennent de l'optimisation globale de l'utilisation de la tranche jusqu'à son déclassement.

La quantité de graphite présente dans le réacteur constitue un stock limité dont il faut optimiser l'utilisation au cours du temps. C'est pourquoi, le problème à traiter est un problème d'optimisation dynamique.

1/ Décisions et critère économique

Les variables décisionnelles qui doivent être optimisées sont les niveaux de puissance auxquels la tranche est utilisée au cours du temps. Elles constituent les commandes qui font évoluer l'état du stock résiduel de graphite.

Le critère économique que l'on maximise est le bilan économique de la tranche, jusqu'à son déclassement. Il s'agit d'un bilan actualisé permettant de comparer des valeurs relatives à des dates différentes.

Ce bilan économique représente le gain réalisé en substituant la production de la tranche à celle de tranches de coût proportionnel plus élevé, ou en diminuant les risques de défaillance du système électrique. On remarquera que, pour une date de déclassement fixée, les charges fixes d'exploitation ainsi que les coûts liés au déclassement de la tranche ne dépendent pas de la stratégie adoptée pour l'utiliser. Il n'est donc pas nécessaire de les faire figurer dans le critère économique.

Compte tenu des aléas susceptibles d'affecter le système électrique pendant les 15 ans étudiés (niveau de la consommation d'électricité, prix des combustibles fossiles et disponibilité du parc de production), la valeur de substitution de la tranche est calculée en espérance mathématique.

Le problème consiste donc à rechercher le fonctionnement futur qui rende maximale la valeur de substitution de la tranche tout en respectant l'usure maximale autorisée pour l'empilement du graphite.

2/ Optimisation à la marge de la gestion du système électrique

L'évaluation de la valeur de substitution de la tranche est faite à la marge de la gestion optimale du système électrique, c'est-à-dire en supposant que la gestion des autres moyens de régulation n'est pas remise en cause par la gestion de BUGEY 1. Cette hypothèse ne constitue pas une approximation importante compte tenu de la place occupée par BUGEY 1 dans le parc de production (<1 % de l'énergie produite, 0,7 % de la puissance installée).

Le critère économique est calculé à partir des coûts marginaux de satisfaction de la demande d'électricité (incluant un coût de défaillance) issus de modèles d'optimisation globale du système électrique, en avenir aléatoire.

3/ Incertitude pesant sur la durée de vie de BUGEY 1

Il ne peut pas être exclu qu'un incident technique ou que le vieillissement prématuré d'un composant conduise à arrêter la tranche avant la durée limite de 30 années. Cette incertitude est représentée par un taux de défaillance, supposé constant dans le temps.

Dans la méthode de calcul du critère économique actualisé, l'introduction d'un taux de défaillance est pratiquement équivalente, pour des valeurs faibles des taux, à l'augmentation du taux d'actualisation d'un terme égal au taux de défaillance.

4/ Evolution de la quantité de graphite

Les calculs de tenue de l'empilement de graphite nécessaire au respect des normes de sûreté permettent d'évaluer la masse en dessous de laquelle il n'est plus possible d'exploiter la tranche. De plus, des prélèvements réguliers de graphite et des extrapolations à partir de modèles physiques permettent d'estimer les vitesses de corrosion en fonction du niveau de puissance auquel la tranche fonctionne.

Ces éléments permettent de représenter l'empilement de graphite comme un stock dont on connaît le niveau initial et la loi d'évolution sous l'effet des décisions d'exploitation. Les évaluations précédentes sont susceptibles d'évoluer légèrement en fonction des résultats des études et des mesures qui se poursuivent.

5/ Méthode d'optimisation

La formulation du problème d'optimisation de la gestion de BUGEY 1 conduit à une gestion de stock en avenir aléatoire qui est résolue par une méthode de programmation dynamique stochastique bien adaptée à ce type de problème.

6/ Résultats du modèle économique

        Pour différents scénarios caractérisant l'environnement
économique des prochaines années, il est possible de définir la
stratégie optimale d'utilisation de BUGEY 1. Celle-ci est
caractérisée par les énergies produites au cours du temps et par les
durées d'appel aux différents niveaux de puissance de fonctionnement
de la tranche. De plus, la méthode de résolution utilisée permet de
déterminer la valeur marginale du stock de graphite en fonction de
la puissance à laquelle est appelée la tranche.

        Ces valeurs permettent de définir la place de BUGEY 1 dans
l'ordre d'appel des moyens de production, utilisé pour la gestion du
système électrique.

VI - EXEMPLES D'APPLICATION

1/ Hypothèses générales

   - l'étude porte sur la période 1987-2001 correspondant à une durée
     de vie de 30 ans pour BUGEY 1 ;

   - le scénario étudié correspond à l'un des scénarios utilisés pour
     les études à moyen et long terme de l'établissement (scénario haut
     sur la consommation) ;

   - le taux d'actualisation est celui actuellement en vigueur, soit
     8 %.

2/ Hypothèses relatives à BUGEY 1

   - le taux de défaillance est de 2 % par an ;

   - le stock résiduel de graphite correspond à une production de
     12 TWh à 470 MW ou de 27 TWh à 400 MW, ou de 6 TWh à 540 MW. Le
     fonctionnement à 200 MW n'affecte pas le stock résiduel de
     graphite ;

   - l'entretien périodique est réalisé tous les ans pendant l'été,
     période la moins chère en énergie de substitution ;

   - le taux d'indisponibilité fortuite est de 15 % ;

   - le coût proportionnel de BUGEY 1 est inférieur à celui des
     tranches au charbon, lui-même plus petit que celui des tranches au
     fioul ;

   - plusieurs représentations des contraintes dynamiques de
     fonctionnement de la tranche peuvent être faites dans le modèle ;
     les résultats ci-après sont issus d'une étude pour laquelle il n'a
     pas été tenu compte de ces contraintes.

3/ Résultats

        Les différentes grandeurs qui peuvent être obtenues sont
caractérisées par des valeurs moyennes et des distributions de
probabilité. Des exemples sont données ci-dessous :

a/ Evolution de la valeur de substitution

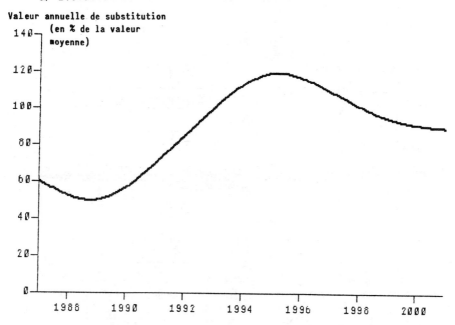

Figure I : Valeur annuelle de substitution rapportée à la
valeur annuelle moyenne.

b/ Evolution des énergies annuelles produites

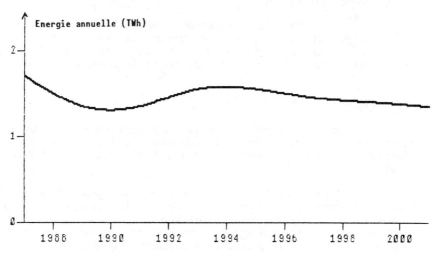

Figure II : Energie annuelle produite (espérance mathématique).

c/ Durées d'appel aux différents paliers de puissance

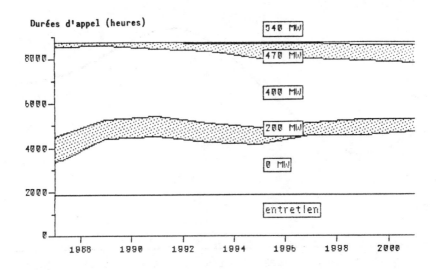

Figure III : Durée d'appel aux paliers de puissance

d/ Commentaires

Les résultats précédents montrent l'intérêt économique de ne pas utiliser BUGEY 1 au maximum de ses possibilités pendant les prochaines années afin de mieux valoriser le potentiel énergétique restant en fin de vie de la tranche.

VII - CONCLUSION

L'exemple précédent montre que la prolongation de la durée de vie d'une tranche peut conduire à optimiser la fin de vie de celle-ci lorsqu'un composant essentiel qui n'est pas réparable introduit une limitation.

Dans le cas de BUGEY 1, cette limitation pouvait se représenter sous la forme d'une contrainte de stock accompagnée d'une loi d'évolution dépendant de la puissance fournie par la tranche. L'optimisation dynamique qui en résulte consiste alors à répartir entre les années futures le potentiel énergétique résiduel de la tranche de manière à maximiser la valeur actualisée de la production, en tenant compte de l'ensemble des aléas qui influent sur le système électrique.

MODELISATION DE LA GESTION DE BUGEY 1

I - SYSTEME DYNAMIQUE

L'usure du graphite fait de Bugey 1 un système dynamique (c'est-à-dire qui évolue dans le temps). De manière classique, un système dynamique est décrit par un état et des commandes qui font évoluer cet état au cours du temps.

L'état est ici la quantité de graphite restant dans le réacteur.

Les commandes qui font évoluer cet état sont les décisions de production d'énergie.

La loi d'évolution de l'état est la loi de décroissance de la quantité de graphite.

II - MODELISATION DU SYSTEME DYNAMIQUE

Le pas de temps considéré sera la semaine.

La période d'étude (paramétrée) sera de plusieurs années.

On notera : T le nombre de semaines de la période allant de l'instant initial à la date de déclassement de la tranche, t sera l'indice d'une semaine quelconque.

1/ Représentation de l'état du système

Soit Q(t) la quantité de graphite restant au début de la semaine t.

A tout instant cette quantité doit être supérieure à une valeur donnée par les critères de sûreté soit $\underline{Q}$ cette valeur.

La relation $Q(t) \geqslant \underline{Q}$ doit être vérifiée pour tout instant t.

Par ailleurs la quantité initiale de graphite est connue soit Qo cette quantité.

On a donc Q (1) = Qo

2/ Représentation des commandes du système

La semaine est décomposée en N postes horaires de durée di.

Soit $P_i(t)$ la puissance fournie par la tranche sur le poste horaire i de la semaine t.

La décision de production pour la semaine t, notée u(t), correspondra à l'ensemble des puissances de fonctionnement prévues sur les N postes horaires :

$$u(t)=(Pi(t), i=1,N)$$

Les décisions possibles pour une semaine forment un ensemble correspondant aux possibilités de la tranche : paliers de fonctionnement prédéterminés, nature des variations de puissance au cours de la semaine (baisse de nuit, arrêt de week-end....)

3) Nature des aléas

Les aléas affectant la gestion de Bugey 1 sont de deux natures :

- aléa sur la disponibilité de la tranche ;

- aléas sur l'ensemble du système se traduisant pas un aléa sur la valeur des coûts marginaux, résultant d'un modèle de gestion global.

On se placera dans l'hypothèse où l'aléa sur les coûts marginaux pour une semaine est connue en début de semaine.

4) Représentation de la loi d'évolution de l'état

Soit $q(P)$ la diminution de la quantité de graphite par unité de temps lorsque la tranche fonctionne à la puissance P.

Lorsque la tranche est indisponible (probabilité $1-k(t)$) l'état n'évolue pas : $Q(t+1)=Q(t)$

Lorsque la tranche est disponible (probabilité $k(t)$) l'état évolue sous l'effet des commandes $u(t)$:

$$Q(t+1) = Q(t) - \sum_{i=1}^{N} d_i \, q \, (Pi(t))$$

5) Représentation du critère économique

Le critère à maximiser est la valeur de substitution actualisée de la tranche sur la période étudiée.

Celle-ci est, pour une semaine donnée et un poste horaire donné, le produit de l'énergie fournie par la différence entre le coût marginal de production et le coût proportionnel de la tranche.

Soit $G_{wt}(u(t))$ le gain sur la semaine t correspondant à la décision $u(t)$.

L'expression de $G_{wt}(u(t))$ est la suivante :

$$G_{wt}(u(t))= \left[\sum_{i=1}^{N} P_i(t) \times d_i \times (cm_{wi}(t) - cp)) \right] \times k(t)$$

où $cm_{wi}(t)$ est le coût marginal de production sur le poste i de la semaine t correspondant à l'aléa w, cp le coût proportionnel de production de BUGEY 1, k(t) le taux de disponibilité totale pour la semaine t.

Le critère, sur la période considérée est alors l'espérance mathématique, prise sur tous les aléas, des gains actualisés :

$$C(u(t)) = \underset{W}{E} \sum_{t=1}^{T} \frac{G_{wt}(u(t))}{(1+a')^{t-1}}$$

6) Maximisation du critère économique

Le problème d'optimisation se résume ainsi :

Max   (C(u(t))
u(t)
sous les contraintes :

(1) Q (1) = Qo

(2) Q (t) $\geqslant$ $\underline{Q}$ pour tout t

(3) équations d'évolution du stock du 4)

(4) u(t) appartenant à un ensemble admissible.

III - REMARQUES

1) Dérive des coûts au cours du temps

La dérive des coûts différente suivant leur nature, intervenant dans le calcul du critère économique ne figure pas dans la présentation ci-dessus afin de ne pas alourdir les notations. Ces dérives sont prises en compte dans le modèle.

2) Contraintes dynamiques

Des contraintes dynamiques de fonctionnement (temps minimum d'arrêt, ...) peuvent être représentées dans le modèle bien qu'elles ne figurent pas dans la formulation ci-dessus.

DESCRIPTION DE LA TRANCHE

La centrale nucléaire BUGEY 1 est équipée d'un réacteur à circuit primaire intégré dans un caisson en béton précontraint, utilisant un combustible annulaire.

Le modérateur est constitué d'un empilement de briques de graphite représentant une masse de 2 000 tonnes. Celui-ci est traversé par 850 canaux verticaux contenant chacun 15 éléments combustibles.

L'élément combustible contient de l'uranium très faiblement enrichi sous forme métallique. La masse totale d'uranium contenu dans le réacteur est de 320 tonnes. Le renouvellement du combustible s'effectue de façon continue pendant la marche du réacteur.

Le gaz de refroidissement est du gaz carbonique, circulant sous une pression de 41 bars, dans l'espace compris entre le caisson et le corps du réacteur, puis à travers les éléments combustibles qu'il refroidit et à travers les échangeurs qu'il réchauffe provoquant la vaporisation de l'eau. La circulation du gaz carbonique est assurée par des soufflantes, entraînées par des turbines à condensation. Le circuit de gaz utilise 280 tonnes de gaz carbonique. La température est de 400°C à la sortie du réacteur.

La centrale est équipée de deux groupes turbo-alternateurs d'une puissance de 280 MW.

La tranche nucléaire BUGEY 1 est la dernière réalisation de la filière UNGG (Uranium naturel, gaz, graphite). Elle a été mise en service en 1972 pour une puissance électrique nette de 540 MW, elle a produit 41,5 TWh et totalise 97 000 heures de fonctionnement à la fin de l'année 1986. La figure 4 ci-dessous indique la répartition de cette production au cours du temps.

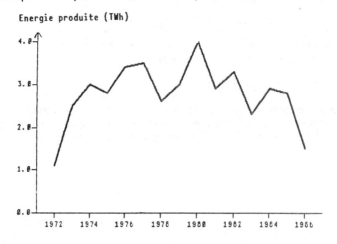

Figure IV : Production réalisée par BUGEY 1

ECONOMIC MODELING FOR LIFE EXTENSION DECISION MAKING*

M.A. Farber
Temple, Barker & Sloane, Inc.
Lexington, Massachusetts

D.L. Harrison
U.S. Department of Energy
Washington, D.C.

D.D. Carlson
Sandia National Laboratories
Albuquerque, New Mexico

ABSTRACT

This paper presents a methodology for the economic and financial analysis of nuclear plant life extension under uncertainty and demonstrates its use in a case analysis.

While the economic and financial evaluation of life extension does not require new analytical tools, such studies should be based on the following three premises. First, the methodology should examine effects at the level of the company or utility system, because the most important economic implications of life extension relate to the altered generation system expansion plan. Second, it should focus on the implications of uncertainty in order to understand the factors that most affect life extension benefits and identify risk management efforts. Third, the methodology should address multiple objectives, at a minimum, both economic and financial objectives.

An analysis of the role of life extension for Virginia Power's generating system was performed using the MIDAS model, developed by the Electric Power Research Institute. MIDAS is particularly well suited to this type of study because of its decision analysis framework. The model incorporates modules for load analysis, capacity expansion, production costing, financial analysis, and rates. The decision tree structure facilitates the multiple-scenario analysis of uncertainty. The model's output includes many economic and financial measures, including capital expenditures, fuel and purchases power costs, revenue requirements, average rates, external financing requirements, and coverage ratio.

Based on findings for Virginia Power's Surry 1 plant, nuclear plant life extension has economic benefits for a utility's customers and financial benefits for the utility's investors. These benefits depend on a number of economic, technical and regulatory factors. The economic analysis presented in this paper identifies many of the key factors and issues relevant to life extension planning.

---

* This work performed at Sandia National Laboratories, which is operated for the U.S. Department of Energy under contract number DE-ACO4-76DP00789.

PROLONGATION DE LA DUREE DE VIE DES CENTRALES NUCLEAIRES : MODELISATION ECONOMIQUE POUR LA PRISE DE DECISION*

RESUME

Cette communication présente une méthode d'analyse économique et financière de la prolongation de la durée de vie des centrales nucléaires dans des conditions d'incertitude et démontre son utilisation dans une analyse de cas.

L'évaluation économique et financière de la prolongation de la durée de vie des centrales nucléaires ne nécessite pas de nouveaux outils analytiques, mais ces études doivent se conformer aux trois exigences suivantes. Première- ment, la méthodologie doit examiner les effets au niveau de la compagnie elle-même et du réseau interconnecté parce que l'incidence économique essen- tielle de la prolongation de la durée de vie des centrales nucléaires concerne la modification du programme modifié de développement des moyens de production. Deuxièmement, elle doit être axée sur les conséquences de l'incertitude afin de comprendre les facteurs qui influent le plus sur les avantages de la pro- longation de la durée de vie des centrales et qui déterminent les efforts à accomplir dans la gestion des risques. Troisièmement, elle doit viser des objectifs multiples et, notamment, les aspects économiques et financiers.

L'analyse de l'importance de l'extension de la durée de vie des moyens de production de la compagnie Virginia Power a été élaborée en utilisant le modèle MIDAS, mis au point par l'Institut de recherche sur l'énergie élec- trique (EPRI). MIDAS est particulièrement bien adapté à ce type d'étude grâce à sa structure d'analyse de décision. Il comprend des modules pour l'analyse de la charge du réseau, le développement de la puissance installée, le coût de production de l'énergie, l'analyse financière et les tarifs. Lastructure en forme d'arbre de décision facilite l'analyse d'incertitude à scénarios mul- tiples. Le modèle livre un grand nombre de valeurs économiques et financières

---

* Cette étude a été réalisée aux Laboratoires nationaux Sandia pour le compte du ministère américain de l'énergie dans le cadre d'un contrat portant la référence DE-ACO4-76DP00789.

dont les dépenses d'investissement, le coût du combustible et des achats
d'électricité, les recettes nécessaires, les tarifs moyens, les besoins de
financement externes et le taux de couverture.

Sur la base des données concernant la tranche Surry 1 de la compagnie
Virginia Power, la prolongation de la durée de vie des centrales nucléaires
présente des avantages économiques pour les abonnés et des avantages financiers pour les investisseurs. Ces avantages dépendent d'un grand nombre de
facteurs économiques, techniques et réglementaires. L'analyse économique
présentée dans cette communication met en évidence plusieurs des facteurs
déterminants et les problèmes essentiels relatifs à la planification de la
prolongation de la durée de vie des centrales nucléaires.

INTRODUCTION

This paper presents a methodology for the economic and
financial analysis of nuclear plant life extension under uncertainty and demonstrates its use in a case study. Three
important characteristics of the methodology are described: a
utility planning model capable of capturing the relevant corporate-level effects of life extension; an approach for examining
key uncertainties; and a multiobjective framework for looking
at both economic and financial issues. The methodology is
illustrated with a study of life extension at Virginia Power's
Surry Unit 1.

METHODOLOGY

As utilities explore, plan, and ultimately implement life
extension programs, economic and financial considerations will
become very important. The methodology presented here is
intended for a screening analysis at the early stages of investigation.

The methodology is both specific and generic. It is
specific in suggesting the usefulness of a computer model
called MIDAS. On the other hand, it is generic because
utilities can perform similar evaluations with their own
planning models.

Characteristics of the Methodology

Even at the early screening stage, an evaluation methodology should meet the following three criteria:

- The methodology should examine effects at the level of the company or utility system;

- It should focus on the implications of uncertainty; and

- It should include multiple objectives.

First, a generating system-level analysis, rather than a plant-level analysis, is required because the benefits of life extension depend on many system-level characteristics, including alternative options for replacement capacity, short-term replacement energy costs during nuclear plant outages, corporate financial situation, and rate-making and accounting policies.

Analysis of uncertainty, the second characteristic, is important in part because of the long planning horizon determined by the licensing lead time, the lead time for possible replacement capacity, and the period of extended operation. Furthermore, the lack of industry experience with life extension creates uncertainty about capital and operating costs, regulatory requirements, and long-term plant performance.

Third, multiple objectives are important for any major investment analysis. At a minimum, the analysis must consider effects on both customers and investors.

The Computer Model

This project has used MIDAS (Multiobjective Integrated Decision Analysis System), a utility planning tool for the analysis of uncertainty.[1] MIDAS was sponsored by the Electric Power Research Institute (EPRI) and was developed by Temple, Barker & Sloane, Inc., and M.S. Gerber & Associates, Inc.

MIDAS's demand, capacity, production cost, financial, and rate modules are incorporated into a generalized decision analysis framework to help utilities analyze uncertainty. The entire system runs on a microcomputer.

MIDAS is a general utility planning model; it was not designed specifically for life extension studies. It is particularly useful for this application, however, because it successfully addresses the three guidelines outlined above: corporate-level scope, focus on uncertainty, and multiple objectives.

The simulation portion of the model has five modules:

- Load Analysis. Projects daily, monthly, and annual load shapes based on input historical load patterns, peak and energy forecasts, and demand-side management program results.

- Capacity Additions. Calculates additions of new generating units necessary to meet the specified reserve margins and mix of baseload, cycling, and peaking capacity.

- Production Cost Analysis. Computes generation, fuel use, and total production cost for every unit in the utility's system, and incorporates off-system purchases and sales with other utilities and cogenerators.

- Financial Analysis. Determines revenue requirements, cash flow, and financing needs, and projects complete financial statements, e.g., Balance Sheet, Income Statement, and Funds Flow Statement.

- Rates. Classifies and allocates revenue requirements to compute average electricity rates to customers.

The next section describes the application of MIDAS to the evaluation of Surry life extension.

VIRGINIA POWER CASE STUDY

The methodology is demonstrated with an analysis of Surry Unit 1 at Virginia Power. The MIDAS model was used to prepare 30-year projections of Virginia Power's loads, capacity plans, production costs, and financial results. Projections were made both with and without a 20-year life extension to examine the economic and financial implications of the strategy. In addition, sensitivity analyses were performed to identify and analyze key issues.

The MIDAS data base was constructed with the support of the company's power supply and financial planning staff. Virginia Power staff also compared MIDAS results to those of their more detailed corporate models. The projections and findings, however, represent the independent analyses and forecasts of the consultant, not the utility.

Because MIDAS is currently constrained to 30 years of projections, the planning period of this study only addresses a portion of the refurbishment period (which encompasses life extension research, planning, and implementation) and extended life periods. The interval from 1995 to 2024 was selected to examine the most significant portion of reach, as illustrated in Figure 1.

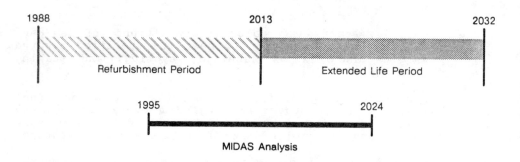

Figure 1:   The Planning Period

A number of key assumptions influence the economic results. Life extension will require approximately $100 million of capital expenditures and an average of $2 million in annual maintenance and monitoring costs over the refurbishment and extended life periods (1987 dollars).   In addition, a continuation of the current $25 million per year in ongoing capital and $27 million in ongoing operating and maintenance (O&M) costs was assumed throughout the extended life period.   Replacement capacity, on the other hand, is assumed to be a conventional coal-fired steam generating unit with a capital cost of approximately $1,800/kW and a fuel cost of approximately $21/MWh (1987 dollars).

The results are discussed below in two sections.   The first addresses the analysis of the base case (referred to here as the Most Likely Scenario) from the perspective of multiple economic and financial objectives.   The second section discusses a number of key issues affecting the results.

Throughout this paper, all cost figures are adjusted for inflation to constant 1987 dollars, unless otherwise noted.

Multiobjective Analysis of the Most Likely Scenario

The economic and financial implications of life extension were analyzed by comparing forecasts of two strategies: retirement of the plant in 2012 and a 20-year life extension until 2032. Both cases are based on a business-as-usual scenario, including moderate load growth, no major new technological developments, and continued cost-based regulation.

The major implications of life extension are discussed below:

- **Life Extension Costs**. The direct costs of implementing life extension estimated to be approximately $100 million during the refurbishment period, plus approximately $2 million per year in annual maintenance and monitoring costs.

- **Replacement Power Cost**. In addition, only about $1 million per year (1987 dollars) of replacement power cost (from internal generation and purchases) will be incurred during the refurbishment period, since most refurbishment activities are expected to be performed within routine plant outages. The fuel mix for the replacement power on Virginia Power's system is projected to be approximately half coal and half natural gas.

- **Postponed Construction**. Based on a reference expansion plan incorporating 750 MW coal-fired steam generating units, Surry's 20-year life extension permits postponement of one unit from 2013 to 2033.

- **Fuel Savings**. Annual fuel savings exceed $115 million (1987 dollars)--nuclear fuel cost increases by $35 million, but fossil fuel cost is reduced by $150 million.

- **Depreciation**. Depreciation decreases initially because of the lower depreciation rate associated with an extended life. By 2008 depreciation actually increases because of the higher depreciable base caused by refurbishment costs. In addition, after 2012, the postponed coal plant significantly reduces depreciation.

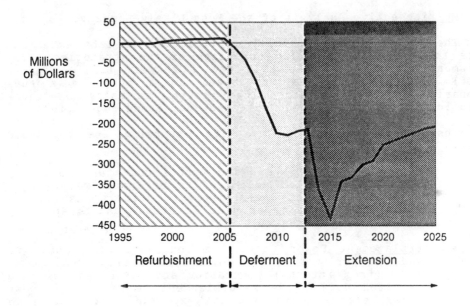

Figure 2: Annual Incremental Revenue Requirements
(1987 dollars)

- **Revenue Requirements**. Figure 2 presents incremental
  revenue requirements, the consolidation of the cost
  components discussed above. The graph distinctly
  shows three periods: refurbishment, capacity deferment (part of the refurbishment period), and extended
  life.

  -- Prior to 2005, revenues increase slightly because
     of the capital, operation and maintenance, and
     replacement energy associated with refurbishment
     activities.

  -- The years 2005 to 2012 are characterized by sav-
     ings because of the postponed coal plant since
     Virginia Power earns a cash return on approxi-
     mately 85 percent of construction work in pro-
     gress.

  -- After 2012, the reduced revenues are due to lower
     fuel costs and lower capital-related costs (de-
     preciation, operating income, and taxes) associ-
     ated with the lower ratebase.

As shown in Figure 3, after a small increase in revenue requirements because of refurbishment, the cumulative present value of incremental revenue requirements are reduced by $760 million by the end of the
study period (which is only the 12th year of the
20-year extended life period).   On the basis of an
engineering economic analysis, which does not have a
truncated planning horizon, the total benefits are
expected to be approximately $1 billion.

- **External Financing**. As shown in Figure 4, the incremental financing requirements of the refurbishment
  program (which peak in 2002 at $25 million) are quite
  small compared to the postponement of the financing
  associated with the replacement capacity (which peaks
  in 2008 at almost $2.5 billion).

- **Financial Ratios**. The interest coverage ratio and the
  ratio of internal to external funds also reflect the
  minor financial burden of refurbishment and the
  greater financial benefits of postponed construction
  of replacement capacity.

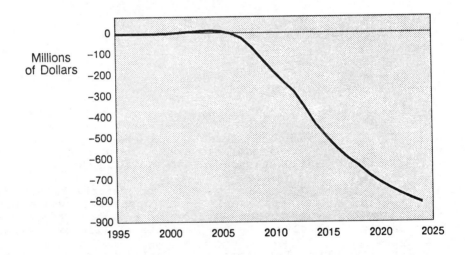

Figure 3:   Cumulative Incremental Revenue Requirements
(Present Value)

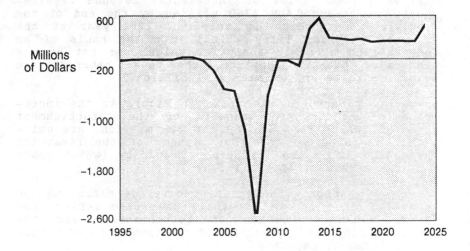

Figure 4:   Incremental External Financing
(current dollars)

Issues Analysis

The benefits of life extension for the Most Likely Scenario depend on many economic, technical, and regulatory
assumptions. This section presents the highlights of the
analysis of a number of important issues. For most of these
issues, sensitivity analyses were performed with MIDAS.

- Life Extension Costs. Surry's refurbishment and
  ongoing costs (both capital and operating) would have
  to exceed current expectations by a factor of approximately 10 to eliminate the benefits of life extension.

- Surry's Plant Performance. Similarly, even significant deterioration of Surry's plant performance does
  not eliminate the benefits because of the availability of inexpensive, coal-fired energy on Virginia
  Power's system. For example, the benefits are still
  positive for a capacity factor of 20 percent.

- **License Extension.** Regarding the length of the license extension, even a one-year extension justifies
  the refurbishment investments since replacement capacity can be postponed for the same one-year period.

- **Replacement Capacity.** By 2012, when replacement
  capacity is needed, coal-fired, central station steam
  units may well not be the dominant technology. Figure 5 presents a two-variable sensitivity analysis of
  the capital cost (vertical axis) and fuel cost (horizontal axis) of replacement capacity. Only for capital and fuel cost combinations in the lower left corner is nuclear life extension not preferred. To be
  more cost-effective than life extension, a new technology must, therefore, have much lower costs than any
  currently envisioned technology--on the order of $300
  per kW and $6 per MWh (1987 dollars).

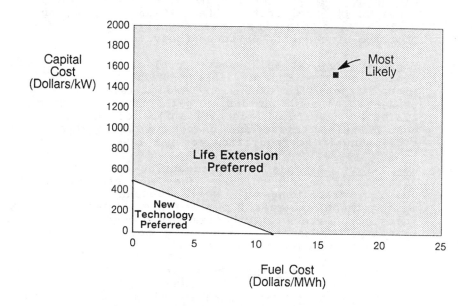

Figure 5: Joint-Event Break-Even Analysis of the
Replacement Capacity's Capital and Fuel Cost

- **Fuel Prices**. The benefits of life extension are sensitive to the fuel cost of the replacement capacity, as shown in Figure 5. If this technology is not coal-based, however, then the prices of coal or other fuels used in Virginia Power's generating system have a minor effect on life extension's benefits because other generating units are not dispatched very differently.

- **Load Growth**. If the utility can accurately predict load growth and adjust expansion plans accordingly, then the economic benefits of life extension are insensitive to the level of load growth. Furthermore, life extension possesses the attributes necessary to help a utility cope with uncertain load growth: short lead time and low cost for low risk exposure and for economic flexibility.

- **Licensing Delay**. Early decision of the licensing issue will facilitate life extension planning and analysis and minimize the possibility of excess or shortage of capacity or unnecessary costs.

- **Economic Regulation**. State public utility commissions and the Federal Energy Regulatory Commission might affect life extension through rate recovery and prudence investigations, performance regulation, financing approval, certification of need, least-cost-planning tests, and changes in accounting practice, securities regulation, or tax laws.

- **Capital vs. Expense**. The accounting classification of life extension expenditures does not affect its economic attractiveness. While accounting treatment might affect external financing needs, near-term rate increases, internal authorization procedures, or rate recovery, in general, accounting policies should not be used to manage such concerns.

- **Alternative Financing Mechanisms**. Financing approaches such as sale/leaseback, joint ventures, limited partnerships, turnkey financing, or industrial revenue bonds should be considered for life extension--as they should be for any capital investment--but will not likely alter the project's viability.

- **Decommissioning Financing.** While life extension will alter the rate of accrual of the decommissioning reserve, it should not substantially alter the constant-dollar reserve ultimately accrued. Furthermore, under present rules, there seems to be limited applicability of funds already accrued for financing life extension.

Summary of the Case Study

In summary, this study has shown the following:

- Nuclear plant life extension has significant economic benefits.

- These benefits stem from lower fuel and capital costs than any currently known replacement technology.

- These findings are quite robust with regard to the costs and performance of the nuclear plant as well as the costs of potential new technologies.

[1] MIDAS Model Documentation (Draft). Electric Power Research Institute, RP 2317, October 1986

DISCUSSION

Y. INABA, IEA

The US nuclear plant life extension (NUPLEX) overnight construction cost assumptions range from $ 300/kW to $ 1700/kW. Are these numbers based on detailed technical assessments ? If so, please explain the determinant factors which cause such a difference in NUPLEX capital investment.

D.L. HARRISON, United States

The evaluation by Data Resources, Inc. was an economic feasibility of nuclear PLEX in the US. The uncertainty in estimating the capital cost for extending the life of plants (technical, safety and economic regulatory, etc.) resulted in using a bounding approach, i.e. $ 300-1700 kW. The upper-limits also provides insights into breakeven or limiting values for capital finance. We now believe the bounds are $ 200-$ 1000/kW (at 1987 prices). We wanted to be extremely conservative in this first economic evaluation.

R. DODDS, United Kingdom

Table II of Mr. Fletcher's paper shows that the same NEWCOAL construction cost of $ 1300/kW has been assumed in the three scenarios, base, optimistic and pessimistic. Given the possibility of improved coal burning technology and perhaps even lifetime extensions in such plants, would it not be reasonable to reflect this in the respective cost assumptions made ?

T.T. FLETCHER, United States

I agree that the coal industry is looking at alternatives to compete with nuclear plant life extension. One can easily conclude that those costs should not be constant across the scenarios. In the optimistic case we should have had lower realistic capital values. But an important thing about the analysis is that it will give you a feel for how and what type of parameters we used in deriving cost savings.

In my paper, I had not considered the possible impact of new technologies competing with NEWCOAL as well as NUPLEX in the coming future. I would like to know what other technologies might be expected to be competitive in the time frame of NUPLEX of current plant (2000-2050).

D.L. HARRISON, United States

Looking at nuclear research only, the alternatives are the advanced LWRs, small and large modular Liquid Metal Reactors (converters), possibly breeders and HTGRs. Of course, advances in fossil and renewables (fusion, solar, etc.) could also compete if major significant technological accelerations occur.

R. VIDAL, France

De nouvelles filières sont à l'étude en France, mais elles ne seront pas compétitives dans les prochaines décennies. La filière des surgénérateurs n'est qu'au stade du prototype et ce n'est que dans une vingtaine d'années que l'on pourra espérer le lancement progressif des centrales industrielles. Pour les REP avancés, la conception générale est très voisine des REP actuels, la différence ne porte que sur le coeur et le combustible et ne concerne donc que l'amélioration du coût de fonctionnement. Les REP actuels n'ont à craindre dans les trente prochaines années ni l'obsolescence technique ni l'obsolescence économique.

T.T. FLETCHER, United States

Dr. Marchese, has a higher discount rate than the 5 per cent mentioned in the paper been tried ?

C.J. MARCHESE, United Kingdom

The test discount rate most closely matching historical costs is 2 per cent. The 5 per cent choice of base cases complies with the requirements of our UK Government as indicated in my paper. Naturally high discount rates are more penalising for any capital intensive project. However fossil fuel price increases and their uncertainties can also be penalising.

T.T. FLETCHER, United States

Would you explain the sensitivities in Net Effective Cost estimates and also the use of the Net Avoidable Cost ?

C.J. MARCHESE, United Kingdom

One per cent change in background costs associated with uranium and fuel fabrication produces a one per cent change in effective costs of nuclear production. However a one per cent change in fossil fuel costs produces an eight per cent change in net effective costs.

The Net Effective Cost Model includes all capital and interest changes and is used in project assessment prior to commitment. The Net Avoidable Cost Method is used for operating units and excludes past capital payments.

In M. Martel's assessments, has the optimisation of the Bugey 1 operating power showed the need for variations within a given year or over a whole life ?

A. MARTEL, France

La valeur de la production de Bugey 1 est maximisée lorsque les puissances de fonctionnement les plus élevées sont utilisées tous les ans, pendant les périodes de forte demande d'électricité.

Il est donc plus judicieux de ne pas diminuer la puissance de fonctionnement d'une façon systématique mais de faire varier celle-ci continûment au cours du temps.

J.W. HARROW, United Kingdom

A definite limit for graphite loss due to radiolytic corrosion was indicated in the presentation of M. Martel as the basis for the future service life of Bugey 1. How definite is this limit and what are the consequences of reaching this limit earlier or later ?

A. MARTEL, France

Les prévisions d'évolution du stock de graphite sont basées sur des analyses régulières de prélèvements et sur des extrapolations numériques issues de code de calcul. Le seuil minimal en dessous duquel il n'est plus possible de fonctionner est déterminé par des critères de tenue de l'empilement. Tous ces paramètres sont régulièrement revus en fonction des connaissances du moment. Les fluctuations des prévisions qui en résultent constituent un élément moins incertain que les autres paramètres économiques du problème. Pour en tenir compte, il convient de refaire les études d'optimisation régulièrement au fur et à mesure de l'accroissement de l'information disponible sur l'ensemble des paramètres évolutifs.

C.J. MARCHESE, United Kingdom

For those members of the symposium not familiar with graphite reactor technology, the design of the interlocking graphite bricks and keyways is important in lifetime assessment. Different design will be differently affected by the degradation from radiolytic corrosion. The CEGB is funding significant R&D to evaluate the sensitivity of the different designs to graphite weight loss. Such work has given confidence in the integrity of structures in the face of some weight loss in the graphite core at the stations most affected.

Y. INABA, IEA

I have an observation on the methodology taken by the US. If I understood correctly, their analysis deals with only a portion of the useful lives of the two options. But I believe the present value of the total cost of the NUPLEX option should be compared with that of the NEWCOAL option. The results of their analysis seem to exaggerate the benefits of NUPLEX.

D.D. CARLSON, United States

Engineering economic analysis over a much longer period of time have been performed to confirm the conclusions of our limited 30-year case study. Of course, the final decision should include benefits over the full planning cycle.

D.L. HARRISON, United States

The computer code used to analyze the Surry 1 PLEX option is software limited to a maximum term of 30 years. To augment confidence that this limitation is not significant, the benefits analysis included results from the separate Economic Lifecycle Study funded by Virginia Power and their corporate mainframe based analysis. Further, the basic results were comparable to other PLEX economic analysis recently completed in the USA. The generic conclusion of all these economic feasibility studies is that "PLEX has significant national and regional benefits".

J. BAUMIER, France

M. Carlson, à l'horizon envisagé dans votre étude, on peut penser que le contexte nucléaire actuel, si difficile aux Etats-Unis, aura évolué. Peut-être que vos efforts actuels, concernant la standardisation et la simplification de vos relations avec les Autorités administratives, aboutiront, et, dans ce cas, les coûts diminueront peut-être d'une façon importante, par exemple de 50 pour cent. Dans ce cas, il vous faudra comparer des coûts de rénovations qui porteront sur de vieilles centrales hétérogènes, au niveau par exemple de 30 pour cent du coût des centrales anciennes, avec le coût de centrales modernes qui serait par exemple égal à 50 pour cent de ces centrales anciennes. Qu'en pensez-vous ?

D.D. CARLSON, United States

Costs for new nuclear construction may well change in the future making new nuclear construction a viable alternative to extending the lives of existing plants. When the utility decides its best options for future genera- tion, all alternatives - coal, new nuclear, extending operating plants, new technologies - must be considered to determine the most cost-effective means of generating power.

D.R. HOSTETLER, United States

The planning for life extension will be periodically reviewed as situa- tions change. With the long lead time for replacement generation US utilities will have to choose between replacement and life extension beginning in the mid-1990s. If during the intervening years, the nuclear option appears viable PLEX will be compared with that alternative. If replacement nuclear generation is cheaper PLEX will not take place.

J.W. HARROW, United Kingdom

In view of experiences in Italy and Spain presented earlier in the Symposium, is it not unreasonable to assume the main bulk of the refurbishment activities can be undertaken during normal plant outages ?

What is the effect of extended plant down time for refurbishment on the financial benefits presented in this paper for life extension ?

D.D. CARLSON, United States

The assumption is highly uncertain. Yet the case study analysis suggest that up to $ 1 billion or more could be spent for life extension and still be economically preferable to new generating capacity. This cost could include major capital expenditures as well as long term outages for refurbishment. Thus, even with extended outages, PLEX should be economically viable.

D.R. HOSTETLER, United States

Based on what has been identified thus far in the pilot studies, major outages are not anticipated. We are speaking of incremental PLEX outages. Replacement activities in Italy and Spain were required to achieve the design life. There will no doubt be additional new requirements within the original 40 year licence period. At that time the decision will be made to do the work or shut down. The decision might be different if it is known that additional life beyond 40 years will result.

P.R. PARKMAN, United Kingdom

Are we sure that the required amounts of private finance will be forthcoming for life extension, in view of current public attitudes to nuclear power ?

D.L. HARRISON, United States

If the demand is critical, the supply side will accommodate. By that, I mean normal supply and demand forces will occur. Public attitudes pro or con nuclear will impact the ultimate unit cost of energy. Public opinions will·be felt through the safety and economic regulatory process. This perspective is nothing new. The public is the ultimate end user of electrical energy, consequently willingness to pay at a certain level for electrical energy is theirs alone.

D.D. CARLSON, United States

Only when a license renewal has been granted, taking into consideration public attitudes through the public hearing process, will substantial investments be made. With license renewal granted much uncertainty will have been removed from the process and financing should be of less concern.

D.L. HARRISON, United States

The issue of financial resources availability for nuclear PLEX is debatable. We believe the growth of demand for energy will continue to increase. Even if the growth was "zero" PLEX would be still needed in the US. Therefore, the issue "financial resources availability" is more related to how much will the energy cost. US utilities will provide the energy.

SESSION VI

CLOSING SESSION

SEANCE VI

SEANCE DE CLOTURE

Chairman – Président

P.R. PARKMAN

(United Kingdom)

Implications of Plant Life Extension

Conséquences de la prolongation de la durée de vie des centrales

R. Vidal
(France)

Au cours de la première séance nous avons étudié les problèmes généraux liés à l'augmentation de la durée de vie des centrales nucléaires et nous en avons analysé toutes les implications.

Ces implications couvrent plusieurs domaines :

- le domaine technique largement débattu dans les différentes séances ;

- le domaine économique auquel la Séance V a été entièrement consacrée ;

- le domaine de la sûreté qui a été souvent évoqué mais qui n'est pas l'objectif principal du symposium ;

- le domaine industriel qui concerne essentiellement les constructeurs d'abord par le ralentissement du programme de renouvellement des centrales. Mais aussi par le développement des interventions pour réparation et rénovation.

Toutes ces implications conduisent à des analyses différentes :

- selon les pays concernés en particulier en raison de la réglementation nucléaire existante ;

- selon les producteurs d'électricité suivant la variété de leur moyen de production, l'importance, la composition et l'âge du parc nucléaire et du parc des centrales classiques ;

- selon le type de centrales : réacteurs à eau légère, réacteurs à gaz ou réacteurs à eau lourde.

En raison de l'importance du parc de centrales à eau légère en service dans le monde les analyses techniques présentées couvrent en majorité ce type de centrales.

Enfin il me paraît souhaitable de préciser ce que l'on entend par "Extension de la durée de vie".

Il s'agit d'évaluer le bénéfice qu'on peut espérer d'une poursuite du fonctionnement au-delà d'une durée limite mais on admet en général la durée prévue lors de la conception qui est généralement moins de 40 ans pour les tranches récentes.

Ceci nécessite une bonne conaissance :

- du vieillissement des composants donc de leur durée de vie ;

- des méthodes et moyens pour assurer la rénovation ;

- des méthodes économiques d'aide à la décision pour engager la rénovation.

Je rappellerai brièvement les points essentiels de communications présentées dans la Séance I.

En France, ainsi que dans les pays à forte production nucléaire, la part du nucléaire atteindra au début des années 90 près de 75 pour cent de la production totale. Les tranches REP sont jeunes puisque leur moyenne d'âge ne dépasse guère 5 ans ; elles présentent donc une plus grande résistance aux phénomènes d'obsolescence technique mais aussi économique principalement à cause des importantes économies de combustible qu'elles procurent par rapport aux centrales classiques.

Par ailleurs les investissements nécessaires à la réalisation des centrales nucléaires sont lourds. Des réparations importantes et des refontes de longue durée, même si elles représentent une fraction significative de l'investissement initial, peuvent ainsi se trouver justifiées.

Les exploitants de centrales nucléaires auront donc tout intérêt à prolonger aussi longtemps que possible l'exploitation de leurs centrales dans la mesure, bien entendu où la sûreté de ces installations reste toujours garantie.

Mais ce problème ne se pose pas encore en France ni au producteur d'électricité, ni au constructeur.

Aux Etats-Unis, si on arrêtait les centrales après 40 ans de fonctionnement, la puissance nucléaire installée qui atteindra un maximum voisin de 100 Gigawatts vers 1994-1995, diminuerait entre 2010 et 2030 de 5 Gigawatts chaque année. Ainsi sans augmentation de la durée de vie, 95 pour cent de la capacité nucléaire serait ainsi retirée du réseau.

Même avec une faible croissance de la demande d'électricité et une augmentation de la durée de vie des centrales classiques, le besoin de nouvelles capacités de production dans la période de 2010 à 2030 sera très importante.

La prolongation de la durée de vie est donc un moyen de satisfaire cette demande.

Pour une large gamme d'hypothèses économiques l'augmentation de la durée de vie conduit à un important bénéfice pour les consommateurs d'électricité dont la majeure partie provient de l'économie de construction de centrales classiques. [Avec les meilleures hypothèses ce programme peut économiser près de 200 milliards de dollars jusqu'en 2030.]

D'un autre côté, le programme de Prolongation de la durée de vie va entraîner de profondes répercussions sur les programmes futurs de construction de centrales nucléaires.

Ainsi pour l'ensemble des pays de l'OCDE, l'étude de M. Inaba montre qu'en prenant comme base une durée de vie de 30 ans la seule prolongation jusqu'à 40 ans permettrait dans les 25 prochaines années de maintenir en service une capacité de production de 100 Gigawatts et ainsi de réduire à une valeur négligeable le programme de construction des centrales de remplacement.

Notons aussi que ce programme aura des conséquences plus importantes à court terme dans les pays comme les Etats-Unis et la Grande-Bretagne qui ont été les premiers à s'engager dans l'énergie nucléaire.

Le fonctionnement des centrales les plus anciennes constituera, dans les prochaines années, une source intéressante de données techniques. Dans ce domaine il faut encourager les programmes internationaux qui permettront à chaque pays d'acquérir ces informations. Chacun pourra ensuite évaluer l'intérêt et le gain que peut apporter l'augmentation de la durée de vie suivant sa propre situation économique.

M. Bertron nous a présenté les objectifs qui ont été assignés au programme d'étude de la prolongation de la durée de vie engagé par EDF. Ces objectifs, qui pourraient nous aider à définir des recommandations, sont les suivants :

- Etablir la <u>liste des matériels sensibles</u> et des informations dont on dispose pour évaluer leur durée de vie.

- Définir les <u>actions de R-D</u>, de surveillance et de retour d'expérience qui permettront d'améliorer nos connaissances.

- Déterminer les <u>conditions d'exploitation</u> susceptibles d'atténuer l'effet du vieillissement.

- Proposer des <u>indicateurs technico-économiques</u> à partir desquels une décision de réparation, de remplacement ou d'arrêt définitif de l'installation pourrait être prise.

Dans une centrale nucléaire la durée de vie de la plupart des équipements n'a guère de limite physique pourvu qu'on leur assure un entretien et une surveillance convenable et qu'on procède aux remises en état ou au remplacement des matériels. Tout peut être changé. Il suffit d'y mettre le prix. La prolongation de la durée de vie ne se pose donc qu'en terme économique.

J'ajouterai à mon exposé deux questions importantes qui ont fait l'objet de discussions :

- Quelle durée faut-il estimer pour la période de rénovation ?

En général on prévoit d'effectuer les rénovations importantes au cours de l'arrêt décennal quitte à l'allonger. Cet arrêt qui ne devrait pas dépasser 6 mois permettrait de garder la centrale en service pendant les périodes de pointe.

- Peut-on profiter de la rénovation pour augmenter les performances de la centrale ?

Les centrales anciennes ont été dimensionnées avec des marges, on pourrait donc augmenter les performances mais une modification sensible de celles-ci devrait conduire à présenter un dossier complet aux Autorités de sûreté.

Les centrales récentes sont optimisées on ne peut donc espérer gagner sur les performances, par contre on peut gagner sur la qualité de la réalisation en bénéficiant du retour d'expérience et ainsi reconstruire un équipement qui aura une plus longue durée de vie.

Plant and Component Lifetimes

Durée de vie des composants et des centrales

V.J. Streicher
(Federal Republic of Germany)

It was one of the purposes of this session to point out how lifetimes of single components influence the lifetime of the plant.

As already mentioned in the introduction to this session, we had a really interesting and informative combination of papers.

Safety issues were not a central focus of this symposium but, as we all know, they too will influence lifetime expectancy as well as refurbishment considerations.

As most of the participants are not primarily safety experts or regulatory people, the Secretariat invited Dr. Novak and Dr. Podest from the IAEA and Dr. McDonald from the NEA Division of Nuclear Safety so we could receive information concerning international activities in this field.

From these presentations we learned that:

- in the IAEA both safety and technical aspects of NPP ageing are studied by both the Divisions of Nuclear Safety and Nuclear Power. A state-of-the-art report on "Safety Aspects of Ageing" will be released in the near future. A symposium on "Safety Aspects of Ageing and Maintenance" will be held in Vienna at the beginning of July this year.

- the NEA hosted a workshop on these issues last week. Dr. McDonald gave us a detailed summary; we have to thank him for doing this in such a tight schedule. It was the goal of this workshop to define "technical issues which limit the long-term integrity of water reactor pressurised components"

In particular, all those phenomena which cause a loss of safety margins or component functions were pointed out, such as:

- neutron irradiation

- thermal ageing

- fatigue, creep corrosion effects, etc.

I am convinced that the full report announced by Dr. McDonald will be of major interest for our community. I hope it will be available from NEA later on.

The next two presentations dealt with methods by which the actual and the expected residual lifetime of reactor components, particularly the RPV, can be evaluated.

In spite of the fact that until 1996 none of the Japanese NPPs reaches its assumed lifetime, Mr. Nakajima gave us a scenario with very clear ideas about the basic concept and extended research items, which should enable the actual degradation of components to be monitored as well as being able to estimate their residual lifetime. He reported on his experimental work on crack initiation and crack growth in different reactor steel. This contribution confirmed my opinion that only an expert system, monitoring simultaneously a lot of different parameters and using long-term data bases, which is not available at present, can give us clear information about the usage and residual lifetime of reactor components. One part of such an expert system definitely has to be the fatigue monitoring system like that introduced by Dr. Schücktanz in the presentation that followed. This system can continuously evaluate the actual usage factor for the relevant parts and zones of the reactor pressure circuit boundary, taking into consideration static and cyclical loading as well as thermal stresses.

In the second half of our session we heard about some of the practical problems occurring when plants constructed in the '60s exhaust their residual lifetime.

We received information and case histories from four countries:

- In the United Kingdom twelve reactors of the Magnox type are still in service, the two oldest of them for over 24 years. A large amount of operating experience has been gained. This provides a good base for extending their lifetimes beyond the originally planned limits. A so-called "Long Term Safety Review" was required by the UK licensing process. This review and the different plant improvements performed in the last years are expected to enable operation to continue on the two earliest plants.

- In contrast to this we heard about two case histories from France and Germany where the plants at Chinon A2 and Gundremmingen had to be shut down and decommissioned due to their non-compliance with present safety requirements and guidelines.

In both these cases not a single component was replaced. It was cheaper to replace the whole plant by new and more powerful units.

- Mr. Hart's presentation on the CANDU 300 project was not the last paper in this session but I have put it at the end of this summary because it gives a glance into the future. This reactor type is designed for a lifetime of at least 100 years. From past experience, this goal will be achieved by:

- good access to relevant components, hence easy replacement possibilities and flexibility in additional requirements; and

- high lifetime of the few components which are not replaceable.

To summarise just let me mention that this session at least touched on all those issues important for lifetime expectancy and extension:

- safety aspects and regulatory requirements;

- parameters relevant to plant ageing;

- evaluation, calculation and monitoring of these parameters;

- long term operational experience with existing plants;

- last but not least the possibility of planned replacement and refurbishment of components or systems.

Projects of Plant Life Extension

Projets de prolongation de la durée de vie des centrales

D.R. Hostetler
(United States)

Session III focussed on life extension project activities on LWR.

The joint EPRI/DOE nuclear plant life extension program is intended to support U.S. utilities through the identification of the requirements for extended life and support of activities leading to the development of a licence renewal process, U.S. law providing for licence renewal but no commercial licensing has been renewed.

Based on their planning horizon U.S. utilities will need to know with certainty whether or not the plant licence will be renewed up to 12 years in advance of licence expiration. This lead time is required to plan, design and construct replacement generation if the licence is not renewed. Thus a licence renewal process is needed by the early 1990s to permit a decision by the mid-1990s.

The NUPLEX Steering Committee has been established to co-ordinate the technical, licensing and codes and standards activities associated with the development of a viable life extension licence renewal program. To this end NUPLEX has developed a technical program and initiated discussion with NRC with respect to licence renewal.

The two LWR pilot studies, the Monticelli PWR and Surry 1 PWR, which form the basis for the NUPLEX plan, have completed phase 1, i.e. feasibility and issue identification. These studies are the first detailed plant specific PLEX studies.

Each project identified potential critical plant elements which could have a significant impact on life extension. Detailed evaluation including a review of design base, of regulation requirements, codes and standards, O&M history, potential degradation mechanics to estimate where possible remaining life, will identify R&D needed and recommend potential follow-on implementation activities such as modified O&M practice, additional monitoring and inspection and physical changes.

Conclusions from both studies were similar:

1. Life extension of 20 or more years appears technically feasible.

2. Preventative and mitigating action to preserve the life extension option should be implemented in the near future.

3. Records retention and retrieval are not currently adequate to support life extension. Substantial upgrades are needed (the licence renewal application will rely heavily on adequate records).

Significant, genuine R&D is needed. Both pilot studies are in Phase II (implementation). Activities include upgrading records storage and retrieval, transient validation, developing and implementing procedures for life extension, inspection and monitoring activities. Monitoring in the broad sense includes surveillance, testing and inspection as well as on-line monitoring.

You will note that these activities focus on preserving the options on life extension; major expenditure will be deferred until the licensees are assured that the licence will be renewed.

EDF is evaluating the performance of its standardized PWR to obtain the best estimate of the safe economical life. Available data on ageing and maintenance on a limited number of major components are being evaluated. The large data base made possible by the EDF system makes this approach potentially meaningful and very valuable.

There appears to be no practical limit on the containment life. Reactor vessels and other major components appear to have very good potential for extended life. However, it is not certain that all degradation mechanisms have been fully evaluated. For example, steam generators and turbines are subject to degradation and possible failure. Maintenance programs to detect and mitigate these effects can be developed but at what cost? A major object of the study is to identify risks and bring them under control to prevent performance degradation as the systems age.

The last paper described what is, in effect, an actual life extension program. The Trino unit was the first wholly commercial LWR placed in service (in 1964). Over the life span of almost 22 years substantial modification and improvements were made in two long outages.

The first outage was necessary to repair failure in the reactor internals and to instal a monitoring and surveillance system. The second outage was primarily for safety upgrades. The ECCS was replaced. Additional modifications derived from post-TMI concerns and systematic evaluation plans were also made.

The above modifications were made at a cost of about $80 million and took a number of years but, as a result, the standard of safety has improved and the potential for extension of life beyond that originally estimated is enhanced.

Refurbishment Experience and Monitoring

Expérience et contrôle des travaux de rénovation

G. Schücktanz
(Federal Republic of Germany)

The first part of Session IV dealt with the replacement of aged components, the experience gained during execution of replacement work and covered
the design of some replacement components. Repair techniques were presented
and discussed as alternatives to component replacement. In the second part of
Session IV the present status of monitoring systems was reported.

In the design of replacement components, of course, the latest state-
of-the-art has been taken into consideration. An example is the selection of
corrosion resistant material for replacement piping for BWRs and for tubing
for steam generator replacement. In combination with a more protective chemistry in the coolant it can be expected that failures caused by stress corrosion cracking will not occur in the future. For repairs and replacement more
sophisticated techniques are available, most of them using remole controlled
devices or even automatically operating robots. The experience has shown that
the use of such equipment does minimise the risk of failures during repair.
On the other hand, the installation of remote controlled equipment could require more time and cause more radiation exposure of personnel than a manually
performed repair work. Pros and cons of the use of automatic equipment have
to be considered carefully.

As an alternative to replacement of components, repair techniques were
discussed such as shot peening, rote peening, heat treatment and sleeving of
tubing of steam generators as well as, for instance, overlay cladding of
cracked piping of BWRs. With regard to the two options, repair or replacement,
two aspects were discussed.

There is a lack of knowledge with regard to the effectiveness of some
repair techniques. It is obvious that, for instance, shot peening will prolong
the lifetime of a steam generator, but it is very difficult to say for how
long. Organisations such as NEA, IAEA or EPRI were asked to consider compiling
a data base on the effectiveness of repair techniques which would help the
utilities in deciding the most economic option. Another aspect with regard to
replacement versus repair is that of licensing. Some repair techniques do not
really remove the defect. Overlay cladding of BWR piping for instance just
increases the wall thickness in the vicinity of the cracks. Licensing authorities might accept such repairs only for limited periods and may ask for additional measures such as extended in-service inspection or continuous crack

monitoring. Replacement may then be the more economic and less risky solution, as has been reported from Spain and Switzerland.

In the second part of the Session several monitoring systems for the primary systems components of nuclear power plants were presented, such as loose parts monitoring systems, vibration monitoring systems, leakage monitoring systems, noise analysis systems, etc. All these systems have been installed in nuclear power plants in operation and have performed well.

The question was raised to what extent such systems contribute to the extension of the life to power plants, as they only detect failures when they have already occurred. An early detection helps, of course, to avoid major damage and also helps to optimise the scheduling of repair activities.

Nevertheless, systems monitoring the actual ageing of components would be an advantage. A system for fatigue monitoring was discussed in another session; systems monitoring the embrittlement of RPV steel and systems monitoring the corrosive environment in components were not discussed. There seems to be a need for preparation of a complete concept for monitoring all the effects limiting the lifetime of components. Together with a cost benefit analysis this would help the utilities in installing the most appropriate system.

In summary :

   1) Repair and replacement of components is technically no problem.

   2) To decide whether to repair or to replace utilities requires more
      information on the effectiveness of repair techniques.

   3) An overall concept for monitoring the effects limiting the life of
      components, combined with a cost benefit analysis, would help the
      utilities in optimising their plant operation with respect to plant
      life extension.

Economic Analyses of Plant Life Extension

Analyse économique de la prolongation de la durée de vie des centrales

T.T. Fletcher
(United States)

In summmary, Session V focussed on the economic cost and benefit of nuclear plant life extension.

The paper which I presented this morning concluded that, in the absence of any major technological breakthroughs making the present generating option obsolete and under the most cost-inefficient assumptions for nuclear plant life extension, consumers will save approximately $ 180 billion on their electric bills over the period 2010-50. However, nuclear PLEX could lose money for consumers in comparision with new coal power plants, but only under the extremely pessimistic scenario for nuclear PLEX. Savings in our analysis are most sensitive to changes in plant construction costs. In the case of the US, the main factors are relevant in a NUPLEX-vs-NEWCOAL decision.

The second paper, presented by Dr. Marchese from the UK, focused on factors contributing to the economic worth of CEGB Magnox PLEX with emphasis being placed on the marginal savings which could arise from extending the operations of these plants. The paper's basic conclusion shows a net economic worth of savings; about one billion pounds resulting from life extension of a Magnox plant.

The third paper was presented by M. Martel of the nuclear and fossil generating group of France. He discussed the economics of life extension in the case of BUGEY 1, a unit of GCR type. The basic conclusion indicates that by extending the plant lifetime the end of this life may be optimised when the basic components, which cannot be repaired, introduces a constraint. In the case of BUGEY 1 this constraint can be represented as a stock constraint whose development is governed by the power supply of the unit.

The last paper was given by Mr. Carlson of Sandia. He discussed a cost/benefit analysis for nuclear plant life extension in regard to a public utility as opposed to the US as a whole. The methodology he used is based on a computer model focusing not only on economic aspects of nuclear plant life extension but also on financial aspects.

R. NOEL, France (Statement)

1.   Safety aspects of life extension in France

The licences given to EDF by the safety authorities refer explicitly to the safety justifications supplied by the technical files attached to the applications. In these documents the applicant demonstrates that convenient margins of safety are ensured within a lifetime of 40 years, provided the operation conforms to the various design hypothesis (i.e. fluence on the vessel wall, number and severity of transients, and so on).

So there is no doubt that the safety authority would not consider cancelling these authorisations, provided EDF can demonstrate that all safety margins are respected at any time.

Of course, a life extension beyond the 40 years would require additional data. Obviously, severe unexpected technical issues could also lead to cancellation of the authorisations.

2.   Economical aspects of life extension

There is no doubt that a life extension of the EDF PWR plants may represent an important saving of money, provided:

a) No competitive system, with large cost advantage, is available at the time of the extension or replacement decision.

b) The cost of the necessary "refurbishing" for an extension of life is not prohibitive.

A major objective of any life extension study is to allow a correct evaluation of this cost.

3.   Life forecast of heavy components

Unless a worldwide in-service experience of the critical component of a nuclear plant is gained over 30 or 40 years, any attempt at life prediction can only be analytical. Therefore the quality of the forecast is very dependent on the quality of the models used to predict the time dependent evolution of the ageing process.

When making a review of all available data in these fields, there are two possibilities:

a) If a correct technical model of the damage is available (e.g. fatigue, irradiation embrittlement...): the extrapolation in future behaviour of the component is easy.

b) If no model of the damage is available (e.g., corrosion): a long term prediction is risky. I think basic work to clarify this kind of phenomena is very important for the future.

N.R. McDONALD, NEA,

I would support M. Noel's comments about corrosion. The workshop on which I reported identified the role of the chemical environment on integrity as a major area of uncertainty and requiring, in particular, the development of further guidance material (there is much fundamental understanding -practical implications are less clear). One aspect here is the need for corrosion, water chemistry and fracture assessment experts to interact more closely and better understand each others practical requirements. The workshop recommended that NEA look at means to facilitate this interaction and develop guidance material, taking account also of the work of international groups such as the International Committee on Crack Growth Rate.

We see a similar need for greater interdisciplinary interaction in other areas. For example we plan to bring together fracture mechanics and non-destructive examination experts to discuss advances in their respective areas with regulatory people and encourage a better mutual understanding among all three groups of their respective capabilities and interests.

R. GINIER, France (Statement)

Apport de la R&D à la prolongation de la durée de vie

La prolongation de la durée de vie nécessite de reprendre l'analyse des marges qui interviennent à différent titres:

- au niveau de la conception : incertitudes liées aux outils de calculs mécaniques ou thermohydrauliques, à la connaissance des matériaux,

- au niveau de la réalisation : marges de dimensionnement, incertitudes liées aux matériaux utilisés,

- au niveau de l'utilisation : connaissance des scénarios de fonctionnement réels, surveillance locale, ...

Les programmes de R&D peuvent apporter des éléments à ces différents niveaux, en particulier à celui de la conception avec le développement d'outils de calcul plus élaborés et une meilleure connaissance des matériaux soumis au vieillissement sur de longues durées.

Concernant les outils de calcul, il y a bien entendu les outils de calcul mécanique, mais aussi les outils de calcul thermohydraulique qui fournissent les données d'entrée au dimensionnement mécanique. Comme il s'agit fréquemment de géométries complexes, il faut prévoir le développement de codes multidimensionnels, nécessitant des validations au moyen d'essais suffisamment représentatifs tant au niveau des maquettes utilisées que des conditions de fonctionnement, de façon à minimiser les incertitudes liées à la transposition au réacteur.

Concernant les matériaux, il faut penser que les programmes de vieillissement, par nature, sont longs à mettre en oeuvre. Il faut donc être très attentifs au choix des éprouvettes, aux conditions d'irradiation ou de vieillissement thermique. Les lois utilisées pour l'extrapolation présentent encore bien des incertitudes et la possibilité de disposer d'un ou de paramètres permettant de suivre le vieillissement in situ serait d'un grand intérêt.

Il en va de même pour les aspects corrosion; des "maladies" peuvent mettre un certain temps à se déclarer et il est important de disposer de méthodes de contrôle non destructif fiables et qualifiées.

Enfin, tout cet ensemble de développement et d'amélioration des connaissances ou des moyens doit être intégré dans la réglementation qu'il faut donc faire évoluer en parallèle.

P.R. PARKMAN, United Kingdom

Mr. Ginier touched upon the issue of plant data, which might be an area on which other delegates would like to express opinions.

D.R. HOSTETLER, United States

We certainly believe that retention of plant data is essential for life extension. We are working very hard to collect data for supporting life extension programmes of Surry and Monticello.

C.J. MARCHESE, United Kingdom

In the CEGB we are currently extending the coverage of our reliability and availability data bases. Furthermore in the area of record keeping, we are developing Laser Disc Archival Storage and Retrieval. This utilises computerised record access. The importance of this aspect lies in the ability to perform programmed and structured enquiries of the information contained on the discs. Its uses cover video recorded data, still photographs and many printed records, e.g. NDT reports.

M.J. BOYER, France (Statement)

R&D dans le projet extension durée de vie: La surveillance en ligne

Certains orateurs ont parlé de l'interêt d'une surveillance en ligne, je souhaiterais que l'on revienne sur ce sujet afin de voir quelles actions la R&D pourrait engager compte-tenu des objectifs visés pour allonger la durée de vie de conception, compte-tenu du bénéfice que l'on attend c'est-à-dire un allongement de 10, 15, 20 ans, etc.

   a) Quels sont les objectifs de la surveillance en ligne pour le projet
      d'extension de durée de vie ?

Actuellement les concepteurs et les exploitants disposent d'informations concernant la comptabilisation des situations, la maintenance, les analyses de comportement, les inspections en service...

Qu'attend-on d'une surveillance en ligne vis-à-vis de la fatigue des composants (approche KWU) ; de la détection d'anomalies de fonctionnement notamment pour les matériels ayant une fonction de sauvegarde; de la conformité des matériels par rapport aux critères de sûreté de conception (qualification des matériels électriques en particulier)?

   b) Peut-on définir des critères de définition de la surveillance en
      ligne ?

G. SCHüCKTANZ, Federal Republic of Germany (Statement)

The main objective of monitoring systems should definitely be to provide information on the actual state of ageing. One cannot talk about extension of life if one doesn't know the actual degradation in the function of a component. Of course, there are a number of factors affecting the life of components. Material fatigue is just one of them.

I feel that it is necessary to develop an overall concept for plant life monitoring taking into consideration all life limiting mechanisms. I think this cannot be done without some effort, probably also including some R&D work.

M. MIKSCH, Federal Republic of Germany (Statement)

The participants of the Symposium discussed the target of calculating fatigue usage factors of representative locations of the steam supply system with time, which enables us to define available safety margins in respect to crack initiation.

I have to mention that one of the most important objectives of fatigue monitoring and data acquisition is to provide utility personnel with actual data defining the operational behaviour of the plant. From these data, modifications to plant operation in order to minimise severe cyclic loads and transients which may have an impact on fatigue damage may then be made.

H.-P. ADLER, Switzerland (Statement)

One of the aims of refurbishing should be to comply with recent safety criteria. Therefore as a first step a PRA (Probabilistic Risk Assessment) for an individual plant seems to be necessary. Since 1974 (Rasmunssen) PRA has made steady progress and is nowadays a useful tool available from commercial companies. In some cases the core melt frequency can be much lower than presumed on a generic basis. Some national safety authorities require this assessment before allowing refurbishing.

Refurbishing should include not only the replacement of worn components but also the installation of new safety systems, e.g. third water supply for decay heat removal. Some older plants may also be insufficiently protected against external events (air plane crash, flood) and this influences structural elements. Thus refurbishing may have to be very comprehensive and expensive, perhaps to the extent that other options have to be considered: derated electricity production (less fuel elements) or, in the case of Switzerland, production of steam only for district heating.

L. REYNES, France

Pour répondre au Dr. Alder, je dirai qu'il n'y a pas de lien entre l'extension de la durée de vie et les études probabilistes de sûreté. En effet, la conception des réacteurs s'appuie sur des méthodes déterministes. L'analyse probabiliste apporte à ce stade un complément utile dans le choix entre différentes solutions techniques ; elle est ensuite utilisée sur les systèmes des centrales en service pour apprécier le niveau de sûreté d'ensemble et faire apparaître les points afin de les corriger. Cela étant, il faut souligner que les études probabilistes ne peuvent pas donner de valeurs absolues d'occurrence d'incidents.

Dans ces conditions, il me paraîtrait irréaliste de vouloir apprécier le vieillissement d'une centrale par des calculs probabilistes. Contrairement à une voiture dont on pense qu'il est possible de laisser se dégrader l'état avant sa mise à la ferraille ; un réacteur doit satisfaire à ses spécifications techniques d'exploitation jusqu'au terme de son exploitation. On peut dire que la veille de son déclassement, un réacteur devra fonctionner avec un niveau de sûreté comparable à celui de sa vie durant.

D.D. CARLSON, United States

The DOE sponsored work to apply results of analysing Surry PRA results to identify the most important components to risk if their reliability were degraded. This bounding analysis added to our understanding of PLEX-important components.

G. ECKERT, Federal Republic of Germany

With political obstacles, as well as the problem of public acceptance to prolonging life time, I would seek high availability of a plant during its secured lifetime rather than life extension beyond 40 years.

It seems to be more important to look at components which have to be improved so that they can operate a plant reliably for the secured period.

D.R. HOSTETLER, United States

It is certainly much more important to assume a lifetime of 40 years than life extension. However, in a life extension programme, one of the benefits that we see is to improve knowledge about the areas where improvements can be made on current operation, and to make life extension more feasible as a consequence.

S. MORI, NEA

From the standpoint of the Secretariat, I think one of the main purposes of holding an international symposium of this kind is to learn something useful from other countries' efforts. I guess there would be similar approaches towards plant life extension between those countries with the same reactor type, e.g. PWR, because they could share a common technical basis.

My question is directed to U.S. and/or French delegates, who are promoting the pioneering projects for their LWRs. In the process of your projects, you have identified the critical components and R&D items required for plant life extension. Do you think these technical outputs from your projects will also be applicable to other plants not only in your country but in other Member countries? If not directly applicable, I wonder what would be most needed to take into account. Can you identify any factors that are considered to be plant-specific?

D.D. CARLSON, United States

The important components from the two US projects were the reactor pressure vessel, vessel internals, primary system components, the containment building, large concrete structures and so forth. These are important for both PWR and BWR. We are currently investigating whether these critical components will also be important for LWRs in general in the United States. We have also found a few plant-specific components which I guess are probably design-specific.

I think many critical components for our study would also be important for light water reactors in general. As plant-specific matters, I would refer to graphite concerns and some other concerns for other reactor types, such as CANDU, because there are particular material questions.

L. REYNES, France

Si j'ai bien compris la question, il s'agit de savoir si les études d'allongement de la durée de vie faites dans un pays sont applicables dans un autre.

Je répondrai à cette question en disant qu'il est sûrement possible et certainement profitable d'avoir des échanges internationaux dans le domaine de la recherche et développement. On peut certainement s'inspirer de la méthodologie mise au point dans d'autres pays. Cela étant, il paraît évident que chaque exploitant devra faire son propre programme d'allongement de durée de vie.

M. PODEST, IAEA

We really think that it is necessary to provide a forum for international exchange of experience in this field.

An international data base will also be useful to Member countries to obtain necessary information. But it is necessary to start by identifying what is useful and what is possible, because we cannot get all the information and there is some difference between reactor types.

N.R. McDONALD, NEA

The Nuclear Energy Agency is currently giving considerable attention to its international data bases in this area. We are trying to improve the quality of input information, which is of vital importance.

I think one has to be very selective and choose topics which provide good opportunity for getting useful information. What we are endeavouring to do in our work, e.g. the PISC (Programme for the Inspection of Steel Components) and some other areas on material integrity, is to try to assist experts in different countries to get better mutual understanding of the underlying technical issues so that they can arrive at similar interpretations and applications of the information in each country in terms of regulations, safety assessment or whatever.

C.J. MARCHESE, United Kingdom

There is certainly a need for international co-operation in the area of operating experience feedback. As a utility envisaging LWR stations it has been of great assistance to have timely feedback as provided by INPO and UNIPEDE.

This has been typified by the recent SURRY events and the swift reporting of information by INPO and its members and associate members on this subject is of great value. Therefore, in general, there is great need for international co-operation but it must provide timely feedback to utilities to be of use in operation and PLEX activities.

CLOSING REMARKS

P.R. Parkman
Central Electricity Generating Board
London, United Kingdom

In the past three days, we have received an excellent series of papers that have addressed a wide range of issues from complete study methodology to particular techniques but have generally pointed out the important areas that need further work. We have identified some of the constraints. We have deliberately not discussed the safety issues but we have seen quite clearly how the regulatory and the safety aspects will impinge on the viability of the options and their assessment. We have also had a valuable session for the engineers amongst us on the economic aspects which have been addressed admirably in the sessions today.

I believe that this Symposium will have been useful to all those attended ; focussing our thoughts on those aspects applicable each to our own particular areas of interest. I would like to thank all the speakers who have prepared papers and I am particularly grateful to the five session chairmen on my left, who have supported me so very strongly and have just presented a masterly summary of each of their sessions. I would also like to thank the NEA staff ; the translators for dealing with difficult technical jargon and managing admirably, the administrative staff who have served us so well with papers and those yellow question sheets, Martin Crijns and Soichi Mori, who have put a tremendous amount of effort into making this Symposium successful. Finally, I would like to express our thanks to Mr. Horiuchi, Deputy Director of NEA for arranging this Symposium, and invite him to close the proceedings.

CLOSING ADDRESS

S. Horiuchi
Deputy Director
OECD Nuclear Energy Agency

Thank you Mr. Chairman, ladies and gentlemen,

It is my great pleasure to have the last word at the Symposium on behalf of the Nuclear Energy Agency.

You will certainly agree with me that this Symposium has been a most successful meeting. Even though the studies on nuclear plant life extension are just on their starting line, the discussions and the exchange of views and information have stimulated our recognition of the future direction of factors influencing nuclear plant life extension.

We will leave this Symposium with a greater knowledge of the recent development. At the same time, I am sure that we will all be even more aware than we were before of the importance of plant life extension in the process of nuclear power development.

The success of the meeting is due to the efforts of many people and I would like to thank the various people who have been involved in.

First of all, I would like to thank the participants, in particular, those who presented the excellent papers and also those who took part in discussions.

I would also like to thank all the chairmen, Mr. Parkman, Mr. Vidal, Mr. Streicher, Mr. Hostetler, Dr. Schücktanz and Mr. Fletcher who accepted the roles with such energy and good humour.

In addition, I would like to give thanks to the IAEA and IEA staffs who have co-operated in organizing this Symposium. I believe a co-operation of this kind could be a reference case to improve our efficiency and also to meet the demand from our Member countries.

Now, many of us are going to make a field trip to Chinon tomorrow. I would like to remind you that this trip is arranged by the courtesy of Electricité de France. I would like to thank them for their hospitality on this occasion. I hope we will have good weather and a nice trip.

Last but not the least, I would like to express my sincere thanks on behalf of us all to the interpreters who have done an excellent job. I am always impressed by their ability to translate our technical jargon, often at a high speed without pre-prints. This successful international Symposium would not have been possible without their efforts. Let us give them a big hand.

All in all, it has been a great pleasure for us to act as your host and we hope that many of the associations which were formed during the past three days and some to be formed tomorrow may continue in the future.

Thank you very much for your attention and I wish you "Bon Voyage".

The Symposium is now closed.

LIST OF PARTICIPANTS

LISTE DES PARTICIPANTS

AUSTRIA - AUTRICHE

CECH, F., OEST-ALPINE, Postfach 2, 4010 Linz

BELGIUM - BELGIQUE

DE HEERING, D., Divison Commerciale - Projets Spéciaux, Belgonucléaire,
25 rue du Champ de Mars, B-1050 Bruxelles

SAINT-PAUL, R., Westinghouse Nuclear International, 73 rue de Stalle,
B-1180 Bruxelles

CANADA

HART, R.S., Atomic Energy of Canada, Sheridan Park Research Community,
Mississauga, Ontario L5K 1B2

KUPCA, S., Atomic Energy of Canada, Research Company, Chalk River,
Ontario K0J 1J0

FINLAND - FINLANDE

OTTOSSON, C., Finnish Centre for Radiation and Nuclear Safety, P.O. Box 268,
SF-00101 Helsinki

PAAVOLA, O.M.T., Teollisuuden Voima Oy, SF-27160 Olkiluoto

FRANCE

ALBIN, M. FRAMATOME, Tour Fiat, Cedex 16, F-92084 Paris La Défense

BARRE, B., Commissariat à l'Energie Atomique, Centre d'Etudes Nucléaires de
Cadarache, DRE, F-13108 Saint-Paul-lez-Durance Cedex

BAUMIER, J., Commissariat à l'Energie Atomique, 31-33 rue de la Fédération,
F-75015 Paris

BERTRON, L., Chef Adjoint du Service de la Production Thermique, Electricité de France, 3 rue de Messine, F-75384 Paris Cedex 08

BITSCH, D., FRAMATOME, Tour Fiat, Cedex 16, F-92084 Paris La Défense

BONEH, B., FRAMATOME, Tour Fiat, Cedex 16, F-92084 Paris La Défense

BOYER, J., Commissariat à l'Energie Atomique, Centre d'Etudes Nucléaires de Cadarache, DRE/BCT-E, F-13108 Saint-Paul-lez-Durance Cedex 22

BRETON, A., Département des Liaisons du Service de la Production Thermique, Electricité de France, 3 rue de Messine, F-75384 Paris Cedex 08

DUMONT, J., Chef du Centre de Production Nucléaire de Chinon, Electricité de France, B.P. 80, F-37420 Avoine

GARCIA, J.L., Commissariat à l'Energie Atomique, Centre d'Etudes Nucléaires de Cadarache, DRE/STRE, F-13108 Saint-Paul-lez-Durance Cedex

GINIER, R., Commissariat à l'Energie Atomique, Centre d'Etudes Nucléaires de Cadarache, DRE/STRE, F-13108 Saint-Paul-lez-Durance Cedex

HAMMER, P., Commissariat à l'Energie Atomique, Boîte Postale n° 510, F-75752 Paris Cedex 15

MARMONIER, P., Commissariat à l'Energie Atomique, Centre d'Etudes Nucléaires de Cadarache, D.R.N.R./SYTC, F-13108 Saint-Paul-lez-Durance Cedex

MARTEL, A., Electricité de France, 3 rue de Messine, F-75384 Paris Cedex 08

NOEL, R., Chargé de Mission au Service de la Production Thermique, Electricité de France, 3 rue de Messine, F-75384 Paris Cedex 08

PAPIN, B., Commissariat à l'Energie Atomique, Centre d'Etudes Nucléaires de Cadarache, DRE/SEN, F-13108 Saint-Paul-lez-Durance

PALLISSIER TANON, A., FRAMATOME, Tour Fiat, Cedex 16, F-92084 Paris La Defense

POIGNET, B., Commissariat à l'Energie Atomique, Centre d'Etudes Nucléaires de Cadarache, DRE/SCOS, F-13108 Saint-Paul-lez-Durance Cedex

RAYNAL, A., Chef de la Centrale de Chinon A, Centre de Production Nucléaire de Chinon, Electricité de France, B.P. 80, F-374210 Avoine

REMOND, A., FRAMATOME, Tour Fiat, Cedex 16, F-92084 Paris La Défense

REYNES, L., SEPTEN, Electricité de France, 12 rue Dutrievoz, F-69628 Villeurbanne Cedex

VIDAL, R., Commissariat à l'Energie Atomique, DEDRE/CRE, Centre d'Etudes Nucléaires de Saclay, F-91191 Gif-sur-Yvette Cedex

VIGNESOULT, N., Commissariat à l'Energie Atomique, IPSN/DAS, B.P. n° 6, F-92265 Fontenay-aux-Roses Cedex

FEDERAL REPUBLIC OF GERMANY - REPUBLIQUE FEDERALE D'ALLEMAGNE

ECKERT, G., Kraftwerk Union A.G., Berliner Str. 295-303, Postfach 962,
D-6050 Offenbach am Main

GNUTZMANN, H., Technischer Überwachungs-Verein Baden e.V., Dudenstrasse 28,
D-6800 Mannheim 1

IVENS, G., Arbeitsgemeinschaft Versuchsreaktor AVR GmbH, Postfach 1411,
Luisenstrasse 105, D-4000 Düsseldorf

MIKSCH, M., Kraftwerk Union A.G., Dept. RT 214, Postfach 3220, D-8520 Erlangen

SCHÖCKTANZ, G., Kraftwerk Union A.G., Dept. RT 21, Postfach 3220,
D-8520 Erlangen

STANG, W., Projektleiter Stillegung Block A, Kernkraftwerke Grundremmingen,
Betriebsgesellschaft mbH (KRB), Grundremmingen/Guenzburg

STEIGER, W.O., Geschäftsführer Kernkraftwerk-Betriebsgesellschaft mbH,
D-7514 Eggenstein-Leopoldshafen

STREICHER, V.J., Kraftwerk Union A.G., Dept. R 542, Postfach 3220,
D-8520 Erlangen

ZIERMANN, E., Arbeitsgemeinschaft Versuchsreaktor AVR GmbH, Postfach 1411,
Luisenstrasse 105, D-4000 Düsseldorf

INDIA - INDE

KOTHARI, C.M., Narora Atomic Power Project, Nuclear Power Board, Department
of Atomic Energy, P.O. NAPP Township, Narora, Bulandshahr District, Uttar
Pradesh

ITALY - ITALIE

BUONO, A., Capa Gruppo Reattore, Secteur Réacteur et Sécurité, Direction de
la Construction, ENEL, Via G.B. Martini 3, I-00198 Roma

COMINI, R., ENEL DPT, Via G.B. Martini 3, I-00198 Roma

DE AGOSTINO, E., ENEA-DISP, Via V. Brancati 48, I-00144 Roma

DI PALO, L., ENEA-DISP, Via Vitaliano Brancati 48, I-00144 Roma

JAPAN - JAPON

KOYAMA, T., Hitachi Limited, Energy Research Laboratory, 1168 Moriyama-cho,
Hitachi-shi, Ibaraki-ken 316

NAKAJIMA, H., Japan Atomic Energy Research Institute, Tokai Research
Establishment, Materials Engineering Laboratory, Department of Fuels and
Materials Research, Tokai-mura, Ibaraki-ken 319-11

ONO, Y., Mitsubishi Heavy Industries, Ltd., Shuwa Shiba Park Building,
4-1 Shibakoen, 2-chome, Minato-ku, Tokyo

TSUNODA, T., Nippon Atomic Industry Group Co. Ltd, Nuclear Engineering
Department, 4-1 Ukishima-cho, Kawasaki-ku, Kawasaki-shi, Kanagawa 210

SPAIN - ESPAGNE

ARANA, J., Chef de la Section des Centrales nucléaires en opération,
Ministère de l'Industrie et de l'Energie, Paseo de la Castellana 160,
28046 Madrid

IBANEZ, M., Planning Department, Union Electrica S.A., Francisco Gervas 3,
28020 Madrid

OLASO, J., Nuclenor S.A., Hernan Cortès 26, 39003 Santander

PERRAMON, F., Asociacion Nuclear Vandellos, Travessera de les Corts 39-43,
1a planta, 08028 Barcelona

SWITZERLAND - SUISSE

ALDER, H., Swiss Federal Institute for Reactor Research (EIR),
CH-5303 Würenlingen

TURKEY - TURQUIE

KURBANOGLU, O., Turkish Atomic Energy Authority, Karanfil Sok. n° 67,
Bakanliklar, Ankara

UNITED KINGDOM - ROYAUME-UNI

DODDS, R., British Nuclear Fuels Ltd., A Block, Risley, Warrington WA3 6AS

HARROW, J.W., South of Scotland Electricity Board, Cathcart House, Spean
   Street, Glasgow G44 4BE

MARCHESE, C.J., Central Electricity Generating Board, Sudbury House,
   15 Newgate Street, London EC1A 7AU

PARKMAN, P.R., Chairman, Head of Nuclear Safety Operations Branch, Health and
   Safety Department, Central Electricity Generating Board, Courtenay House,
   15 Newgate Street, London EC1A 7AU

UNITED STATES - ETATS-UNIS

CARLSON, D.D., Sandia National Laboratories, Division 6513, Post Office
   Box 5800, Albuquerque, New Mexico 87185

FLETCHER, T.T., Data Resources Inc., 1750 K Street NW, Washington D.C. 20006

HARRISON, D.L., U.S. Department of Energy, Office of Nuclear Energy, NE-42,
   Washington D.C. 20545

HOSTETLER, D.R., Corporate Technical Assessment, Virginia Power,
   P.O. Box 26666, Richmond, Virginia 23261

COMMISSION OF THE EUROPEAN COMMUNITIES
COMMISSION DES COMMUNAUTES EUROPEENNES

JUUL, K., Commission des Communautés Européennes, 200 rue de la Loi,
   B-1049 Bruxelles, Belgique

INTERNATIONAL ATOMIC ENERGY AGENCY
AGENCE INTERNATIONALE DE L'ENERGIE ATOMIQUE

NECHAEV, A., P.O. Box 100, Wagramerstrasse 5, A-1400 Vienna, Austria

NOVAK, S., Division of Nuclear Safety, P.O. Box 100, Wagramerstrasse 5,
   A-1400 Vienna, Austria

PODEST, M., Division of Nuclear Power, P.O. Box 100, Wagramerstrasse 5,
   A-1400 Vienna, Austria

INTERNATIONAL ENERGY AGENCY
AGENCE INTERNATIONALE DE L'ENERGIE

INABA, Y., Energy Economic Analysis Division, 2 rue André Pascal, 75775 Paris
Cedex 16, France

LANGLOIS, L., Economic Analysis Division, 2 rue André Pascal, 75775 Paris
Cedex 16, France

NUCLEAR ENERGY AGENCY
AGENCE POUR L'ENERGIE NUCLEAIRE

CRIJNS, M.J., Nuclear Development Division, 37bis boulevard Suchet,
75016 Paris, France

HORIUCHI, S., Deputy Director, Nuclear Development Division, 38 boulevard
Suchet, 75016 Paris, France

McDONALD, N.R., Nuclear Safety Division, 38 boulevard Suchet, 75016 Paris,
France

SHAPAR, H.K., Director General, 38 boulevard Suchet, 75016 Paris, France

Scientific Secretary - Secrétaire scientifique

MORI, S., Nuclear Development Division, 37bis boulevard Suchet, 75016 Paris,
France

Secretariat

CARON, F., Publications Section, OECD/NEA, 38 boulevard Suchet, 75016 Paris,
France

DAWSON, M., Nuclear Development Division, OECD/NEA, 37bis boulevard Suchet,
75016 Paris, France

KOUSNETZOFF, C., Publications Section, OECD/NEA, 38 boulevard Suchet,
75016 Paris, France

QUARMEAU, S., Nuclear Development Division, OECD/NEA, 37bis boulevard Suchet,
75016 Paris, France

SOME OTHER NEA PUBLICATIONS

QUELQUES AUTRES PUBLICATIONS DE L'AEN

Remote Handling in Nuclear Facilities
(Proceedings of the Joint NEA/IAEA Seminar, 1984)

Télémanipulation dans les installations nucléaires
(Compte rendu d'un séminaire conjoint AEN/AIEA, 1984)

ISBN 92-64-02669-X

£32.00   US$64.00   F320.00   DM140.00

The Economics of the Nuclear Fuel Cycle
(A report by an Expert group, 1985)
ISBN 92-64-12714-3

Les aspects économiques du cycle du combustible nucléaire
(Rapport établi par un groupe d'experts, 1985)

ISBN 92-64-22714-8

£12.50   US$25.00   F125.00   DM56.00

Electricity, Nuclear Power and Fuel Cycle in OECD Countries-Main Date
Annual
previous known as:
Summary of Nuclear Power and Fuel Cycle Data in OECD Member Countries

Electricité, énergie nucléaire et cycle du combustible dans les pays de l'OCDE – Données principales
Annuel
précédemment publié sous le titre :
Quelques données sur l'énergie nucléaire et le cycle du combustible dans les pays de l'OCDE

Free on request – Gratuit sur demande

Projected Costs of Generating Electricity from Nuclear and Coal-fired Power Stations for Commissioning in 1995
(A report by an Expert Group, 1985)
ISBN 92-64-12805-0

Prévision de coûts de l'électricité produite par des centrales nucléaires ou au charbon mises en service en 1995
(Rapport établi par un groupe d'experts, 1985)

ISBN 92-64-22805-5

£9.00   US$18.00   F90.00   DM40.00

Decommissioning of Nuclear Facilities:
Feasibility, Needs and Costs
(A report by an Expert Group, 1986)
ISBN 92-64-12894-8

Déclassement des installations nucléaires : faisabilité, besoins et coûts
(Rapport établi par un groupe d'experts, 1986)

ISBN 92-64-22894-2

£11.00   US$22.00   F110.00   DM49.00

Nuclear Spent Fuel Management
(A report by an Expert group, 1986)

ISBN 92-64-12883-2

Gestion du combustible nucléaire irradié
(Rapport établi par un groupe d'experts, 1986)

ISBN 92-64-22883-7

£15.00   US$30.00   F150.00   DM67.00

Nuclear Energy and its Fuel cycle: Prospects to 2025
ISBN 92-64-12919-7

L'énergie nucléaire et son cycle du combustible : Perspectives jusqu'en 2025
ISBN 92-64-22919-1

£15.00   US$30.00   F150.00   DM67.00

OECD SALES AGENTS
DÉPOSITAIRES DES PUBLICATIONS DE L'OCDE

ARGENTINA - ARGENTINE
Carlos Hirsch S.R.L.,
Florida 165, 4° Piso,
(Galeria Guemes) 1333 Buenos Aires
Tel. 33.1787.2391 y 30.7122

AUSTRALIA-AUSTRALIE
D.A. Book (Aust.) Pty. Ltd.
11-13 Station Street (P.O. Box 163)
Mitcham, Vic. 3132   Tel. (03) 873 4411

AUSTRIA - AUTRICHE
OECD Publications and Information Centre,
4 Simrockstrasse,
5300 Bonn (Germany)   Tel. (0228) 21.60.45
Local Agent:
Gerold & Co., Graben 31, Wien 1 Tel. 52.22.35

BELGIUM - BELGIQUE
Jean de Lannoy, Service Publications OCDE,
avenue du Roi 202
B-1060 Bruxelles   Tel. (02) 538.51.69

CANADA
Renouf Publishing Company Ltd/
Éditions Renouf Ltée,
1294 Algoma Road, Ottawa, Ont. K1B 3W8
Tel: (613) 741-4333
Toll Free/Sans Frais:
Ontario, Quebec, Maritimes:
1-800-267-1805
Western Canada, Newfoundland:
1-800-267-1826
Stores/Magasins:
61 rue Sparks St., Ottawa, Ont. K1P 5A6
Tel: (613) 238-8985
211 rue Yonge St., Toronto, Ont. M5B 1M4
Tel: (416) 363-3171
Sales Office/Bureau des Ventes:
7575 Trans Canada Hwy, Suite 305,
St. Laurent, Quebec H4T 1V6
Tel: (514) 335-9274

DENMARK - DANEMARK
Munksgaard Export and Subscription Service
35, Nørre Søgade, DK-1370 København K
Tel. +45.1.12.85.70

FINLAND - FINLANDE
Akateeminen Kirjakauppa,
Keskuskatu 1, 00100 Helsinki 10   Tel. 0.12141

FRANCE
OCDE/OECD
Mail Orders/Commandes par correspondance :
2, rue André-Pascal,
75775 Paris Cedex 16
Tel. (1) 45.24.82.00
Bookshop/Librairie : 33, rue Octave-Feuillet
75016 Paris
Tel. (1) 45.24.81.67 or/ou (1) 45.24.81.81
Principal correspondant :
Librairie de l'Université,
12a, rue Nazareth,
13602 Aix-en-Provence   Tel. 42.26.18.08

GERMANY - ALLEMAGNE
OECD Publications and Information Centre,
4 Simrockstrasse,
5300 Bonn   Tel. (0228) 21.60.45

GREECE - GRÈCE
Librairie Kauffmann,
28, rue du Stade, 105 64 Athens Tel. 322.21.60

HONG KONG
Government Information Services,
Publications (Sales) Office,
Beaconsfield House, 4/F.,
Queen's Road Central

ICELAND - ISLANDE
Snæbjörn Jónsson & Co., h.f.,
Hafnarstræti 4 & 9,
P.O.B. 1131 – Reykjavik
Tel. 13133/14281/11936

INDIA - INDE
Oxford Book and Stationery Co.,
Scindia House, New Delhi 1 Tel. 331.5896/5308
17 Park St., Calcutta 700016   Tel. 240832

INDONESIA - INDONÉSIE
Pdii-Lipi, P.O. Box 3065/JKT.Jakarta
Tel. 583467

IRELAND - IRLANDE
TDC Publishers - Library Suppliers,
12 North Frederick Street, Dublin 1.
Tel. 744835-749677

ITALY - ITALIE
Libreria Commissionaria Sansoni,
Via Lamarmora 45, 50121 Firenze
Tel. 579751/584468
Via Bartolini 29, 20155 Milano Tel. 365083
Sub-depositari :
Editrice e Libreria Herder,
Piazza Montecitorio 120, 00186 Roma
Tel. 6794628
Libreria Hœpli,
Via Hœpli 5, 20121 Milano   Tel. 865446
Libreria Scientifica
Dott. Lucio de Biasio "Aeiou"
Via Meravigli 16, 20123 Milano Tel. 807679
Libreria Lattes,
Via Garibaldi 3, 10122 Torino Tel. 519274
La diffusione delle edizioni OCSE è inoltre
assicurata dalle migliori librerie nelle città più
importanti.

JAPAN - JAPON
OECD Publications and Information Centre,
Landic Akasaka Bldg., 2-3-4 Akasaka,
Minato-ku, Tokyo 107   Tel. 586.2016

KOREA - CORÉE
Kyobo Book Centre Co. Ltd.
P.O.Box: Kwang Hwa Moon 1658,
Seoul   Tel. (REP) 730.78.91

LEBANON - LIBAN
Documenta Scientifica/Redico,
Edison Building, Bliss St.,
P.O.B. 5641, Beirut   Tel. 354429-344425

MALAYSIA - MALAISIE
University of Malaya Co-operative Bookshop
Ltd.,
P.O.Box 1127, Jalan Pantai Baru,
Kuala Lumpur   Tel. 577701/577072

NETHERLANDS - PAYS-BAS
Staatsuitgeverij
Chr. Plantijnstraat, 2 Postbus 20014
2500 EA S-Gravenhage   Tel. 070-789911
Voor bestellingen: Tel. 070-789880

NEW ZEALAND - NOUVELLE-ZÉLANDE
Government Printing Office Bookshops:
Auckland: Retail Bookshop, 25 Rutland Street,
Mail Orders, 85 Beach Road
Private Bag C.P.O.
Hamilton: Retail: Ward Street,
Mail Orders, P.O. Box 857
Wellington: Retail, Mulgrave Street, (Head
Office)
Cubacade World Trade Centre,
Mail Orders, Private Bag
Christchurch: Retail, 159 Hereford Street,
Mail Orders, Private Bag
Dunedin: Retail, Princes Street,
Mail Orders, P.O. Box 1104

NORWAY - NORVÈGE
Tanum-Karl Johan
Karl Johans gate 43, Oslo 1
PB 1177 Sentrum, 0107 Oslo 1 Tel. (02) 42.93.10

PAKISTAN
Mirza Book Agency
65 Shahrah Quaid-E-Azam, Lahore 3 Tel. 66839

PORTUGAL
Livraria Portugal,
Rua do Carmo 70-74, 1117 Lisboa Codex.
Tel. 360582/3

SINGAPORE - SINGAPOUR
Information Publications Pte Ltd
Pei-Fu Industrial Building,
24 New Industrial Road No. 02-06
Singapore 1953   Tel. 2831786, 2831798

SPAIN - ESPAGNE
Mundi-Prensa Libros, S.A.,
Castelló 37, Apartado 1223, Madrid-28001
Tel. 431.33.99
Libreria Bosch, Ronda Universidad 11,
Barcelona 7   Tel. 317.53.08/317.53.58

SWEDEN - SUÈDE
AB CE Fritzes Kungl. Hovbokhandel,
Box 16356, S 103 27 STH,
Regeringsgatan 12,
DS Stockholm   Tel. (08) 23.89.00
Subscription Agency/Abonnements:
Wennergren-Williams AB,
Box 30004, S104 25 Stockholm.
Tel. (08)54.12.00

SWITZERLAND - SUISSE
OECD Publications and Information Centre,
4 Simrockstrasse,
5300 Bonn (Germany)   Tel. (0228) 21.60.45
Local Agent:
Librairie Payot,
6 rue Grenus, 1211 Genève 11
Tel. (022) 31.89.50

TAIWAN - FORMOSE
Good Faith Worldwide Int'l Co., Ltd.
9th floor, No. 118, Sec.2
Chung Hsiao E. Road
Taipei   Tel. 391.7396/391.7397

THAILAND - THAILANDE
Suksit Siam Co., Ltd.,
1715 Rama IV Rd.,
Samyam Bangkok 5   Tel. 2511630

TURKEY - TURQUIE
Kültur Yayinlari Is-Türk Ltd. Sti.
Atatürk Bulvari No: 191/Kat. 21
Kavaklidere/Ankara   Tel. 25.07.60
Dolmabahce Cad. No: 29
Besiktas/Istanbul   Tel. 160.71.88

UNITED KINGDOM - ROYAUME-UNI
H.M. Stationery Office,
Postal orders only: (01)211-5656
P.O.B. 276, London SW8 5DT
Telephone orders: (01) 622.3316, or
Personal callers:
49 High Holborn, London WC1V 6HB
Branches at: Belfast, Birmingham,
Bristol, Edinburgh, Manchester

UNITED STATES - ÉTATS-UNIS
OECD Publications and Information Centre,
2001 L Street, N.W., Suite 700,
Washington, D.C. 20036 - 4095
Tel. (202) 785.6323

VENEZUELA
Libreria del Este,
Avda F. Miranda 52, Aptdo. 60337,
Edificio Galipan, Caracas 106
Tel. 32.23.01/33.26.04/31.58.38

YUGOSLAVIA - YOUGOSLAVIE
Jugoslovenska Knjiga, Knez Mihajlova 2,
P.O.B. 36, Beograd   Tel. 621.992

Orders and inquiries from countries where Sales
Agents have not yet been appointed should be sent
to:
OECD, Publications Service, Sales and
Distribution Division, 2, rue André-Pascal, 75775
PARIS CEDEX 16.

Les commandes provenant de pays où l'OCDE n'a
pas encore désigné de dépositaire peuvent être
adressées à :
OCDE, Service des Publications. Division des
Ventes et Distribution. 2. rue André-Pascal. 75775
PARIS CEDEX 16.

70712-04-1987

PUBLICATIONS DE L'OCDE, 2, rue André-Pascal, 75775 PARIS CEDEX 16 - N° 44104 1987
IMPRIMÉ EN FRANCE
(66 87 04 3) ISBN 92-64-02967-2